THE ENERGY OF PHYSICS

Part I: Classical Mechanics and Thermodynamics

By Christopher J. Fischer
University of Kansas

cognella®
academic publishing

Bassim Hamadeh, CEO and Publisher
Michael Simpson, Vice President of Acquisitions
Jamie Giganti, Managing Editor
Jess Busch, Senior Graphic Designer
Mark Combes, Acquisitions Editor
Mirasol Enriquez, Project Editor
Luiz Ferreira, Senior Licensing Specialist
Mandy Licata, Interior Designer

ISBN: 978-1-62661-435-2 (pbk)/ 978-1-62661-436-9 (br)

www.cognella.com   800-200-3908

To Katherine and Emily.

May you both enjoy a lifetime of learning.

CONTENTS

CHAPTER THREE: ENERGY AND ENERGY CONSERVATION

CHAPTER FOUR: ENERGY-BASED MECHANICS

CHAPTER FIVE: CIRCULAR AND ROTATIONAL MOTION

CHAPTER SIX: OSCILLATORY MOTION

CHAPTER SEVEN: FORCES

CHAPTER EIGHT: NEWTONIAN MECHANICS I

CHAPTER NINE: NEWTONIAN MECHANICS II

CHAPTER TEN: TORQUE AND ROTATIONAL MOTION

CHAPTER ELEVEN: FURTHER APPLICATIONS OF NEWTONIAN MECHANICS

CHAPTER TWELVE: NEWTONIAN MECHANICS FOR SYSTEMS OF MOVING OBJECTS

CHAPTER THIRTEEN: LINEAR MOMENTUM

CHAPTER FOURTEEN: ANGULAR MOMENTUM

CHAPTER FIFTEEN: HEAT AND THE 1ST LAW OF THERMODYNAMICS

CHAPTER SIXTEEN: ENTROPY AND THE 2ND LAW OF THERMODYNAMICS

APPENDIX A

APPENDIX B

APPENDIX C

APPENDIX D

APPENDIX E

APPENDIX F

FORWARD

I was motivated to write this book because I felt that the standard presentation of introductory classical mechanics and thermodynamics was disjointed, and, furthermore, did not effectively emphasize the generally applicable concepts of the material. In contrast, energy conservation is the common theme applied to all the material in this book. Having this unifying theme enables students to develop a more universally applicable strategy for solving physics problems, to better understand the relationship between classical mechanics, thermodynamics, and statistical mechanics, and, finally, to be well prepared for advanced STEM courses. This presentation also allows for this book to be shorter in length since space need not be devoted to the discussion of one special case after another. Instead, this book demonstrates how basic principles can be generalized to solve different specific problems and, thereby, helps students to develop their critical thinking skills.

This book is intended for the first semester of a two semester calculus-based physics curriculum. As such, I assume that students using this book are comfortable with simple differentiation and integration. Furthermore, since I anticipate that students using this book will likely also be simultaneously enrolled in one or more additional calculus courses, applications of more advanced calculus, such as partial differentiation, are introduced in the last chapters of the book. Indeed, another motivation for writing this book was to develop an introductory physics curriculum that would give students a better opportunity to practice and further develop their skill with calculus.

I would like to thank all of the people who contributed to this book and/or supported me as I wrote it. First, I wish to thank Professor Matthew Antonik for originally proposing that students in introductory physics be taught about energy and energy conservation before being taught about forces. Thanks, as well, to Professor Michael Murray and Professor Phil Baringer for putting up with me while I tried out this approach in our general physics class. I appreciate the fact that neither of you ever tried to "pull rank" and insist that I teach that course the standard way. I would also like to thank my department chair, Professor Hume Feldman, for fostering such a creative and supportive environment in the department.

I would especially like to thank graduate students Allen Eastlund and Koan Briggs for taking time away from their research to help me with the writing and editing of this book. I've appreciated your counsel throughout the development of this book and the associated in-class material.

Finally, I would like to thank my family for their support, especially my wife and daughters. I love all of you!

CHAPTER ONE
Why Things Move

The focus of this book is classical mechanics, which involves both the description and causes of motion. This is a broad area of study encompassing everything from the motion of a baseball to the orbits of planets. The beauty and elegance of physics is that the movements of baseballs and planets are both governed by the same set of fundamental physical laws. Indeed, because of these fundamental laws we are able to form general conclusions about the motion of objects and, more importantly, predict the future motion of these same objects.

One of these fundamental physical laws is the law of conservation of energy. The concept of energy conservation is central to all of physics and, therefore, will be used as the basis for all discussion and problem solving throughout this book. Thus, the first step to each problem is to consider the following question:

What happens to the energy?

1-2 Energy

Because we will employ an energy-based approach in this book, we must begin with a definition of energy. Ironically, despite its fundamental usefulness, energy is a concept that is difficult to define. The most practical, though not very informative or insightful, definition of energy is that it is a scalar quantity associated with the state of an object or collection of objects.

Energy: A scalar quantity associated with the state of an object or collection of objects.
Scalar: A mathematical quantity specified by a magnitude (or size) only.

The definition of the state (or condition) of an object or collection of objects naturally depends upon the scale of the investigation. For example, when describing the energy of a pencil lying on a desk, we might be interested in the energy associated with the position of the pencil relative to the surface of the Earth, with the energies associated with the individual atoms that constitute the pencil, or, perhaps, all of these energies. In this book, we will initially restrict ourselves to a scale and set of objects corresponding to everyday life, which we will refer to as a *macroscopic* scale. Accordingly, we will define the state of objects in terms of their macroscopic motion and position only. Later in this book, we will more broadly apply a smaller, or *microscopic*, scale to the analysis of objects and consider also the energies of their constitute parts, such as their molecules and atoms.

Throughout this book, we will consider two main forms of energy: energy that is associated with the motion of an object, referred to as **kinetic energy**, and energy associated with the position of an object, referred to as **potential energy**.

> *Kinetic energy: Energy associated with motion. Kinetic energies are denoted by the variable K.*
> *Potential energy: Energy associated with position. Potential energies are denoted by the variable U.*

We will use subscripts to label the specific type of kinetic or potential energy as well as the object with which the energy is associated.

Since the motion of an object is associated with a change in the object's position, it is not surprising that the kinetic and potential energies of an object are related to each other. Furthermore, it is this connection between an object's kinetic and potential energies that allows us to describe and predict how the object will move and, thus, will be the starting point for our discussion of classical mechanics.

Throughout this book, we will use the word **system** to denote the object or collection of objects that is of interest to a particular problem or discussion.

> *System: An object or a collection of objects.*

We will then define the **energy of the system** to be the sum of all the kinetic and potential energies associated with all of the objects in the system[1].

> *Energy of a system: The sum of all kinetic and potential energies of all objects in a system. The total energy of a system will be denoted by the letter E.*

1-3 Energy Conservation

Energy has a very interesting fundamental property: it can be neither created nor destroyed. This property of energy is referred to as the law of conservation of energy or the 1st law of thermodynamics. Energy can be converted from one type to another or transferred between objects, however. For example, the potential energy of a skydiver is converted into kinetic energy as she falls toward

---

1   This quantity is sometimes referred to as the internal energy of the system.

the ground. Or during a collision, the kinetic energy of one car may be transferred to the kinetic energy of another car.

We can divide these changes in energy or transfers of energy into those that occur within a system and those that result from interactions between the system and something outside the system (more generally, with the environment outside the system). When a ball is thrown up into the air and then falls back down to the ground again, the initial kinetic energy of the ball is converted into potential energy, which is then converted back into kinetic energy. These changes all occur internal to the system of the ball[2]. In contrast, a person changed the energy of this system through the external interaction of throwing the ball.

If all external interactions with the outside environment are prevented, the system is referred to as an ***isolated system***.

> *Isolated system: A system for which interactions with the outside environment are prevented.*
> *The total energy of an isolated system is constant.*

Conservation principles, such as the conservation of energy, are very powerful and can be used to generate other physical laws. Over the next several chapters we will also see how the conservation of energy can lead to equations describing the motions of systems. But where do conservation principles come from? Well, it turns out that the conservation of energy is the result of time being homogeneous, meaning that time is smoothly and evenly flowing, and that there is no absolute origin for time[3]. Later on, we will learn about momentum, which is another intrinsic property of systems that is governed by a conservational principle. The conservation of momentum results from the homogeneity of space, which is also smooth and has no absolute origin[3].

1-4 Why Do Things Move?

The law of conservation of energy explains how energy can be converted or transferred but doesn't explain why these processes occur. It is the 2nd law of thermodynamics that explains why. We will discuss the 2nd law of thermodynamics more formally in Chapter 16; for now we will express it as:

> *Systems will always arrange themselves in order to minimize their total potential energy.*

This is often referred to as the *principle of minimum potential energy*. A ball thrown up into the air will fall back down because by doing so the potential energy of the ball is minimized. In Chapter 3, we will learn our first definitions of the different kinds of kinetic and potential energy and apply them to understanding why objects move. Before that, however, we must learn how to describe the position and motion of objects mathematically since this is required for quantitative calculations involving kinetic and potential energies. This will be the subject of Chapter 2.

---

2   We will discuss this example more carefully in Section 3-5 and Section 13-4.

3   Please be inspired to take additional physics classes to learn why this is true.

1-5 Potential Energy Curves

Even without a quantitative description of position and motion, we can nevertheless make predictions about the behavior of a system from plots of its potential energy as a function of its position. Consider a system that consists of an object whose potential energy depends on its height above the ground, as shown in Figure 1.1.

Let's imagine that we release the object at an initial position above the ground (see Figure 1.1). According to the principle of minimum potential energy, this system will always arrange itself in order to minimize its potential energy. In this case, the object will move closer to the ground (*i.e.*, it will decrease its height above the ground). Metaphorically, we can think of the object sliding down the potential energy curve to the minimum accessible potential energy.

It follows that an object would not change its position if it were released at rest at a point where its potential energy curve had no slope (*e.g.*, if placed on a flat surface, a ball will not move away from where it was released). We refer to these locations as **equilibrium points**.

> *Equilibrium point: A location where the potential energy curve has no slope.*

As shown in Figure 1.2, there are three varieties of equilibrium points, which are differentiated based upon the curvature of the potential energy curve at that location.

At **neutral equilibrium points** the potential energy curve is flat. This is an example of a ball on a flat surface: it will not move when released at rest. At **unstable equilibrium points** the potential energy curve is convex; if you place a ball on top of a pole, it can and will fall off with only the slightest push or bump. Finally, at **stable equilibrium points** the potential energy curve is concave. If you

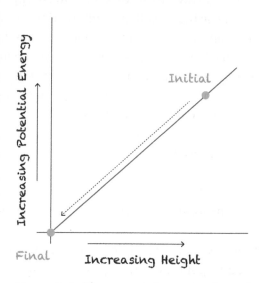

Figure 1.1: The potential energy of an object as a function of its height above the ground. An object initially at a position with high potential energy will automatically move to a position with lower potential energy. In this case, the object will move closer to the ground.

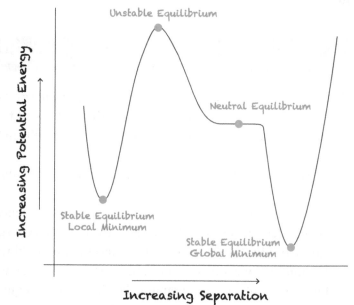

Figure 1.2: Identification of equilibrium points on a potential energy curve. All points correspond to locations where the slope of the potential energy curve is zero. They are further distinguished by the curvature of the potential energy curve at that location.

place a ball at the bottom of a bowl, it will always return to that same position if moved slightly away from it.

> *Neutral equilibrium point: An equilibrium location of the system where the system's potential energy curve is flat.*
> *Unstable equilibrium point: An equilibrium location of the system where the system's potential energy curve is convex.*
> *Stable equilibrium point: An equilibrium location of the system where the system's potential energy curve is concave.*

Stable equilibrium points can be further classified as local or global minima depending upon the associated magnitude of the potential energy at that point; the global minimum corresponds to the lowest possible potential energy, whereas local minima are other stable equilibrium points that, while stable, have higher potential energy than the global minimum.

1-6 System Energy

It is always important to remember that energy is an ***extensive*** parameter. This means that the energy of a system is the sum of all the energies of the individual objects that constitute the system.

> *Extensive parameter: A parameter of a system that is the sum of properties of the components of the system.*

The motions and/or positions of objects in a system can often be related to each other. As we will see, this allows us to use relationships between the variables denoting the motions and positions of objects in a system to simplify the equation for the energy of that system. It is always beneficial to take advantage of these relationships when they exist.

Consider, for example, the system shown in Figure 1.3 that consists of two blocks, A and B, which are connected to each other by a rope that passes over a pulley.

Because the rope connects the two blocks, we know that the two blocks cannot move independently of one another. For example, block A will move to the right if block B moves down. Similarly, block B would move upwards if block A moves to the left. In either case, it is important to note that the distance moved by block A must be equal to the distance moved by block B (even though these two motions are occurring along different directions) since the two blocks are connected by a rope[4]. It is this kind of correlation between the distances travelled by objects in systems that will be the basis for our future discussion of the coupled motions of these objects. Furthermore, since the positions and motions of the two blocks in the system shown in Figure 1.3 are coupled to each other, so, too, are the potential and kinetics energies of these blocks.

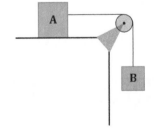

Figure 1.3: A system consisting of two blocks, a rope, and a pulley.

---

4   We will assume that the ropes behave ideally and, thus, do not stretch.

In other words, it is possible to write expressions for the kinetic and potential energies of the two blocks in Figure 1.3 using a common set of variables. Of course, this, in turn, then also allows for a more simplified mathematical description of the energy conservation occurring within the system.

Furthermore, the energy of the system is also a **state function**[5]. This means that the energy depends upon the arrangement of the system (*i.e.,* the positions and motions of the objects in the system) but does not depend upon the process by which the system arrived at its arrangement (*i.e.,* how each object obtained its position and motion).

State function: A property of a system that depends upon only the arrangement of the system.

The energy of the system shown in Figure 1.3 depends upon only the positions and motions of the two blocks, the pulley, and the rope. Knowledge of these quantities for these objects is sufficient to determine the energy of the system regardless of how these objects came to have them.

1-7 Units

Physics is an experimental science, and experimental measurements require units. The system of units used in science is the International System of Units (known by its French acronym, SI). This system is commonly referred to as the metric system. We are already familiar with some metric units in our daily lives (*e.g.,* seconds, liters), whereas others may not be so familiar (*e.g.,* candela). A list of the seven basic SI units and several additional derived units is shown in Appendix A. Also in Appendix A, is a list of the prefixes that are used to describe very large or very small quantities with SI units.

1-8 Looking Ahead

The energy-based approach for understanding classical mechanics presented in this book will provide a common framework for the treatment of a wide variety of problems. In this sense, it is a generally applicable way to understand physics. As with any physics course, it is always important to pay close attention to terminology and to be careful with your mathematics! And remember, the first step to each problem you encounter is to consider the following question:

What happens to the energy?

Summary

- **System:** A single object or a collection of objects.
- **Energy:** An extensive scalar quantity associated with the location and motion of an object.
- **Kinetic energy:** Energy associated with the motion of an object.
- **Potential energy:** Energy associated with the position of an object.
- **Energy of a system:** The sum of all the kinetic and potential energies associated with all of the objects in the system. The energy of a system is a state function, which means that it depends

---

5   We will discuss state functions in more detail in Chapter 15 and Chapter 16.

upon only the current positions and motions of the objects in the system and not how these objects came to possess these quantities.

- **Isolated system:** A system that cannot exchange energy with the outside environment. The total energy of an isolated system is, therefore, constant.
- **The law of conservation of energy:** Energy can be neither created nor destroyed but can be converted from one type to another or transferred between objects. This is also referred to as the 1st law of thermodynamics.
- **The principle of minimum potential energy:** All systems will arrange themselves in order to minimize their total potential energy. This follows from the 2nd law of thermodynamics.
- **Equilibrium point:** A location where the potential energy curve for a system has no slope. A neutral equilibrium point occurs when the potential energy curve is flat; an unstable equilibrium point occurs when the potential energy curve is convex; and a stable equilibrium point occurs when the potential energy curve is concave.

Problems

1. Do you get better gas mileage with your car when the air conditioning is turned on or when it is turned off? Why?

2. A system consists of two long parallel wires carrying electricity in opposite directions. The presence of this electricity in the two wires results in a potential energy being created for the system. This potential energy has a dependence on the separation distance between the two wires that can be described using the figure at right. The two wires are initially held in place close together and then released. After they are released, what will happen? Specifically, will the two wires move closer together, move farther apart, or stay in the same position?

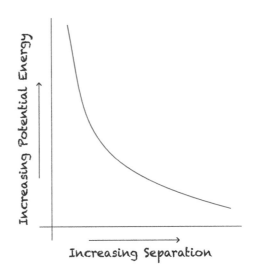

3. The potential energy existing between two atoms in a diatomic molecule has a dependence upon the separation of the two atoms as shown in the figure below. Three points are labeled on this potential energy curve. Describe the behavior of the system at each point. In other words, how will the atoms move if released from rest at that point? Are any of these points equilibrium points? If so, what kind of equilibrium point?

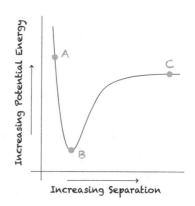

4. A system consists of two blocks, A and B, connected by a single rope that passes over two pulleys, as shown in the figure below. How far does block A move to the right if block B moves down 2 m?

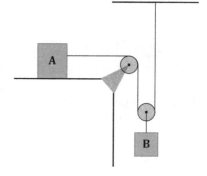

CHAPTER TWO

Kinematics

As discussed in the previous chapter, potential energies are functions of the positions of objects, and kinetic energies are functions of the motions of objects. Using energy as a basis for a mathematical description of the world around us, therefore, requires mathematical definitions of both position and motion.

We first recognize that defining where an object is located or how an object is moving requires two pieces of information. For example, we could describe a chair as being "1 m from the northeast corner of the room." This description includes a specification of both magnitude (1 m) and direction (from the northeast corner). Similarly, if we state that a car is moving "west at 20 mph," the magnitude is 20 mph and the direction is west. Descriptions such as these that include both a magnitude and a direction are referred to as **vector** quantities.

Vector: A mathematical quantity specified by both a magnitude and a direction.

The direction of a vector can be described in many ways and with respect to many different reference points. For example, while someone in St. Louis would describe the position of Chicago as being 300 miles to the north-northeast, someone in Detroit would describe the position of Chicago as being 250 miles to the west. Because of this potential subjectivity, we must always designate the reference point, or origin, for our vectors as the first step in using them. We will limit our initial discussion to 1-dimensional vectors and 1-dimensional motion but will return to multi-dimensional vectors in Chapter 9. A summary of vectors and vector mathematics can be found in Appendix B.

2-2 Position and Displacement

Since position is a vector, identifying the location of an object requires specifying the origin (or reference point) for the measurement. For 1-dimensional motion, we will denote the origin of a 1-dimensional coordinate axis as the zero point for referencing the magnitude of the position (*i.e.*, the distance from the origin) and a positive (+) or negative (−) sign to denote the direction. For example, in Figure 2.1 we denote moving to the right along the coordinate axis to be the positive direction and moving to the left to be the negative direction.

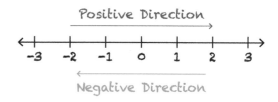

Figure 2.1: 1-dimensional coordinate axis for describing position.

The increments along this axis (−1, 0, 1, *etc.*) indicate measurements of distance from the origin. Although there are many units of distance that would be applicable for describing position (miles, feet, *etc.*), most scientific fields measure distances using the SI unit meter, which is denoted by the symbol m. We will follow this convention, too.

Let's now label the 1-dimensional axis the "*x*-axis." As shown in Figure 2.2, we can then denote the position of the blue circle that is 2 meters away from the origin of the *x*-axis in the negative direction as having a position of −2 m. Similarly, the green circle that is 1 meter away from the origin in the positive direction has a position of +1 m. These

Figure 2.2: The positions of two objects along a 1-dimensional axis, denoted as the x-axis, using a (±) sign to denote the direction of the vectors.

positions can also be described mathematically with the equals sign (=). For example, the position of the two circles can be expressed as $x_{blue} = -2$ m and $x_{green} = +1$ m, where the subscript (blue or green) denotes the object. Often, the positive sign is omitted when designating the direction of a 1-dimensional vector and, thus, we could also have written $x_{green} = 1$ m; the absence of a negative sign implies the presence of the positive sign.

A change in the position of an object is referred to as a *displacement* since the object is *displaced* from its original position. For our positions defined on the *x*-axis, we can denote the displacement as Δx.

$$\Delta x = x_{final} - x_{initial}$$

Throughout this book, we will use the Greek letter Δ, uppercase delta, to represent "*change in*"; specifically, the difference between a final value and an initial value of a variable. In addition, we will use the subscript "*f*" to denote the final value of a variable and the subscript "*i*" to denote the initial value. Therefore, we can also write this equation for the displacement as

$$\Delta x = x_f - x_i \tag{2-1}$$

Now, let's consider the situation shown in Figure 2.3 in which an object initially at $x_i = -2$ m, moves to a final position at $x_f = 1$ m. The displacement of this object can then be calculated using Equation 2-1 to be

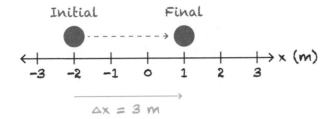

Figure 2.3: The displacement of this object is 3 m. Namely, the magnitude of the displacement is 3 m and the direction of the displacement is positive.

$$\Delta x = \left(1\,\text{m}\right) - \left(-2\,\text{m}\right) \quad \rightarrow \quad \Delta x = 3\,\text{m}$$

Since displacement has both magnitude and direction, it is a vector; this also follows from the fact that it is defined in terms of position, which is also a vector. For 1-dimensional motion, we can denote the direction of the displacement using the same ($\pm$) sign convention as for position.

The displacement of an object is independent of the origin of the coordinate axis used to measure position. This is true since changing the location of the origin of the coordinate axis shifts both the initial and final positions of the object by the same amount. Indeed, if we denote the magnitude of this change as x_{shift}, then according to Equation 2-1 we have

$$\Delta x = \left(x_f + x_{shift}\right) - \left(x_i + x_{shift}\right) \quad \rightarrow \quad \Delta x = \left(x_f - x_i\right) + \left(x_{shift} - x_{shift}\right)$$

$$\Delta x = x_f - x_i$$

Thus, shifting the location of the origin of the coordinate axis has no effect on the displacement (Figure 2.4).

The displacement of an object is independent of the reference point for the measurement of the position of the object.

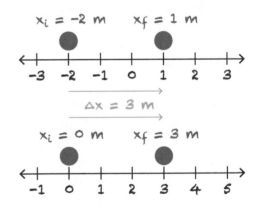

Figure 2.4: The displacement of an object is independent of the origin of the coordinate axis. In the first case,

$$\Delta x = 1\text{m} - (-2\text{m}) = 3\text{m}$$

and in the second case,

$$\Delta x = 3\text{m} - 0\text{m} = 3\text{m}$$

2-3 Velocity and Acceleration

If we know the time interval (Δt) over which a displacement occurs, we can define an average velocity for the displacement as

$$v_{avg} = \frac{\Delta x}{\Delta t} = \frac{x_f - x_i}{t_f - t_i} \qquad \textbf{(2-2)}$$

Average velocity is our first method of describing the motion of an object that includes time. The units of average velocity are the units of displacement (m) divided by the units of time (s), or m/s. Average velocity is a simplified way of describing the motion of an object, but not necessarily a useful one. Imagine that you fly from New York to Chicago in 2 hours, have a 1 hour layover in Chicago, and then fly from Chicago to Los Angeles in 4 hours. The time interval used to determine the average velocity of your trip from New York to Los Angeles would include both the 6 hours spent in the air and the 1 hour spent on the ground in Chicago. Thus, your average velocity would not necessarily be a good description of your motion from New York to Los Angeles as it would be an average of the periods when you were moving and the period when you were not moving.

A more useful measurement would be the velocity of an object at any *instant* of time. Not surprisingly, we refer to this quantity as the instantaneous velocity, or simply the velocity. Mathematically, the velocity of an object is the first derivative of the position of the object with respect to time.

$$v = \frac{dx}{dt} \qquad \textbf{(2-3)}$$

In Equation 2-3, the variable x is the position of the object as a function of time (*i.e.*, *x(t)*) and the units of instantaneous velocity are m/s. The magnitude of any velocity vector is referred to as the **speed** of the object.

Speed: The magnitude of the velocity vector.

The magnitude of the average velocity is the average speed, and the magnitude of the instantaneous velocity is the instantaneous speed; however, we often refer to the instantaneous speed as simply the speed. Thus, although we use the words velocity and speed interchangeably in everyday language, in physics they refer to entirely different quantities.

Another useful description of the motion of a system is *acceleration*. The acceleration describes the rate at which the velocity is changing and has the units m/s². The instantaneous acceleration of an object is defined as the first derivative of the velocity with respect to time, or the second derivative of position with respect to time.

$$a = \frac{dv}{dt} = \frac{d^2 x}{dt^2} \qquad \textbf{(2-4)}$$

Similarly, the average acceleration of a system is defined to be

$$a_{avg} = \frac{\Delta v}{\Delta t} = \frac{v_f - v_i}{t_f - t_i} \tag{2-5}$$

Like position and velocity, acceleration is a vector, but unlike velocity, there is no separate name for the magnitude of the acceleration.

2-4 Kinematics

We can use Equations 2-3 and 2-4 to relate the position, velocity, and acceleration of an object and, thereby, mathematically describe the motion of the object. We call this process **kinematics**.

Kinematics: A mathematical description of the motion of an object or group of objects.

If we know an equation for the position or the velocity as a function of time, then we can determine the corresponding velocity or acceleration using Equation 2-3 or Equation 2-4, respectively.

Example 2-1:

Problem: The position of an object moving in 1-dimension along the *x*-axis is given by the equation:

$$x(t) = 5\,\mathrm{m} + \left(2\frac{\mathrm{m}}{\mathrm{s}}\right)t + \left(4\frac{\mathrm{m}}{\mathrm{s}^2}\right)t^2$$

What is the velocity of this object?

Solution: We determine the velocity using Equation 2-3.

$$v(t) = \frac{d}{dt}\left(5\,\mathrm{m} + \left(2\frac{\mathrm{m}}{\mathrm{s}}\right)t + \left(4\frac{\mathrm{m}}{\mathrm{s}^2}\right)t^2\right)$$

$$v(t) = 2\frac{\mathrm{m}}{\mathrm{s}} + \left(8\frac{\mathrm{m}}{\mathrm{s}^2}\right)t$$

Integrating Equation 2-3 allows us to relate the displacement of an object to the velocity of the object across a particular time interval.

$$v = \frac{dx}{dt} \quad \rightarrow \quad \int_{t_i}^{t_f} v\,dt = \int_{x_i}^{x_f} dx \quad \rightarrow \quad \int_{t_i}^{t_f} v\,dt = x_f - x_i \quad \rightarrow \quad \int_{t_i}^{t_f} v\,dt = \Delta x$$

In this equation, the object is located at position x_i at time t_i and at position x_f at time t_f. As shown in Figure 2.5, since the displacement of an object is the integral of the velocity of the object with respect to time, it is the same as the area under the velocity curve. From Equation 2-4 we identify the acceleration as the slope of this curve.

It is important to emphasize that the integral of the velocity with respect to time determines the displacement rather than the absolute position. Determining the position of the object

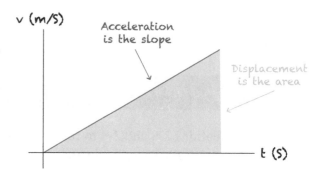

Figure 2.5: The relationship between acceleration, velocity, and displacement.

requires both the velocity as a function of time and the position of the object at one time point. Similarly, an integration of the acceleration over time determines only a change in velocity, not the velocity itself.

Example 2-2:

Problem: The acceleration of an object as a function of time is shown in Figure 2.6. The velocity of the object at $t = 0$ s is -4 m/s. What is the velocity of the object at $t = 6$ s?

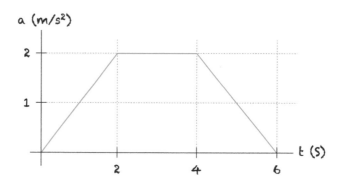

Figure 2.6: The acceleration of the object in Example 2-2 as a function of time.

Solution: We begin with Equation 2-4.

$$a = \frac{dv}{dt} \quad \rightarrow \quad dv = a\,dt \quad \rightarrow \quad \int_{v_i}^{v_f} dv = \int_{t_i}^{t_f} a\,dt \quad \rightarrow \quad \Delta v = \int_{t_i}^{t_f} a\,dt$$

In this equation, the object has velocity v_i at time t_i and velocity v_f at time t_f. The change in the velocity is, thus, the integral of the acceleration with respect to time, which is simply the area under the curve of a plot of acceleration versus time. For our figure, this area is

$$\int_{t_i}^{t_f} a \, dt = 8\frac{m}{s} \quad \rightarrow \quad \Delta v = 8\frac{m}{s} \quad \rightarrow \quad v_f - \left(-4\frac{m}{s}\right) = 8\frac{m}{s}$$

$$v_f = 4\frac{m}{s}$$

2-5 Constant Acceleration Kinematics

When the acceleration of an object is constant, there are three often-used equations to relate the object's position, velocity, and acceleration.

$$\Delta v = a\Delta t \quad \rightarrow \quad v_f = v_i + a\Delta t$$

$$\Delta x = v_i \Delta t + \frac{1}{2}a\left(\Delta t\right)^2 \quad \rightarrow \quad x_f = x_i + v_i \Delta t + \frac{1}{2}a\left(\Delta t\right)^2$$

$$v_f^2 = v_i^2 + 2a\Delta x$$

The derivations for these equations can be found in Appendix C. As shown in Figure 2.7, these equations indicate that when acceleration is constant, velocity changes linearly with time, and position changes quadratically with time.

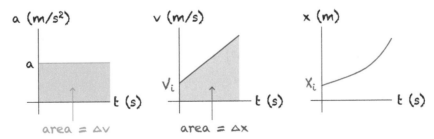

Figure 2.7: Plots of acceleration, velocity, and position as a function of time for motion with constant and positive acceleration. The initial velocity and position are denoted by v_i and x_i, respectively. The area under the curve of acceleration versus time is the change in the velocity, and the area under the curve of velocity versus time is the displacement.

Example 2-3:

Problem: A car has a constant acceleration of 4 m/s². How much time elapses as the car's velocity increases from 10 m/s to 30 m/s?

Solution: Since the acceleration is constant we can use the constant acceleration kinematics equations.

$$\Delta v = a \Delta t \quad \rightarrow \quad \Delta t = \frac{\Delta v}{a}$$

$$\Delta t = \frac{v_f - v_i}{a} \quad \rightarrow \quad \Delta t = \frac{30\frac{m}{s} - 10\frac{m}{s}}{4\frac{m}{s^2}} \quad \rightarrow \quad \Delta t = \frac{20\frac{m}{s}}{4\frac{m}{s^2}}$$

$$\Delta t = 5s$$

Example 2-4:

Problem: A car starts from rest and has constant acceleration while travelling a distance of 100 m in 5 s. What is the speed of the car after it has travelled this distance?

Solution: Since the acceleration is constant we can use the constant acceleration kinematics equations.

$$\Delta x = v_i \Delta t + \frac{1}{2} a (\Delta t)^2 \quad \rightarrow \quad a = \frac{2\Delta x}{(\Delta t)^2}$$

$$\Delta v = a(\Delta t) \quad \rightarrow \quad v_f = \frac{2\Delta x}{(\Delta t)^2}(\Delta t) \quad \rightarrow \quad v_f = \frac{2\Delta x}{\Delta t} \quad \rightarrow \quad v_f = \frac{2(100m)}{(5s)}$$

$$v_f = 40\frac{m}{s}$$

Alternatively, we could have solved the problem starting with a different equation.

$$v_f^2 = v_i^2 + 2a\Delta x \quad \rightarrow \quad v_f^2 = 2a\Delta x$$

$$\Delta v = a\left(\Delta t\right) \quad \rightarrow \quad a = \frac{\Delta v}{\Delta t} = \frac{v_f}{\Delta t}$$

$$v_f^2 = 2\left(\frac{v_f}{\Delta t}\right)\Delta x \quad \rightarrow \quad v_f = \frac{2\Delta x}{\Delta t}$$

2-6 Relative Motion in 1-Dimension

Frequently the solution to a problem requires a kinematic description of more than one moving object. Consider, for example, a police car chasing a speeder along a straight road. The police car has a velocity of 50 m/s and is 500 m behind the speeder, who has a velocity of 45 m/s. How much time will pass from this instant until the police car catches the speeder?

Since the accelerations of both cars are constant, we can use the constant acceleration kinematics equations to solve this problem. Let's label the axis for the 1-dimensional motion of the two cars to be the x-axis and use the subscripts P (police) and S (speeder) to denote the position, velocity, and acceleration of the two cars.

$$\Delta x_S = v_{i,S}\Delta t_S + \frac{1}{2}a_S\left(\Delta t_S\right)^2 \quad \rightarrow \quad x_{f,S} = x_{i,S} + v_{i,S}\Delta t_S$$

$$\Delta x_P = v_{i,P}\Delta t_P + \frac{1}{2}a_P\left(\Delta t_P\right)^2 \quad \rightarrow \quad x_{f,P} = x_{i,P} + v_{i,P}\Delta t_P$$

The next step in our solution is to define the origin and positive direction for the x-axis. We are free to choose any origin that we want, but it makes the calculations simpler to choose the origin to correspond to the initial position of one of the two cars. Let's consider these two options:

Option 1: Origin at the police car ($x_{i,p} = 0$) and positive direction for the x-axis pointing from the police car to the speeder.

As shown in Figure 2.8, for this definition for the x-axis our kinematic equations for the police car and the speeder become

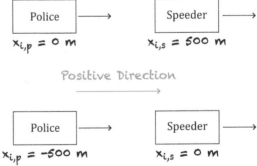

Figure 2.8: Values for the initial position of the police and speeder with different origins for the coordinate axis.

$$x_{f,P} = \left(50\frac{\text{m}}{\text{s}}\right)\Delta t_P \quad \text{and} \quad x_{f,S} = 500\text{m} + \left(45\frac{\text{m}}{\text{s}}\right)\Delta t_S$$

When the police car catches the speeder, both cars are in the same place at the same time. We can express this condition mathematically as

$$x_{f,P} = x_{f,S} \qquad \Delta t_p = \Delta t_s = \Delta t$$

Thus,

$$x_{f,P} = x_{f,S} \quad \rightarrow \quad \left(50\frac{m}{s}\right)\Delta t_p = 500m + \left(45\frac{m}{s}\right)\Delta t_s$$

$$\Delta t_p = \Delta t_s = \Delta t \quad \rightarrow \quad \left(50\frac{m}{s}\right)\Delta t = 500m + \left(45\frac{m}{s}\right)\Delta t$$

$$\left(50\frac{m}{s} - 45\frac{m}{s}\right)\Delta t = 500m \quad \rightarrow \quad \left(5\frac{m}{s}\right)\Delta t = 500m \quad \rightarrow \quad \Delta t = 100s$$

The speeder has less than 2 minutes until he is caught. He must think of a good excuse quickly.

Option 2: Origin at the speeder ($x_{i,S} = 0$) and positive direction for the x-axis pointing from the police car to the speeder.

As shown in Figure 2.8, for this definition for the x-axis our kinematic equations for the police car and the speeder become

$$x_{f,P} = -500m + \left(50\frac{m}{s}\right)\Delta t_p \quad \text{and} \quad x_{f,S} = \left(45\frac{m}{s}\right)\Delta t_s$$

Following through with the same approach in our previous solution gives us

$$x_{f,P} = x_{f,S} \quad \rightarrow \quad -500m + \left(50\frac{m}{s}\right)\Delta t_p = \left(45\frac{m}{s}\right)\Delta t_s$$

$$\Delta t_p = \Delta t_s = \Delta t \quad \rightarrow \quad -500m + \left(50\frac{m}{s}\right)\Delta t = \left(45\frac{m}{s}\right)\Delta t$$

$$\left(50\frac{m}{s} - 45\frac{m}{s}\right)\Delta t = 500m \quad \rightarrow \quad \left(5\frac{m}{s}\right)\Delta t = 500m \quad \rightarrow \quad \Delta t = 100s$$

This is the same solution that we obtained with the previous definition of the origin of the x-axis ($x_{i,p} = 0$). We could have anticipated that the solution to this problem would be independent of the origin of the x-axis since the problem was asking about the displacements of the two cars, which we know to be independent of the origin of the coordinate axis (Section 2-2).

The solution to this example can also be interpreted in terms of how the police car and the speeder are moving with respect to (or *relative to*) each other. As shown in Figure 2.9, rather than using a coordinate axis that has its origin at a fixed position on the ground (*e.g.*, at the initial position of the

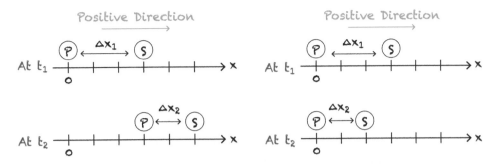

Figure 2.9: The positions of the police car and the speeder as a function of time ($t_2 > t_1$) for different coordinate axes. In the fixed coordinate axis (left), the position of the police car and speeder both change with time, however, in the moving coordinate axis (right), the position of the police car is always at the origin.

police car), we can instead choose a coordinate axis whose origin moves with the position of one of the objects in our system. For example, we could choose the origin of the x-axis to always be at the position of the police car.

Let's refer to the x-axis in which the origin moves with the police car as coordinate system 1. The x-axis in which the origin is fixed at the initial position of the police car will be referred to as coordinate system 2. We can then use subscripts to denote the coordinate system in which the position measurement is being made, as shown in Figure 2.10. For example, $x_{S,2}$ would be the position of the speeder relative to coordinate system 2.

As shown in Figure 2.10, we can then relate the positions of the speeder relative to the two different coordinate systems with the following equation:

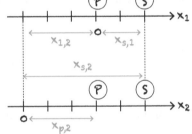

$$x_{S,2} = x_{S,1} + x_{1,2}$$

In this equation, $x_{1,2}$ is the position of coordinate system 1 relative to coordinate system 2, which is the same as the position of the police car relative to coordinate system 2.

Figure 2.10: The relationships between the positions of the speeder measured in two different coordinate systems.

$$x_{1,2} = x_{P,2}$$

In addition to using graphical representations of the position vectors to determine the equation relating the position of an object in different coordinate systems, as in Figure 2.10, we can also rely upon a simple mnemonic to remember how to construct these equations. As shown in Figure 2.11, the order of the subscripts for the different positions dictates their location in the relative position equation.

The equation that relates the velocities of the speeder relative to the two different coordinate systems is found through differentiation of the equation relating the positions of the speeder relative to the two different coordinate systems.

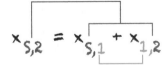

Figure 2.11: Mnemonic for writing relative position equations.

$$\frac{d}{dt}x_{S,2} = \frac{d}{dt}x_{S,1} + \frac{d}{dt}x_{1,2}$$

$$v_{S,2} = v_{S,1} + v_{1,2}$$

In this last equation, $v_{1,2}$ is the velocity of coordinate system 1 relative to coordinate system 2.

Let's now use these equations for relative position and velocity to solve our problem with the speeder and the police car using coordinate system 1. The first step is to solve for the velocity of the speeder relative to this coordinate system.

$$v_{S,2} = v_{S,1} + v_{1,2} \quad \rightarrow \quad v_{S,1} = v_{S,2} - v_{1,2} \quad \rightarrow \quad v_{S,1} = v_{S,2} - v_{P,2}$$

$$v_{S,1} = \left(45\frac{m}{s}\right) - \left(50\frac{m}{s}\right) = -5\frac{m}{s}$$

As expected, the direction of the velocity of the speeder relative to the police car is negative (*i.e.*, the velocity is directed toward the police car), as shown in Figure 2.9. The equations for the position of the police car and speeder in this coordinate system are

$$x_{f,P} = x_{i,P} = 0\,\text{m} \quad \text{and} \quad x_{f,S} = 500\,\text{m} - \left(5\frac{m}{s}\right)\Delta t_{S}$$

We can now use these equations to determine the time interval until the speeder is caught.

$$x_{f,P} = x_{f,S} \quad \rightarrow \quad 0\,\text{m} = 500\,\text{m} - \left(5\frac{m}{s}\right)\Delta t_{S} \quad \rightarrow \quad \Delta t_{S} = 100\,\text{s}$$

As expected this is the same solution as we obtained using coordinate system 2.

Example 2-5:

Problem: A train is moving in 1-dimension with a speed of a 30 m/s. A person on the train is walking in the same direction as that of the train's velocity with a speed of 2 m/s relative to the train. What is the velocity of this person relative to the ground?

Solution: The velocity of the person relative to the ground ($v_{P,G}$) is related to the velocity of the person relative to the train ($v_{P,T}$) through the following equation:

$$v_{P,G} = v_{P,T} + v_{T,G}$$

In this equation, $v_{T,G}$ is the velocity of the train relative to the ground. Let's define the positive direction for our motion to be the direction of the train's velocity. Substitution then yields

$$v_{P,G} = 2\frac{m}{s} + 30\frac{m}{s} \quad \rightarrow \quad v_{P,G} = 32\frac{m}{s}$$

Using relative motion to describe the relationship between the position and velocity of objects in different coordinate systems is also our first example of what is referred to as a ***coordinate transformation***.

Coordinate transformation: A change in the coordinate system used to describe a problem. This can include a change in the origin of the coordinate system and/or a change in the definition of the positive directions for the coordinate axes.

We will use additional simple coordinate transformations in Chapter 4 and Chapter 5 for other 1-dimensional motion calculations and then return to a discussion of relative motion in Chapter 13 and Chapter 14 when we learn about momentum.

2-7 Position, Velocity, and Acceleration for 2-Dimensional Motion

Throughout this course we will rely upon our ability to describe multi-dimensional motion as a collection of separate 1-dimensional motions. Consider, for example, the 2-dimensional motion depicted in Figure 2.12.

If the x-axis and y-axis are perpendicular to each other (*i.e.*, if the angle between the two axes is 90°), then an object can move along the x-axis without changing its position along the y-axis and move along the y-axis without changing its position along the x-axis. Because perpendicular axes allow for this straightforward description of multi-dimensional motions as a combination of separate and independent 1-dimensional motions, we will always use them in our coordinate systems.

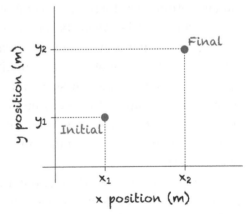

Figure 2.12: 2-dimensional motion from x_1 to x_2 and from y_1 to y_2.

With the appropriate perpendicular axes for our coordinate system, we can now describe the 2-dimensional motion in Figure 2.12 as a combination of two independent 1-dimensional motions: 1-dimensional motion along the x-axis from x_1 to x_2, and 1-dimensional motion along the y-axis from y_1 to y_2. If the object moves from its initial position to its final position during a time interval Δt, then the average velocity for these 1-dimensional motions would be

$$v_{x,avg} = \frac{\Delta x}{\Delta t} = \frac{x_f - x_i}{t_f - t_i}$$

$$v_{y,avg} = \frac{\Delta y}{\Delta t} = \frac{y_f - y_i}{t_f - t_i}$$

Example 2-6:

Problem: An object moves from $x_i = 0$ m and $y_i = 0$ to $x_f = 4$ m and $y_f = 6$ m in 2 s. What are the average x-axis and y-axis velocities for this motion?

Solution: Following the derivation above we have

$$v_{x,avg} = \frac{4\,m - 0\,m}{2s} \quad \rightarrow \quad v_{x,avg} = 2\frac{m}{s}$$

$$v_{y,avg} = \frac{6\,m - 0\,m}{2s} \quad \rightarrow \quad v_{y,avg} = 3\frac{m}{s}$$

Although we can describe the 2-dimensional motion in Figure 2.12 as a combination of independent 1-dimensional motions, there are, of course, several ways in which we can combine those 1-dimensional motions (*i.e.*, there are several paths by which the object can move between its initial and final position). Three possible paths are shown in Figure 2.13. In path 1, the x-axis and y-axis motion occur simultaneously; in path 2, the y-axis motion occurs first and then the x-axis motion occurs; and in path 3, the x-axis motion occurs first and then the y-axis motion occurs. There are, of course, countless more paths that connect the initial and final position of the object.

As we will discover throughout the course of this book, there are some parameters used to describe a system that depend upon the path taken by the system as it changes in configuration (*i.e.*, as the positions and velocities of the objects in the system change), and there are some parameters that are independent of the path taken by the system. For this reason, we must always be aware of the initial state of our system, the final state of our system, and the path by which the system transitions between those two states.

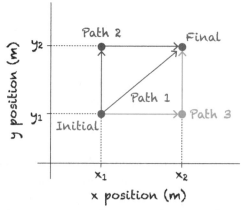

Figure 2.13: 2-dimensional motion from x_1 to x_2 and from y_1 to y_2 can occur over different paths.

Finally, let's consider the system shown in Figure 2.14 that consists of two blocks, A and B, which are connected to each other by a rope that passes over a pulley[1].

We can describe the position of the blocks using two separate 1-dimensional coordinate axes. For block A: the 1-dimensional axis, which we will denote as the x-axis, will be parallel to the horizontal surface on which block A sits and will have a positive direction pointing from block A to the pulley (*i.e.*, to the right in Figure 2.14). We can define an origin for the x-axis ($x = 0$) on this surface, and then denote the position of block A as x_A with respect to this origin (Figure 2.15).

For block B: the 1-dimensional axis will be the vertical direction in Figure 2.14, which we refer to as the y-axis. Furthermore, we can specify the floor or the ground to be the origin of the y-axis ($y = 0$) and denote the position of block B as y_B with respect to this origin (Figure 2.15).

As mentioned in Section 1-6, it is clear that the presence of the rope in this system provides a constraint on the motion of the two blocks. Specifically, if block A moves to the right (positive x-axis direction) 1 m then block B moves down (negative y-axis direction) by 1 m. We can express this relationship between the displacements of the two blocks mathematically as

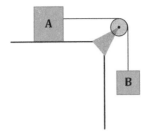

Figure 2.14: A system consisting of two blocks, a rope, and a pulley.

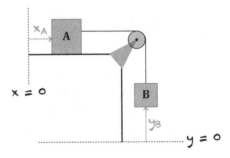

Figure 2.15: Description of the positions of the blocks in the system shown in Figure 2.14.

$$\frac{dy_B}{dx_A} = -1$$

Of course, had we defined different directions to be positive for the x-axis and y-axis in this problem this derivative could have had a different ($\pm$) sign.

Example 2-7:

Problem: A system consists of two blocks, A and B, connected by a single rope that passes over two pulleys, as shown in Figure 2.16. The x and y axes for describing the positions of the two blocks are also shown in the figure. For these axes, what is the value of $\frac{dy_B}{dx_A}$?

Solution: It is clear from Figure 2.16 that as block A moves in the positive x-axis direction, block B will move in the negative y-axis direction. From the orientation of the rope we also

---

1   We have seen this system before (in Section 1-6) and will see it many times again.

see that if block A moves 1 m, block B will move only 0.5 m. Thus,

$$\frac{dy_B}{dx_A} = -\frac{1}{2}$$

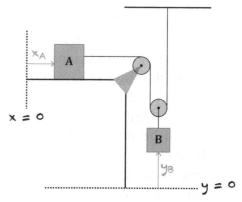

Figure 2.16: A system consisting of two blocks, a rope, and a pulley.

Summary

- **Vector:** A mathematical quantity specified by both a magnitude and a direction.
- **Position:** A vector quantity specifying the location of an object.
- **Displacement:** The change in the position of an object. It is a vector quantity that is independent of the origin of the coordinate system in which it is measured.

$$\Delta x = x_{final} - x_{initial}$$

- **Velocity:** The rate of change of position. Specifically, it is the first derivative of position with respect to time. Velocity is a vector quantity.

$$v = \frac{dx}{dt}$$

- **Acceleration:** The rate of change of velocity. Specifically, it is the first derivative of velocity with respect to time or the second derivative of position with respect to time. Acceleration is a vector quantity.

$$a = \frac{dv}{dt} = \frac{d^2x}{dt^2}$$

- **Equations for constant acceleration kinematics in 1-dimension.** The following equations can be used to relate the position, velocity, and acceleration of an object moving in 1-dimension with an acceleration that is constant in time. These equations are also presented in Appendix C in their vector form.

$$\Delta v = a \Delta t$$

$$\Delta x = v_i \Delta t + \frac{1}{2} a (\Delta t)^2$$

$$v_f^2 = v_i^2 + 2a \Delta x$$

- **The motion of objects in a system can be described using a coordinate axis with an origin external to the system or with an origin internal to the system (*e.g.*, an origin at the location of one of the objects in the system).**
- **Multi-dimensional motion of an object can be described in terms of the independent motion of the object along corresponding perpendicular 1-dimensional axes.**

Problems

1. The position of an object as a function of time is given by the equation:

$$x(t) = \left(2.5 \frac{m}{s^2}\right) t^2 + \left(1 \frac{m}{s^3}\right) t^3$$

   What are the velocity and acceleration of the object at $t = 2$ s?

2. An object is moving with a velocity given by the equation:

$$v(t) = \left(\frac{3}{2} \frac{m}{s^2}\right) t + \left(\frac{3}{2} \frac{m}{s^3}\right) t^2$$

   What is the magnitude of the displacement of the object during the time interval from $t = 0$ s to $t = 2$ s?

3. The figure below shows the acceleration-versus-time graph of an object moving in 1-dimension along the x-axis. The initial velocity of the particle is 2 m/s at $t = 0$ s. What is the particle's velocity at $t = 5$ s?

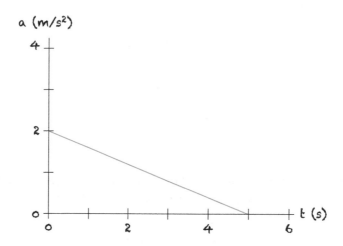

4. The figure below shows the velocity-versus-time graph of an object moving in 1-dimension along the x-axis. The particle was at the origin ($x = 0$ m) at $t = 0$ s. What is the particle's position at $t = 5$ s?

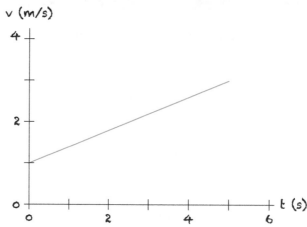

5. The velocity of a car increases from 10 m/s to 30 m/s at a constant acceleration of 4 m/s². What distance does it travel while accelerating?

6. The positions of two objects, labeled A and B, moving in 1-dimension along the x-axis are shown in the figure at right. Do the two objects ever have the same velocity? If so, between which two time points? Do the objects ever have the same acceleration? If so, between which two time points?

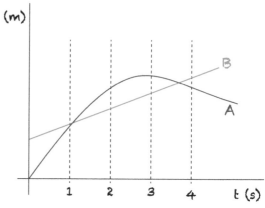

7. The velocity of an object moving in 1-dimension along the x-axis as a function of time is shown in the figure at right. At $t = 0$ s the object was at $x = 2$ m. What is the position of the object at $t = 3$ s?

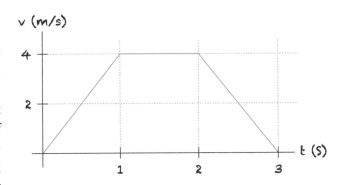

8. A car starts from rest and accelerates at a constant rate travelling a distance of 100 m in 5 s. The car continues to accelerate at the same rate for an additional 300 m. What is the speed of the car after it has travelled the full 400 m?

9. A car starts from rest and accelerates at 3 m/s² in a straight line until it reaches a speed of 36 m/s. The car then accelerates at -2 m/s² until it stops. How much time passes between when the car starts moving and when it stops?

10. Two football players are running directly towards each other. At one instant they are 28 m apart from each other and running with speeds of 3 m/s and 4 m/s, respectively. How much time will pass from this instant until they collide?

11. A train is moving in 1-dimension with a speed of a 25 m/s. A person on the train is walking in the opposite direction of the train's velocity with a speed of 2 m/s relative to the train. What is the speed of this person relative to the ground?

12. While you are driving a pedestrian jumps out onto the road 100 m ahead of you. Because you were texting while driving, you are not immediately aware that the pedestrian is in your path and don't step on the brakes until 1.5 s later. While skidding toward the pedestrian, the magnitude of your car's acceleration is 5 m/s². What is the maximum initial speed you could have had to avoid hitting the pedestrian?

CHAPTER THREE
Energy and Energy Conservation

3-1 Introduction

As we have discussed in the two previous chapters, each object in a system may have kinetic and/or potential energies depending upon its location and motion. Furthermore, since energy is an extensive parameter, the total energy in a system of objects is the sum of all the separate energies of the constituent objects. In this chapter, we will introduce three of these energies that are related to position and motion.

3-2 Translational Kinetic Energy

Kinetic energy is an energy related to the motion of an object (Section 1-2). If an object is moving in any direction at any speed, it has kinetic energy. Because there are several ways in which objects can move (in a straight line, in a circle, *etc.*), there is, naturally, more than one kind of kinetic energy. We define **translational kinetic energy** as the energy associated with the *linear* movement of an object (*i.e.*, the motion of an object along a 1-dimensional axis).

Translational kinetic energy: Energy associated with the linear motion of an object.

The equation for translational kinetic energy for 1-dimensional motion is

$$K = \frac{1}{2}mv^2 \tag{3-1}$$

In Equation 3-1, m is the mass of the object measured in kg, and v^2 is the square of the speed with units of $(m/s)^2$. Notice that since the translational kinetic energy depends upon v^2, the direction of the velocity, which is indicated by a $(\pm)$ sign for 1-dimensional motion (Section 2-2), is not relevant.

All that matters is the magnitude of the velocity (*i.e.*, the speed), which means that translational kinetic energy is a *scalar* quantity. The units of translational kinetic energy are joules (J).

$$1J = 1\frac{kg\,m^2}{s^2}$$

Example 3-1:

Problem: A 2 kg block is moving with a velocity of 2 m/s. The translational kinetic energy of the block then increases by 21 J. What is the new speed of the block?

Solution:

$$\Delta K = K_f - K_i \;\;\rightarrow\;\; K_f = K_i + \Delta K$$

$$K_f = \frac{1}{2}\left(2kg\right)\left(2\frac{m}{s}\right)^2 + 21J \;\;\rightarrow\;\; K_f = 4J + 21J \;\;\rightarrow\;\; K_f = 25J$$

$$\frac{1}{2}\left(2kg\right)v_f^2 = 25J \;\;\rightarrow\;\; v_f^2 = 25\frac{m^2}{s^2} \;\;\rightarrow\;\; v_f = \pm 5\frac{m}{s}$$

The ($\pm$) sign in our solution reminds us that translational kinetic energy is independent of the direction of the velocity[1]. Furthermore, since this question asked for the speed of the object, we need only report the magnitude of our solution.

$$v_f = 5\frac{m}{s}$$

3-3 Gravitational Potential Energy

The gravitational interaction between objects gives rise to a potential energy that depends upon the masses of the objects and the distance between them. Gravitational potential energy is, thus, different from translational kinetic energy since it exists because of the interaction between

---

1   Another way of interpreting this result is that the assignment of the positive and negative directions for the coordinate axis for measurements of position is arbitrary.

two objects. The equation for the gravitational potential energy of two objects (with masses m_1 and m_2) separated by a distance r is

$$U_g = -G\frac{m_1 m_2}{r}$$

(3-2)

In this equation, G is the gravitational constant of the universe.

$$G = 6.67 \times 10^{-11}\frac{\text{Jm}}{\text{kg}^2}$$

It follows that the units of gravitational potential energy are also joules. Furthermore, since the magnitude of the gravitational constant is so small, large masses and/or small distances are required for objects to have significant values for gravitational potential energy. For example, in this course, we will often be concerned with the gravitational potential energy of macroscopic objects (blocks, balls, *etc.*) interacting with the Earth, which has a very large mass.

Strictly speaking, Equation 3-2 is valid only when the distance r is much larger than the physical dimension (length, width, *etc.*) of the objects. However, throughout most of this book, we will use Equation 3-2 even when this requirement is not satisfied. This is the first instance in which we will use an approximation. Approximations are helpful tools that we will employ often to simplify systems and/or the mathematics associated with their descriptions. In this case, we will be invoking what is commonly referred to as the *point particle approximation* in which we treat objects as though they were points without any physical size. When using the point particle approximation, we will usually define the location of the "point" corresponding to an object to be at the geometric center of the object[2].

Example 3-2:

Problem: Consider a 2 kg block lying on the ground. What is the gravitational potential energy of this block and (i) a 4 kg block lying on the ground 3 m away; (ii) the Earth?

Solution: We answer both questions using Equation 3-2.
(i) For the 2 kg block and the 4 kg block, we have

$$U_g = -\left(6.67 \times 10^{-11}\frac{\text{Jm}}{\text{kg}^2}\right)\frac{(2\,\text{kg})(4\,\text{kg})}{3\,\text{m}} \quad \rightarrow \quad U_g = -1.78 \times 10^{-10}\text{J}$$

(ii) To determine the gravitational potential energy of the 2 kg block and the Earth, we define the point corresponding to the Earth to be located at the center of the Earth. Thus,

---

2   We will discuss this further in Section 10-5.

the distance between the object and the Earth that we will substitute into Equation 3-2 is the radius of the Earth.

$$U_g = -\left(6.67\times10^{-11}\,\frac{Jm}{kg^2}\right)\frac{(2kg)(5.97\times10^{24}\,kg)}{6.37\times10^6\,m} \quad \rightarrow \quad U_g = -1.25\times10^8\,J$$

Note that gravitational potential energy of the 2 kg block and the Earth is many orders of magnitude larger than the gravitational potential energy of the 2 kg block and the 4 kg block.

When calculating the gravitational potential energy between the Earth and objects near the surface of the Earth, it is common to use a simplified form of Equation 3-2. Let's consider a small object of mass m that is a height y above the surface of the Earth; we will again invoke a point particle approximation for both the Earth and the object. The gravitational potential between this object and the Earth is

$$U_g = -G\frac{M_E m}{R_E + y} \quad \rightarrow \quad U_g = -G\frac{M_E m}{R_E\left(1+\dfrac{y}{R_E}\right)}$$

In this equation, M_E and R_E denote the mass and radius of the Earth, respectively. We can expand the term in parenthesis in the denominator using the binomial expansion.

$$(1+x)^n = 1 + nx + \frac{n(n-1)}{2!}x^2 + \frac{n(n-1)(n-2)}{3!}x^3 + \ldots$$

Thus,

$$\frac{1}{\left(1+\dfrac{y}{R_E}\right)} = \left(1+\frac{y}{R_E}\right)^{-1} = 1 - \frac{y}{R_E} + \left(\frac{y}{R_E}\right)^2 - \left(\frac{y}{R_E}\right)^3 + \ldots$$

Now, let's restrict our interest to those instances in which the values of y are much smaller than R_E; this will be true for most problems we'll encounter in this book. This assumption allows us to approximate our expansion with only the first two terms. Under these conditions, we have

$$U_g = -G\frac{M_E m}{R_E}\left(1+\frac{y}{R_E}\right)^{-1} \quad \rightarrow \quad U_g \approx -G\frac{M_E m}{R_E}\left(1-\frac{y}{R_E}\right)$$

We, therefore, have two terms for our potential energy equation.

$$U_g = -G\frac{M_E m}{R_E} + G\frac{M_E m}{R_E^2} y \quad \rightarrow \quad U_g = \left(U_g\right)_0 + mgy$$

(3-3)

In Equation 3-3, we have defined the scalar g as

$$g = G\frac{M_E}{R_E^2} \quad \rightarrow \quad g = 9.8\frac{m}{s^2}$$

The first term in Equation 3-3 is the gravitational potential energy between the object and the Earth when the object is at the surface of the Earth.

$$\left(U_g\right)_0 = -\left(6.67\times10^{-11}\frac{Jm}{kg^2}\right)\frac{\left(5.97\times10^{24}\,kg\right)m}{6.37\times10^6\,m} \quad \rightarrow \quad \left(U_g\right)_0 = -\left(6.3\times10^7\frac{J}{kg}\right)m$$

The second term in Equation 3-3 is the additional gravitational potential energy between the object and the Earth when the object is not on the surface of the Earth. As we shall see, this second term is more important than the first for most of our calculations.

Example 3-3:

Problem: A system consists of the Earth and a 2 kg block. The 2 kg block is initially 5 m above the ground and when released from rest falls down to the ground. What is the change in the gravitational potential energy of this system when the block reaches the ground?

Solution:

$$\Delta U_g = \left(U_g\right)_f - \left(U_g\right)_i$$

$$\Delta U_g = \left(\left(U_g\right)_0 + mgy_f\right) - \left(\left(U_g\right)_0 + mgy_i\right)$$

$$\Delta U_g = \left(\left(U_g\right)_0 - \left(U_g\right)_0\right) + \left(mgy_f - mgy_i\right)$$

$$\Delta U_g = mgy_f - mgy_i \quad \rightarrow \quad \Delta U_g = mg\Delta y$$

$$\Delta U_g = \left(2kg\right)\left(9.8\frac{m}{s^2}\right)\left(0-5m\right) \quad \rightarrow \quad \Delta U_g = -98J$$

The negative sign in our solution informs us that the gravitational potential energy of the system has decreased.

It is important to note that although the $\left(U_g\right)_0$ term in Equation 3-3 is much larger than the mgy term, it does not contribute to calculations of ΔU_g since it is a constant and, thus, always cancels out by subtraction, as shown in Example 3-3, or through differentiation, as we shall see in Chapter 4. Indeed, the change in gravitational potential energy of the system in Example 3-3 was dependent upon only the vertical displacement of the block (Δy).

In general, it is changes in the energy of a system rather than absolute values of the energy that are important for mechanics. Because of this, we can effectively ignore the contributions of $\left(U_g\right)_0$ to the gravitational potential energy of systems in our solutions to mechanics problems. We can also consider this as "*redefining*" the zero point of the gravitational potential energy equation (Equation 3-3) to be located at the surface of the Earth. Indeed, since the change in the gravitational potential energy of the object depends upon only the vertical displacement of the object, it must be independent of the origin of the coordinate system used to define the vertical position of the object[3].

3-4 Spring Potential Energy

The potential energy of a spring is a function of both the "*stiffness*" of the spring and the extent to which the spring has been extended or compressed. The equation for this potential energy is:

$$U_s = \frac{1}{2}k\left(l - l_0\right)^2$$

(3-4)

In this equation, k is the spring constant, and l_0 is the normal length of the spring (*i.e.*, l_0 corresponds to the length of the spring when it is neither compressed nor extended). The normal length of a spring is often also referred to as its unstretched length. The spring constant is a measure of the "*stiffness*" of the spring and has units[4] of J/m^2; the larger the value of k, the more difficult it is to compress or extend the spring. Finally, it follows from Equation 3-4 that the units of spring potential energy are also joules.

Example 3-4:

Problem: A spring with a spring constant of 50 J/m² and a normal length of 50 cm is initially compressed to 40 cm. What is the change in the potential energy of the spring if it is further compressed to 30 cm?

---

3   Recall from Section 2-2 that displacements are independent of the origin of the coordinate system used to measure position.
4   We will introduce alternative units for the spring constant in Section 7-2.

Solution:

$$\Delta U_s = \left(U_s\right)_f - \left(U_s\right)_i \quad \rightarrow \quad \Delta U_s = \frac{1}{2}k\left(l_f - l_0\right)^2 - \frac{1}{2}k\left(l_i - l_0\right)^2$$

$$\Delta U_s = \frac{1}{2}k\left(\left(l_f - l_0\right)^2 - \left(l_i - l_0\right)^2\right)$$

$$\Delta U_s = \frac{1}{2}\left(50\frac{J}{m^2}\right)\left(\left(0.3\,m - 0.5\,m\right)^2 - \left(0.4\,m - 0.5\,m\right)^2\right)$$

$$\Delta U_s = \left(25\frac{J}{m^2}\right)\left(0.04\,m^2 - 0.01\,m^2\right) \quad \rightarrow \quad \Delta U_s = 0.75\,J$$

Throughout this book we will assume that springs behave ideally. That is, their potential energy is described by Equation 3-4 regardless of the magnitude of the compression or extension. In real life, however, very large compressions or extensions of springs can result in behavior that cannot be described by this equation alone. Furthermore, we will assume that all springs are massless so that we do not need to consider their kinetic and gravitational potential energies.

3-5 Energy Conservation in Isolated Systems

We know from our discussion in Section 1-3 that the total energy of an isolated system will be constant. Therefore, any energy conversion that occurs for an isolated system must occur within the system and not involve interactions between the system and the outside environment. This fact forms the basis of a powerful problem-solving strategy that we will employ in this book. However, the successful application of this strategy requires us to define the system correctly and usefully.

Let's consider an isolated system that consists of the Earth and a small block that is initially held in place a short distance above the ground (*e.g.*, the system discussed in Example 3-3). When the block is released from rest, this system will react in order to minimize its total potential energy; this is a consequence of the principle of minimum potential energy (Section 1-4). Interestingly, *this reaction will consist of both the block falling down toward the Earth and the Earth moving up toward the block*. Because this system is isolated, as the block and the Earth move toward each other, their gravitational potential energy is converted into the separate and distinct translational kinetic energies of the block and the Earth (Section 1-3). However, because the Earth has a much larger mass than the block, nearly all of this converted energy will be transferred to the translational kinetic energy of the block; we will discuss this further in Chapter 13. Because of this large asymmetry in the energy conversion process, we can ignore the motion of the Earth and approximate this system to consist of only the block. In this definition of the system, the gravitational potential energy that exists between the Earth and the block is defined to be *"possessed"* by the block only since it will be converted almost exclusively into the translational kinetic energy of the block.

Because so many of our examples will involve a gravitational interaction with the Earth, we will continue to use this assumption and limit our definition of systems to include only the objects that are undergoing significant changes in energy as well as anything serving to connect these objects (ropes, springs, pulleys, *etc.*).

Example 3-5:

Problem: A 4 kg block is released from rest 3.6 m above the ground. What is the speed of the block when it hits the ground? You may treat the block as an isolated system.

Solution: In this problem, the system consists of only the block. The energy of this system is the sum of the kinetic and potential energies of the block alone.

$$E = K + U_g$$

Because this system is isolated, its energy will be constant. In other words, the energy of the system will not change as the block falls to the ground.

$$\Delta E = 0 \quad \rightarrow \quad \Delta K + \Delta U_g = 0 \quad \rightarrow \quad \Delta K = -\Delta U_g$$

Therefore, the translational kinetic energy of the block increases as the gravitational potential energy of the block decreases. Another way of saying this is that the gravitational potential energy of the block is *converted* into the translational kinetic energy of the block as the block falls.

Substitution of the equations for the translational kinetic and gravitational potential energy gives us

$$\Delta K + \Delta U_g = 0 \quad \rightarrow \quad \left(\frac{1}{2}mv_f^2 - \frac{1}{2}mv_i^2 \right) + mg\Delta y = 0$$

$$v_f^2 - v_i^2 + 2g\Delta y = 0 \quad \rightarrow \quad v_f^2 = v_i^2 - 2g\Delta y$$

The initial point of this equation refers to when the mass is at rest 5 m above the ground.

$$v_i = 0 \qquad y_i = 5\text{m}$$

The final point of this equation refers to when the mass is moving and has just hit the ground.

$$y_f = 0\,\text{m}$$

Substitution then yields

$$v_f^2 = 0 - 2\left(9.8\,\frac{\text{m}}{\text{s}^2}\right)\left(0\,\text{m} - 3.6\,\text{m}\right) \quad \rightarrow \quad v_f^2 = 70.56\,\frac{\text{m}^2}{\text{s}^2}$$

$$v_f = \pm 8.4\,\frac{\text{m}}{\text{s}}$$

Since the question asked for the speed of the block when it hit the ground, we need report only the magnitude of our result.

$$v_f = 8.4\,\frac{\text{m}}{\text{s}}$$

Example 3-6:

Problem: A block with a mass of 4 kg is moving across a horizontal surface with a speed of 5 m/s when it collides with a horizontally mounted massless spring with a spring constant of 400 J/m² and a normal length of 75 cm. What is the minimum length of the spring following the collision of the block with the spring? You may treat the block and spring together as an isolated system.

Solution: We can use the following picture to denote the variables in our problem and to illustrate the system that constitutes our problem.

Figure 3.1: Pictorial representation of Example 3-6.

In this case, the system consists of the block and the spring. The energy of the system is the sum of the kinetic and potential energies of these two objects.

$$E = K + U_g + U_s$$

Because this system is isolated, its energy will be constant.

$$\Delta E = 0 \quad \rightarrow \quad \Delta K + \Delta U_g + \Delta U_s = 0$$

Since the spring is massless, the only contribution to the gravitational potential energy and the translational kinetic energy of the system comes from the block. However, because the block is moving across a horizontal surface, there will be no change in its gravitational potential energy as it moves.

$$\Delta U_g = mg\Delta y \quad \rightarrow \quad \Delta U_g = \left(4\,\text{kg}\right)\left(9.8\,\frac{\text{m}}{\text{s}^2}\right)\left(0\,\text{m}\right) \quad \rightarrow \quad \Delta U_g = 0\,\text{J}$$

Thus, our equation for energy conservation becomes

$$\Delta K + \Delta U_s = 0 \quad \rightarrow \quad \Delta U_s = -\Delta K$$

In other words, the potential energy of the spring increases as the translational kinetic energy of the block decreases. To put it another way, the translational kinetic energy of the block is converted into the potential energy of the spring as the block compresses the spring.

The maximum compression of the spring occurs when the potential energy of the spring is the largest. Therefore, the maximum compression of the spring will occur when the translational kinetic energy of the block has decreased to its smallest value. The smallest translational kinetic energy of the block is zero, corresponding to when the block has stopped moving[5]. Let's take this to be the final point in our energy conservation equation and use a time before the collision for the initial point. Before the collision has occurred, the length of the spring will be equal to its normal length, and the potential energy associated with the spring will be zero.

$$\Delta K + \Delta U_s = 0 \quad \rightarrow \quad \left(\frac{1}{2}mv_f^2 - \frac{1}{2}mv_i^2\right) + \left(\frac{1}{2}k\left(l_f - l_0\right)^2 - \frac{1}{2}k\left(l_i - l_0\right)^2\right) = 0$$

Let's simplify this a bit.

$$\frac{1}{2}m\left(v_f^2 - v_i^2\right) + \frac{1}{2}k\left(\left(l_f - l_0\right)^2 - \left(l_i - l_0\right)^2\right) = 0 \quad \rightarrow \quad m\left(v_f^2 - v_i^2\right) + k\left(\left(l_f - l_0\right)^2 - \left(l_i - l_0\right)^2\right) = 0$$

---

5 This makes sense. If the block were moving then the length of the spring would be changing. Only when the block has stopped moving is the spring at its minimum length.

Applying our initial and final conditions gives us

$$m\left((0)^2 - v_0^2\right) + k\left(\left(l_f - l_0\right)^2 - \left(l_i - l_i\right)^2\right) = 0$$

$$m\left(0 - v_0^2\right) + k\left(\left(l_f - l_0\right)^2 - 0\right) = 0 \quad \rightarrow \quad k\left(l_f - l_0\right)^2 = mv_0^2$$

Substitution of the values of the variables then yields

$$\left(400\frac{J}{m^2}\right)\left(l_f - l_0\right)^2 = \left(4\,kg\right)\left(5\frac{m}{s}\right)^2 \quad \rightarrow \quad \left(l_f - l_0\right)^2 = 0.25\,m^2$$

$$\left(l_f - l_0\right) = \pm 0.5\,m$$

The ($\pm$) sign is there since the spring can store potential energy by being compressed or by being extended. In this case, the spring must be compressed, and, therefore, the negative sign is appropriate.

$$l_f = l_0 - 0.5\,m \quad \rightarrow \quad l_f = 0.75\,m - 0.5\,m \quad \rightarrow \quad l_f = 0.25\,m$$

Example 3-7:

Problem: A 1.5 kg block is released from rest touching a spring with spring constant of 200 J/m² and an initial compression of 20 cm, as shown in the Figure 3.2. What is the maximum distance travelled by the block up the nearby ramp? You may treat this as an isolated system.

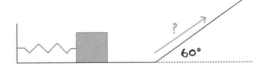

Figure 3.2: The system in Example 3-7.

Solution: Let's choose as the initial and final points for our energy conservation equation to be the instant the block is released and when the block reaches its highest point on the ramp, respectively. When the block has travelled its maximum distance up the ramp, its speed will be zero. Before the block is released, it is also at rest. Therefore, both the initial and final translational kinetic energies of the system are zero, and we can write our energy conservation equation as

$$\Delta U_g + \Delta U_s = 0 \quad \rightarrow \quad mg\Delta y + \left(\frac{1}{2}k\left(l_f - l_0\right)^2 - \frac{1}{2}k\left(l_i - l_0\right)^2\right) = 0$$

$$mg\Delta y + \frac{1}{2}k\left(\left(l_f - l_0\right)^2 - \left(l_i - l_0\right)^2\right) = 0$$

When the block is at its highest point on the ramp, the spring is no longer in contact with the block and, thus, must be at its normal length. Therefore,

$$mg\Delta y - \frac{1}{2}k\left(l_i - l_0\right)^2 = 0 \quad \rightarrow \quad \Delta y = \frac{k\left(l_i - l_0\right)^2}{2mg}$$

$$\Delta y = \frac{\left(200\frac{J}{m^2}\right)\left(0.2m\right)^2}{2\left(1.5kg\right)\left(9.8\frac{m}{s^2}\right)} \quad \rightarrow \quad \Delta y = 27.2cm$$

We can then use trigonometry to relate the distance up the ramp to the change in the height of the block. As shown in Figure 3.3, we can designate a new 1-dimensional coordinate axis, which we will call the s-axis, to be aligned parallel to the surface of the ramp with a positive direction pointing up the ramp. This change in the coordinate axis used to describe the position of the block is another example of coordinate transformation, as discussed in Section 2-6.

We can relate changes in position along the s axis to changes along the y axis using trigonometry.

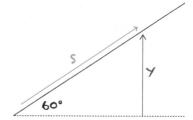

Figure 3.3: Relationship between the s-axis and y-axis for the system in Example 3-7.

$$\sin\left(60°\right) = \frac{y}{s} \quad \rightarrow \quad \sin\left(60°\right)s = y \quad \rightarrow \quad \sin\left(60°\right)\Delta s = \Delta y$$

Thus,

$$\Delta s = \frac{\Delta y}{\sin\left(60°\right)} \quad \rightarrow \quad \Delta s = \frac{27.2cm}{\frac{\sqrt{3}}{2}}$$

$$\Delta s = 31.4\,cm$$

3-6 Energy Conservation in Non-Isolated Systems

In non-isolated systems, energy is exchanged with the outside environment (Section 1-3). A common example is the energy exchange resulting from friction, which is an interaction occurring when two surfaces move past each other. Friction opposes the motion of these surfaces and, thus, decreases their kinetic energies. We refer to this decrease in energy as a *dissipation of energy* from the system and can model it as a rate of energy decrease per distance traveled by the surfaces (*i.e.*, by the corresponding objects).

When objects move through fluids like air or water, they interact directly with the molecules of the fluid (*e.g.*, through collisions). This interaction, which also results in energy dissipation, is referred to as drag. Drag is distinguished from friction in that the magnitude of the drag interaction is dependent upon the velocity of the object moving in the fluid, whereas the magnitude of the friction interaction is independent of the velocity of the moving surfaces.

Friction and drag are both examples of *mechanical interactions* (*i.e.*, pushes or pulls). A change in energy of a system that results from a mechanical is referred to as **work**.

> *Work: A change in energy associated with a mechanical interaction. Work is denoted by the variable W.*

This is another example of words having specific definitions in physics that may differ from the definitions in everyday language. Specifically, work is not a measure of energy but rather a measure of a *change* in energy.

Example 3-8:

Problem: A block with a mass of 4 kg is sliding across a horizontal surface with an initial speed of 5 m/s. Because of friction, the energy of the block will decrease linearly with the distance travelled by the block at a constant rate of 2.5 J/m. How far will the block slide before coming to a rest?

Solution: In this problem, the system consists of only the block. The energy of this system is the sum of the kinetic and potential energies of the block.

$$E = K + U_g$$

The change in the energy of this system resulting from the friction interaction is equal to the work done on the system by friction.

$$\Delta E = W_{friction} \quad \rightarrow \quad \Delta K + \Delta U_g = W_{friction}$$

Because the surface along which the block slides is horizontal, there is no change in the gravitational potential energy of the block as it slides

$$\Delta y = 0 \quad \rightarrow \quad \Delta U_g = 0$$

When the block comes to a rest, its speed and translational kinetic energy are zero. Let's define this to be the final point for our energy conservation equation. The initial point will correspond to when the block had a speed of 5 m/s. Thus,

$$W_{friction} = \Delta K \quad \rightarrow \quad W_{friction} = \frac{1}{2}mv_f^2 - \frac{1}{2}mv_i^2 \quad \rightarrow \quad W_{friction} = -\frac{1}{2}mv_i^2$$

$$W_{friction} = -\frac{1}{2}(4\,\text{kg})\left(5\,\frac{\text{m}}{\text{s}}\right)^2 \quad \rightarrow \quad W_{friction} = -50\,\text{J}$$

We can determine the distance the object slides by dividing this work by the rate at which friction dissipates energy from the system.

$$\Delta x = \frac{-50\,\text{J}}{-2.5\,\dfrac{\text{J}}{\text{m}}} \quad \rightarrow \quad \Delta x = 20\,\text{m}$$

This solution to Example 3-8 demonstrates a useful general statement.

The work done on a system by friction is always negative.

We will return to this statement in Chapter 7 and Chapter 9 to understand why it is true. For now, it is sufficient for us to recognize that the work done by friction or drag is negative since these interactions "*pull back*" on moving objects and, thus, reduce both the speed and the translational kinetic energy of these objects. Similarly, positive work would be done on an object if an object was pushed forward, and its speed and translational kinetic energy increased.

Example 3-9:

Problem: A pitcher is able to accelerate a 140 g baseball from rest to a speed of 40 m/s over a distance of 1.5 m. What is the work done on the ball by the pitcher?

Solution: In this problem, the system consists of only the baseball. The energy of this system is the sum of the kinetic and potential energies of the ball.

$$E = K + U_g$$

The pitcher is able to change the energy of the system by *doing work* on the ball; specifically, by pushing or throwing the ball. We will assume that the system is otherwise isolated, so we can ignore any work done by drag (*i.e.*, air resistance). We will also use the approximation that there is no net change in the vertical position of the ball during the pitch, and, therefore, that there is no change in the gravitational potential energy of the ball. With these assumptions we have

$$\Delta E = W_{pitcher} \quad \rightarrow \quad \Delta K = W_{pitcher}$$

$$W_{pitcher} = K_f - K_i \quad \rightarrow \quad W_{pitcher} = \frac{1}{2}(0.14\,\text{kg})\left(40\frac{\text{m}}{\text{s}}\right)^2 - \frac{1}{2}(0.14\,\text{kg})\left(0\frac{\text{m}}{\text{s}}\right)^2$$

$$W_{pitcher} = 112\,\text{J}$$

The basic model for energy conservation is shown in Figure 3.4. The total energy of a system is the sum of the kinetic and potential energy of the objects that constitute the system. Through processes internal to the system, kinetic and potential energy can be converted back and forth into each other, but these processes cannot affect the total energy of the system. If the system is isolated, its total energy will be constant. However, if the system is not isolated, then its energy can change because of work done by mechanical interactions with the

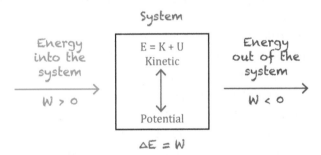

Figure 3.4: The definitions of positive and negative work for the energy conservation model of a system. In this figure the variable W denotes work done on the system.

outside environment. This work done on the system is positive if the associated interaction is adding energy into the system and the work done on the system is negative if it is dissipating energy from the system.

Please note that in Figure 3.4 changes in the energy of the system are related to work done *on the system*. In Chapter 15 we will redraw this figure in terms of work done *by the system,* as this is the more common description for thermodynamics. These two quantities (*i.e.*, work done on the system and work done by the system) are related by a negative sign but, unfortunately, are both commonly denoted by the variable W.

3-7 Graphical Representations of Energy Conservation

Graphical representations of the energy of the system provide a simple way to visualize energy conservation. Consider the system shown in Figure 3.5, which consists of a block sliding along a frictionless surface that inclines upward at an angle θ on both ends. The potential energy of this system as a function of the position of the block is also shown in Figure 3.5; in this plot, we have defined the zero point of the gravitational potential energy to be the horizontal surface upon which the block moves.

Let's assume that the block is released from rest on the incline at position 1 in Figure 3.6. Since the block is released from rest, there is no energy associated with the motion of the block (*i.e.*, it has no translational kinetic energy). Therefore, all of the energy of the system at this position is the gravitational potential energy of the block. Let's denote this energy as E_i. Because the system is isolated (the surface is frictionless), we know that this energy will be constant regardless of the position of the block. We can represent the total system energy, E, as a horizontal line in Figure 3.6 with a constant value of E_i.

From the principle of minimum potential energy (Section 1-4), we know that this system will always arrange itself in order to minimize its total potential energy. It is clear from Figure 3.6 that the total potential energy of this system will be minimized if the block slides down the incline. Because the system is isolated, as the block slides down the incline, the gravitational potential energy of the system is being converted into translational kinetic energy—specifically, into the translational kinetic energy of the block, which is the only object in the system. As shown in Figure 3.6, the translational kinetic energy of the system is simply the difference between the curve for the total energy of the system and the curve for the total potential energy of the system.

Once the block has reached the horizontal surface (*e.g.*, at position 2), the gravitational potential energy of the system is zero, and the translational kinetic energy of

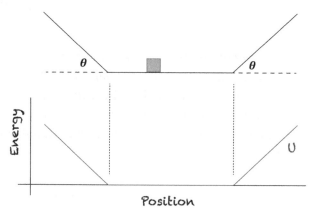

Figure 3.5: A system consisting of a block moving along a frictionless surface (top panel). The total potential energy of this system as a function of the position of the block is shown in the bottom panel. The zero point of the gravitational potential energy is defined to be the horizontal surface.

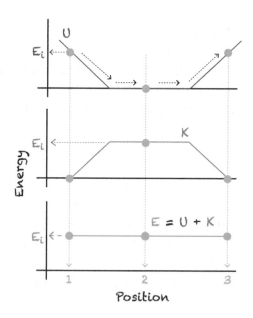

Figure 3.6: The total potential energy (blue), translational kinetic energy (green), and total system energy (red) for the system in Figure 3.5 as a function of the position of the block. The dashed black lines indicate the response of the system to being initially placed in position 1.

the system is equal to the total energy of the system. In other words, at position 2, the translational kinetic energy of the system is equal to the initial potential energy of the system[6].

Because the block has non-zero translational kinetic energy at position 2, it also has a non-zero speed there. It will, therefore, continue to move to the right and, eventually, will slide up the incline on the right side of Figure 3.5. As it moves up this incline, the translational kinetic energy of the system will be continuously converted back into gravitational potential energy. As the translational kinetic energy of the system decreases, the speed of the block also decreases. Eventually, at position 3, the translational kinetic energy of the system has been completely converted to gravitational potential energy and is, thus, zero; at this position the speed is also zero. Therefore, at position 3, the total potential energy of the system is, again, equal to the total energy of the system, as when the object was first released. The object is no longer moving at position 3, and, thus, this position corresponds to the maximum distance travelled by the block up the incline. Since the angle of the two inclines are identical (Figure 3.5), the vertical positions of the object above the horizontal surface at positions 1 and 3 are equal.

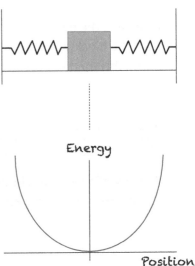

Upon reaching position 3, the block will then begin to slide back down the incline in order to minimize the total potential energy of the system once again. If left alone, the block would constantly move back and forth between positions 1 and 3 forever because no energy will ever be dissipated from the system. These two positions are referred to as turning points; they represent the positions where there is a change in the direction of the velocities of the objects in the system.

We can also use this graphical approach to represent energy conservation for non-isolated systems. Consider the system shown in Figure 3.7, which consists of a block that is attached to two horizontally mounted springs and can slide across a horizontal surface. The springs are neither stretched nor compressed when the block is at the center of the horizontal surface. The total potential energy of this system is shown in Figure 3.7; we have defined the zero point of the gravitational potential energy to be

Figure 3.7: A system consisting of a block attached to two springs (top panel). The total potential energy of this system as a function of the position of the block is shown in the bottom panel.

the horizontal surface, and the origin of our position axis to be at the center of the horizontal surface.

If the surface was frictionless, and the block was initially displaced from the center position (*i.e.*, if one spring was compressed and the other extended) and then released from rest from this position, the block would move back and forth between the two turning points, as shown in Figure 3.8. However, if there is friction present, energy will be dissipated from the system as the block moves back and forth across the horizontal surface.

As shown in Figure 3.8, this net decrease in the energy of the system due to energy dissipation by friction will have several effects on the movement of the block. First, the size of the displacement between the turning points will decrease. In other words, the distance travelled by the block between

---

6   Please note that all positions along the horizontal surface are also neutral equilibrium points, as discussed in Section 1-5.

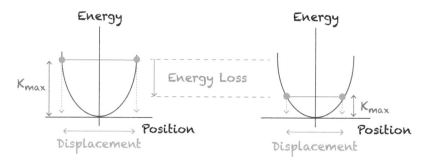

Figure 3.8: As energy is dissipated from the system, both the maximum translational kinetic energy (K_{max}) and the total displacement between turning points (orange circles) will decrease.

each change in the direction of its velocity will decrease. Second, the maximum translational kinetic energy of the block will decrease. Eventually, because of friction, the block will come to rest at the stable equilibrium point corresponding to the minimal potential of the system (*i.e.*, the center of the two springs).

Summary

- **Energy of a system:** The sum of the kinetic and potential energies of the objects in the system.
- **Translational kinetic energy:** Energy associated with the linear motion of an object.

$$K = \frac{1}{2}mv^2$$

- **Gravitational potential energy:** Energy associated with the gravitational interaction between two objects.

$$U_g = -G\frac{m_1 m_2}{r}$$

The gravitational potential energy of objects near the surface of the Earth is

$$U_g = \left(U_g\right)_0 + mgy$$

- **Spring potential energy:** Energy associated with the compression or extension of a spring.

$$U_s = \frac{1}{2}k\left(l - l_0\right)^2$$

- **Work:** A change in the energy of a system associated with a mechanical interaction.
- **Energy conservation:** Systems can convert their potential energy into kinetic energy and their kinetic energy into potential energy without changing their total energy. Mechanical interactions with the outside environment result in work being done on the system, which changes the total energy of the system. As shown in the figure below, this work is positive if the energy of the system is increasing and negative if the energy of the system is decreasing.

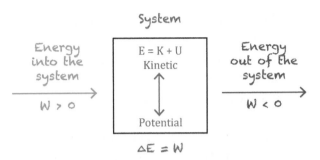

Problems

1. A 5000 kg asteroid is hurtling toward the earth at 100 km/s. What is the asteroid's translational kinetic energy in terms of the number of tons of exploding TNT producing the same energy? The energy released in the explosion of one ton of TNT is 4×10^9J.

2. The masses of the Sun and the Earth are 2×10^{30} kg and 6×10^{24} kg, respectively. What is the gravitational potential energy of their interaction at their average separation of 1.5×10^{11} m?

3. A block is released from rest on a frictionless track at a height h_1 above the ground, as shown in the figure at right. What is the speed of the object as it passes over the subsequent hill with height h_2?

4. The three identical blocks shown in the figure below right have equal masses and are thrown with equal speeds from the same height above the ground. The directions of the arrows indicate the directions at which the blocks were thrown. Rank from highest to lowest the speeds of the blocks when they hit the ground. You may assume each block constitutes an isolated system.

5. A ball is thrown straight up with an initial speed of 20 m/s. The ball was released 2 m above the ground, but when it returns back down it falls into a 11.5 m deep hole. What is the ball's speed at the bottom of the hole? Assume this is an isolated system.

6. Two identical cars, A and B, are moving in a straight line. Car A accelerates from 5 m/s to 10 m/s, and car B accelerates from 10 m/s to 15 m/s. The acceleration of which car required the larger input of energy? Consider these cars to be isolated systems.

7. Two blocks are released from rest at the top of separate ramps, as shown in the figure on the right. The initial vertical displacement of each block above the bottom of the ramp is equal, but the ramps are set at different angles. Which block will have the larger speed at the bottom of the ramp if the surfaces are frictionless? Which block will have the larger speed at the bottom of the ramp if the surfaces are not frictionless?

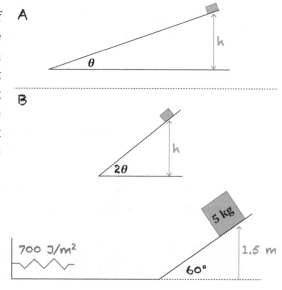

8. A 5 kg block is released from rest at the top of a ramp, as shown in the figure on the right. The block slides down the ramp and then across a horizontal surface before colliding with a spring; all surfaces are frictionless. The initial height of the block is 1.5 m, and the angle of the ramp is 60°.

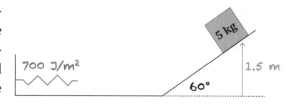

If the spring constant of the spring is 700 J/m², what is the maximum compression of the spring?

9. A 5 kg block is released from rest at the top of a ramp, as shown in the figure below. The block slides down the ramp and then across a horizontal surface before colliding with a spring. As the block slides down the ramp, friction causes energy to dissipate at a rate of 5 J/m. The horizontal surface is frictionless. The initial height of the block is 1.5 m, and the angle of the ramp is 60°.

If the spring constant of the spring is 700 J/m², what is the maximum compression of the spring?

10. You lift a 2 kg block from the ground to a height of 2.2 m. How much work did you do in raising the block?

11. A 2.5 kg block is released from rest at the top of a semicircular track, as shown in this figure. As the block slides back and forth on the track, it loses energy because of friction. What is the total work done by friction when the block has finally come to a rest at the bottom of the track?

12. A 1 kg block is dropped from rest onto a vertically mounted spring with a spring constant of 500 J/m² and a normal length of 1.5 m. What is the length of the spring at its maximum compression? Treat this as an isolated system.

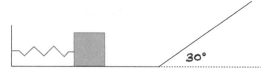

13. A spring is used to propel a 1.5 kg block up a ramp, as shown in the figure below. The horizontal surface along which the block initially moves is frictionless, but there is friction on the ramp, which causes energy to be dissipated at a rate of 2 J/m. The block is initially held in place with the length of the spring compressed by 20 cm. When released, the block will slide up the ramp and then back down again, eventually recompressing the spring. What is the final compression of the spring?

14. A 10 kg object is moving in a straight line with an initial speed of 2 m/s. How long will it take for the speed of the object to increase to 10 m/s if its translational kinetic energy increases at a rate of 20 J/s?

CHAPTER FOUR
Energy-based Mechanics

In Chapter 2, we learned the terms and equations required for a quantitative description of 1-dimensional motion. In this chapter, we will combine this knowledge of kinematics together with the definitions of energy from Chapter 3 to begin our discussion of classical mechanics. Specifically, we will develop methods for using the total energy of a system to make predictions about how the position and velocity of the system will change over time.

4-2 Kinematics with Translational Kinetic Energy

When discussing and calculating equations of motion (*i.e.,* kinematic equations), it is natural to start with the energy of motion, kinetic energy. This will form the basis of our exploration of the physics of kinematics. We have already seen, for example, that the speed of an object can be determined from the object's translational kinetic energy.

$$K = \frac{1}{2}mv^2 \quad \rightarrow \quad v = \left(\frac{2}{m}\right)^{\frac{1}{2}} K^{\frac{1}{2}}$$

Understanding how translational kinetic energy varies with time and/or position can, therefore, allow us to calculate directly the relationship between position and time.

$$v = \frac{dx}{dt} \quad \rightarrow \quad \frac{dx}{dt} = \left(\frac{2}{m}\right)^{\frac{1}{2}} K^{\frac{1}{2}}$$

Alternatively, an equation for the translational kinetic energy can be used to determine directly the corresponding acceleration.

$$a = \frac{dv}{dt} \quad \rightarrow \quad a = \frac{d}{dt}\left(\left(\frac{2}{m}\right)^{\frac{1}{2}} K^{\frac{1}{2}} \right)$$

Let's consider three simple cases:

(i) Translational kinetic energy is constant in both position and time.

If translational kinetic energy is constant, then the speed of the object must also be constant. It is tempting to conclude that this implies that the acceleration must also be zero; however, acceleration is defined as a change in velocity, not speed. Changes in only the direction of the velocity of an object will not affect the object's translational kinetic energy.

(ii) Translational kinetic energy is a function of position.

We take the derivative of the translational kinetic energy with respect to position (*e.g.*, with respect to the *x*-axis) to determine the corresponding acceleration.

$$K = \frac{1}{2}mv^2 \quad \rightarrow \quad \frac{dK}{dx} = mv\frac{dv}{dx} \quad \rightarrow \quad \frac{dK}{dx} = mv\frac{dv}{dt}\frac{dt}{dx}$$

$$\frac{dK}{dx} = mva\frac{1}{v} \quad \rightarrow \quad \frac{dK}{dx} = ma$$

$$a = \frac{1}{m}\frac{dK}{dx}$$

This leads to two interesting conclusions:

If translational kinetic energy is linearly dependent upon position, the acceleration is constant.

The first derivative of translational kinetic energy with respect to position is the product of mass and acceleration.

(iii) Translational kinetic energy is a function of time.

Similarly, we start with the derivative of the translational kinetic energy with respect to time.

$$K = \frac{1}{2}mv^2 \quad \rightarrow \quad \frac{dK}{dt} = mv\frac{dv}{dt} \quad \rightarrow \quad \frac{dK}{dt} = mva$$

$$a = \frac{1}{mv}\frac{dK}{dt}$$

Thus, *if translational kinetic energy is linearly dependent upon time, the acceleration is not constant.*

This leaves us with an interesting tool at our disposal: we can visually examine any equation for translational kinetic energy to determine if the corresponding system is experiencing constant acceleration. Similarly, if given a plot of the translational kinetic energy with respect to time or position, a simple glance will tell us if the relationship is linear or not and, thus, allow us to draw conclusions about the associated acceleration.

Example 4-1:

Problem: The translational kinetic energy of an 8 kg block moving in 1-dimension along the x-axis is given by the equation:

$$K(x) = 25\,\text{J} + \left(16\,\frac{\text{J}}{\text{m}}\right)x$$

In this equation, x denotes the position of the object, and the velocity of the object is in the positive x-axis direction. How long does it take for the object to move from $x = 0$ m to $x = 3.5$ m?

Solution: By looking at this equation, we can see that the translational kinetic energy is linearly dependent upon position. Therefore, we know that the acceleration of the object is constant. We can determine the magnitude of this acceleration using calculus.

$$a = \frac{1}{m}\frac{dK}{dx} \quad \rightarrow \quad a = \left(\frac{1}{8\,\text{kg}}\right)\left(16\,\frac{\text{J}}{\text{m}}\right) \quad \rightarrow \quad a = 2\,\frac{\text{m}}{\text{s}^2}$$

From the constant acceleration kinematics equations in Section 2-5, we know that

$$\Delta x = v_i \Delta t + \frac{1}{2}a(\Delta t)^2$$

From here we need only determine the initial velocity of the object (at $x = 0$ m) to determine the time interval. From our equation for translational kinetic energy, we have

$$K(0) = 25\,\text{J} \quad \rightarrow \quad \frac{1}{2}(8\,\text{kg})v_i^2 = 25\,\text{J} \quad \rightarrow \quad v_i = \pm 2.5\,\frac{\text{m}}{\text{s}}$$

This solution from the quadratic equation has left us with two roots, one positive and one negative. Since the velocity of the object is in the positive x-axis direction, we will use the positive root. Substitution then yields,

$$3.5\,m = \left(2.5\frac{m}{s}\right)\Delta t + \frac{1}{2}\left(2\frac{m}{s^2}\right)(\Delta t)^2$$

This equation has two solutions.

$$\Delta t = 1\,s \quad \Delta t = -3.5\,s$$

However, only the positive root is physically real. Therefore,

$$\Delta t = 1\,s$$

Alternative Solution: We could have also solved this problem using a more general approach (*i.e.*, one that is applicable even when the acceleration is not constant). We begin with the relationship between speed and translational kinetic energy.

$$v = \frac{dx}{dt} \quad \rightarrow \quad v = \left(\frac{2}{m}\right)^{\frac{1}{2}} K^{\frac{1}{2}}$$

Substitution of the equation for translational kinetic energy in this problem then yields

$$\frac{dx}{dt} = \left(\frac{2}{8\,kg}\right)^{\frac{1}{2}}\left(25J + \left(16\frac{J}{m}\right)x\right)^{\frac{1}{2}} \quad \rightarrow \quad \frac{dx}{\left(25J + \left(16\frac{J}{m}\right)x\right)^{\frac{1}{2}}} = \left(\frac{1}{4\,kg}\right)^{\frac{1}{2}} dt$$

We can now integrate both sides of this equation to relate a change in position (*i.e.*, a displacement) to a change in time.

$$\int_{x_i}^{x_f} \frac{dx}{\left(25J + \left(16\frac{J}{m}\right)x\right)^{\frac{1}{2}}} = \int_{t_i}^{t_f} \left(\frac{1}{4\,kg}\right)^{\frac{1}{2}} dt$$

In this integration, we define the object to be at the position x_i at time t_i and at the position x_f at time t_f. Performing the integration yields

$$\frac{1}{8}\left(\left(25J+\left(16\frac{J}{m}\right)x_f\right)^{\frac{1}{2}}-\left(25J+\left(16\frac{J}{m}\right)x_i\right)^{\frac{1}{2}}\right)=\left(\frac{1}{4kg}\right)^{\frac{1}{2}}\Delta t$$

Substitution of the values of x_f and x_i then gives us

$$\frac{1}{8}\left(\left(25J+\left(16\frac{J}{m}\right)(3.5m)\right)^{\frac{1}{2}}-\left(25J+\left(16\frac{J}{m}\right)(0m)\right)^{\frac{1}{2}}\right)=\left(\frac{1}{4kg}\right)^{\frac{1}{2}}\Delta t$$

$$\frac{1}{8}\left((81J)^{\frac{1}{2}}-(25J)^{\frac{1}{2}}\right)=\left(\frac{1}{4kg}\right)^{\frac{1}{2}}\Delta t$$

$$\Delta t = 1s$$

Example 4-2:

Problem: The translational kinetic energy of a 3 kg block moving across a horizontal frictionless surface increases linearly with time, according to the equation:

$$K(t)=\left(6\frac{J}{s}\right)t$$

How far will the object move between $t = 0$ s and $t = 9$ s?

Solution: Since the translational kinetic energy is a linear function of time and not a linear function of position, we know that the acceleration will not be constant. So, instead of using the constant acceleration kinematics equations, we will begin with the general relationship between speed and kinetic energy.

$$v=\frac{dx}{dt} \quad \rightarrow \quad v=\left(\frac{2}{m}\right)^{\frac{1}{2}}K^{\frac{1}{2}}$$

Substitution of the equation for translational kinetic energy in this problem then yields

$$\frac{dx}{dt} = \left(\frac{2}{3\text{kg}}\right)^{\frac{1}{2}}\left(\left(6\frac{\text{J}}{\text{s}}\right)t\right)^{\frac{1}{2}} \quad \rightarrow \quad dx = \left(4\frac{\text{m}^2}{\text{s}^3}\right)^{\frac{1}{2}}t^{\frac{1}{2}}dt$$

We can now integrate both sides of this equation to relate a change in position (*i.e.*, a displacement) to a change in time. In this integration, we define the object to be at the position x_i at time t_i and at the position x_f at time t_f.

$$\int_{x_i}^{x_f} dx = \int_{t_i}^{t_f}\left(4\frac{\text{m}^2}{\text{s}^3}\right)^{\frac{1}{2}}t^{\frac{1}{2}}\,dt$$

Performing the integration gives us

$$\Delta x = \left(4\frac{\text{m}^2}{\text{s}^3}\right)^{\frac{1}{2}}\frac{2}{3}\left(t_f^{\frac{3}{2}} - t_i^{\frac{3}{2}}\right)$$

Substitution of the values of t_f and t_i then gives us

$$\Delta x = \left(4\frac{\text{m}^2}{\text{s}^3}\right)^{\frac{1}{2}}\frac{2}{3}\left((9\text{s})^{\frac{3}{2}} - 0\right)$$

$$\Delta x = 36\,\text{m}$$

4-3 1-Dimensional Kinematics with Constant Energy

The examples of the previous section demonstrate that the kinematics of a system can be readily calculated if an equation for the translational kinetic energy of a system as a function of position or time is known. An equation for translational kinetic energy of this form can often be obtained from the potential energy associated with the system; recall that potential energy is a function of the position of an object or a collection of objects.

Let's consider a block that is falling down toward the surface of the Earth with no energy dissipated because of air resistance; we previously considered such a situation in Example 3-5. We refer to this motion as *free-fall*. The block is moving in 1-dimension with the axis of motion corresponding to the vertical direction, as shown in Figure 4.1.

As discussed in Section 3-5, we can ignore the motion of the Earth in this problem and define the system to consist of the block only. The energy of this system is, consequently, the sum of the kinetic and potential energies of the block.

$$E = K + U_g$$

$$E = \frac{1}{2}mv^2 + mgy + \left(U_g\right)_0$$

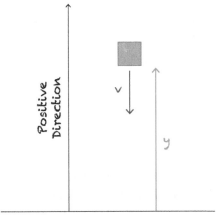

Figure 4.1: An object in free-fall.

The equation for the energy of this system is a function of the speed and the vertical position of the block. We also see from this equation that when released from rest, the block will fall in order to minimize its gravitational potential energy in accordance with the principle of minimum potential energy (Section 1-4). In other words, a decrease in the value of the variable y, which is a measure of the position of the object above the surface of the Earth, will result in a decrease in the potential energy of the system. This is, of course, also consistent with our many observations of objects falling down and not up.

Let's include an additional subscript "y" for the speed in the translational kinetic energy term in our expression for the energy of the system; it will remind us that the translational kinetic energy of the block results from its movement along the y-axis.

$$E = \frac{1}{2}mv_y^2 + mgy + \left(U_g\right)_0$$

Since we are ignoring energy dissipation from friction, we can treat the block as an isolated system. Hence, during free-fall, the total energy of the block is always the same regardless of its position, its speed, or how much time has passed since it was released. We can express these conditions mathematically as

$$\frac{dE}{dy} = 0 \quad \text{or} \quad \frac{dE}{dv_y} = 0 \quad \text{or} \quad \frac{dE}{dt} = 0$$

Let's first apply the condition that the energy is constant regardless of the vertical position of the block.

$$\frac{dE}{dy} = 0 \quad \rightarrow \quad \frac{d}{dy}\left(\frac{1}{2}mv_y^2 + mgy + \left(U_g\right)_0\right) = 0$$

$$\frac{d}{dy}\left(\frac{1}{2}mv_y^2\right) + \frac{d}{dy}\left(mgy\right) + \frac{d}{dy}\left(U_g\right)_0 = 0$$

The first term in this equation is the differentiation of the translational kinetic energy of the block with respect to the position of the block. We know from Section 4-2 that this derivative will be equal to the product of the mass of the block and the acceleration of the block.

$$\frac{d}{dy}\left(\frac{1}{2}mv_y^2\right) = ma_y$$

We have, again, included the subscript "y" to denote that the acceleration is directed along the y-axis. The remaining two derivatives are

$$\frac{d}{dy}\left(mgy\right) = mg \qquad \frac{d}{dy}\left(U_g\right)_0 = 0$$

Putting it all together, we have

$$\frac{dE}{dy} = 0 \quad \rightarrow \quad ma_y + mg = 0$$

$$a_y = -g$$

This solution tells us that the magnitude of the acceleration is equal to the constant g. The direction of this acceleration is indicated by the negative sign. This occurred because there is an implicit vector definition present in our equation for the gravitational potential energy. Namely, that moving up from the surface of the Earth corresponds to the positive vertical direction (an increase in the gravitational potential energy), as shown in Figure 4.1. We will further discuss the relationship between potential energy and the direction of acceleration in Chapter 7.

The same value for the acceleration is obtained using the other expressions for energy conservation. Next, let's consider that the energy of the system is constant in time.

$$\frac{dE}{dt} = 0 \quad \rightarrow \quad \frac{d}{dt}\left(\frac{1}{2}mv_y^2 + mgy + \left(U_g\right)_0\right) = 0 \quad \rightarrow \quad mv_y\frac{dv_y}{dt} + mg\frac{dy}{dt} + 0 = 0$$

$$mv_y a_y + mgv_y = 0 \quad \rightarrow \quad v_y\left(a_y + g\right) = 0$$

This equation has the following two solutions:

$$v_y = 0 \qquad a_y = -g$$

Because we know that the block will be moving after we release it, only the second solution is physically real.

Finally, let's use the constraint that the energy of the system is constant regardless of the speed of the block.

$$\frac{dE}{dv_y} = 0 \quad \rightarrow \quad \frac{d}{dv_y}\left(\frac{1}{2}mv_y^2 + mgy + \left(U_g\right)_0\right) = 0 \quad \rightarrow \quad mv_y + mg\frac{dy}{dv_y} + 0 = 0$$

$$mv_y + mg\frac{dy}{dt}\frac{dt}{dv_y} = 0 \quad \rightarrow \quad mv_y + mgv_y\frac{1}{a_y} = 0 \quad \rightarrow \quad a_y = -g$$

Of course, we could have guessed that the acceleration would be constant from our original equation for the energy of the system. Since energy is conserved, we have

$$\Delta E = 0 \quad \rightarrow \quad \Delta K + \Delta U_g = 0 \quad \rightarrow \quad \Delta K = -\Delta U_g$$

$$\Delta K = -mg\Delta y \quad \rightarrow \quad \Delta K \propto -\Delta y$$

We know that the acceleration of the system will be constant because the translational kinetic energy changes *linearly* with the position of the block (Section 4-2).

It is important to note that the $\left(U_g\right)_0$ term in the equation for gravitational potential energy did not contribute to the solution since it is a constant and, thus, has a derivative of zero regardless of whether we are differentiating with respect to position, time or speed. This is consistent with $\left(U_g\right)_0$ not contributing to calculations of ΔU_g (Section 3-3). Indeed, we would have obtained the same solution for our problem had we redefined the zero point of the gravitational potential energy to be at the surface of the Earth and completely ignored $\left(U_g\right)_0$. As discussed in Section 3-3, such a redefinition of the origin of the coordinate system is another example of how the use of a coordinate transformation (Section 2-6) can simplify calculations.

We can use a graphical representation of the energy of this system, as shown in Figure 4.2, to complement the previous mathematical description of the associated energy conservation process. It is clear from Figure 4.2 that the block will fall down to the ground (*i.e.*, decrease

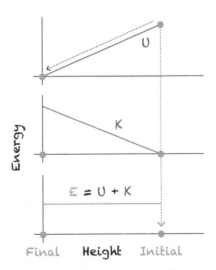

Figure 4.2: The total potential energy (blue), translational kinetic energy (green), and total energy (red) for a block released from rest above the ground as a function of the height of the block above the ground. The zero point of the potential energy is defined to be the surface of the Earth. The dashed line indicates the response of this system from its initial configuration.

its height above the ground) in order to minimize its total potential energy. Since this system is isolated, the total energy of the system is constant. As a result, the gravitational potential energy of the system is converted into the translational kinetic energy of the block as the block falls. Therefore, the translational kinetic energy increases as the height of the block decreases. Since this increase in the translational kinetic energy is linearly dependent upon the height of the block, the acceleration of the system is constant.

Example 4-3:

Problem: A block is sliding down a frictionless ramp, as shown in the Figure 4.3. What is the acceleration of the block?

Solution: The system in this problem consists of the block only. The energy of this system is, consequently, the sum of the kinetic and potential energies of the block.

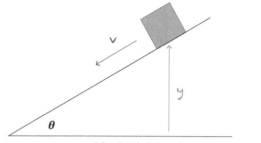

Figure 4.3: A block sliding down a ramp in Example 4-3.

$$E = K + U_g$$

Let's define the zero point of the gravitational potential energy to be the bottom of the ramp. In this case, the equation for the energy of the block is

$$E = \frac{1}{2}mv^2 + mgy$$

The energy of this system is a function of the speed and the vertical position of the block. It is important to realize, however, that the direction of the velocity will not be along the vertical axis as it would be if the block were in free-fall. Indeed, as the block slides down the ramp, it is moving simultaneously in two directions: horizontally and vertically (Figure 4.4). These two motions are linked, however, by the slope of the ramp, and, consequently, the horizontal motion of the block is directly related to its vertical motion resulting in the velocity being directed parallel to the surface of the ramp.

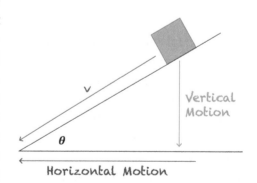

Figure 4.4: As the block slides down the ramp, it is simultaneously moving in both the horizontal and vertical directions.

Because of this, the velocity of this object is not the rate of change of its vertical position, as in the case of free-fall motion, but rather it is the rate of change of its position along the ramp. It is, therefore, convenient for us to use a coordinate transformation (Section 2-6) to define a different axis for describing the position and velocity of the block. This axis will be aligned parallel to the surface of the ramp and will be called the s-axis, as shown in Figure 4.5[1].

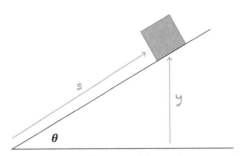

Figure 4.5: Definition of the 1-dimensional axis, denoted as the s-axis, to describe the motion of a block sliding down a ramp in Example 4-3.

Furthermore, we have defined the origin for the s-axis ($s = 0$) to be at the bottom of the ramp and the positive direction for the s-axis to point up the ramp. Using this definition, we can relate the position along the s-axis to the position along the y-axis (*i.e.*, vertical motion of the block) by trigonometry just as we did in Example 3-7.

$$\sin\theta = \frac{y}{s} \;\rightarrow\; y = s\sin\theta$$

The velocity of the object can also be expressed in terms of the position of the block along the s-axis as

$$v_s = \frac{ds}{dt}$$

The equation for the energy of the system can now be written in terms of this new coordinate axis.

$$E = \frac{1}{2}mv_s^2 + mg\left(s\sin\theta\right)$$

We now have an equation for the energy in which both the speed and the position are defined relative to the same coordinate axis. Furthermore, we see that through this coordinate transformation we have also converted a 2-dimensional motion problem (*i.e.*, the motion of the block both horizontally and vertically) into a 1-dimensional motion problem (*i.e.*, motion along the surface of the ramp).

We could have also derived the same equation for the energy of the system by directly including the coupling between the horizontal and vertical motions of the block. To demonstrate, this let's define the 1-dimensional axis for the horizontal motion of the block to be the x-axis and the 1-dimensional axis for the vertical motion of the block to be the y-axis.

---

1   This is the same coordinate transformation we used in Example 3-7.

As shown in Figure 4.6, the movement of the block can then be described in terms of its velocities along these axes.

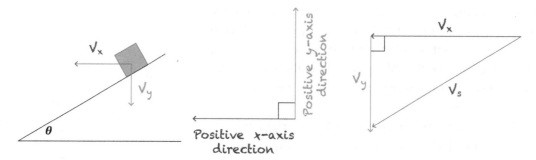

Figure 4.6: The 2-dimensional motion of the block can be described either in terms of its separate velocities along the perpendicular x-axis and y-axis or in terms of a single velocity along the s-axis.

The kinetic energy of the block is thus

$$K = \frac{1}{2}mv_x^2 + \frac{1}{2}mv_y^2 \quad \rightarrow \quad K = \frac{1}{2}m\left(v_x^2 + v_y^2\right)$$

Since the x-axis and y-axis are perpendicular to each other, we can use the Pythagorean Theorem to relate v_x and v_y to v_s and, hence, to express the translational kinetic energy of the block in terms of v_s alone.

$$v_s^2 = v_x^2 + v_y^2 \quad \rightarrow \quad K = \frac{1}{2}mv_s^2$$

This is the same expression for the translational kinetic energy of the block that we obtained before.

Because the surface along which the block moves is frictionless, we can treat the system as being isolated. Hence, the energy of the system must be constant. As before, we can express this condition mathematically as

$$\frac{dE}{ds} = 0 \quad \text{or} \quad \frac{dE}{dv_s} = 0 \quad \text{or} \quad \frac{dE}{dt} = 0$$

Let's apply the first expression to our equation for the energy of this system.

$$\frac{dE}{ds} = 0 \quad \rightarrow \quad \frac{d}{ds}\left(\frac{1}{2}mv_s^2 + mg\left(s\sin\theta\right)\right) = 0$$

$$\frac{d}{ds}\left(\frac{1}{2}mv_s^2\right) + \frac{d}{ds}\left(mg\left(s\sin\theta\right)\right) = 0$$

$$ma_s + mg\sin\theta = 0 \quad \rightarrow \quad a_s = -g\sin\theta$$

The negative sign indicates that the direction of the acceleration will be in the negative s direction (*i.e.*, down the ramp). It is worth noting that this solution agrees with our previous solution for free-fall motion in the limit of a perfectly vertical ramp ($\theta = 90°$)[2].

4-4 Projectile Motion

Consider an object of mass m launched from a horizontal surface with an initial speed v_i at an angle θ relative to this surface (Figure 4.7).

After its launch, this object will be moving in two directions (horizontally and vertically) simultaneously. We refer to this motion as *projectile motion* and the object as a *projectile*. From the discussion of Section 2-7, we know that we can describe projectile motion as independent motions along

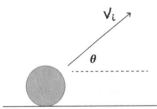

Figure 4.7: The initial velocity for a projectile.

the horizontal and vertical directions since these directions are perpendicular to each other. From the results of Section 4-3, we know that the acceleration along the vertical direction, denoted as the y-axis, will be

$$a_y = -g$$

Furthermore, since the potential energy of the projectile does not depend upon its position along the horizontal direction, denoted as the x-axis, the acceleration along the horizontal direction must be zero.

$$a_x = 0$$

---

2   Whenever possible, always check your solution in a few limiting cases.

Since the accelerations along both axes are constant, we can use the results of Section 2-5 and Section 2-7 to write down time dependent equations for the x-axis and y-axis positions and velocities of the projectile.

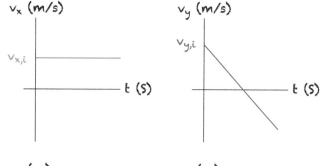

$$V_{x,f} = V_{x,i}$$

$$x_f = x_i + v_{i,x}\Delta t$$

$$v_{y,f} = v_{y,i} + (-g)\Delta t$$

$$y_f = y_i + v_{y,i}\Delta t + \frac{1}{2}(-g)(\Delta t)^2$$

Figure 4.8: The time dependence of the horizontal and vertical velocities and displacements for projectile motion.

Plots of the projectile's position and velocity are shown in Figure 4.8. In these plots, the initial positions of the object on both the x and y axes are zero.

Example 4-4:

Problem: A projectile is launched from the ground with an initial speed v at an angle θ relative to the ground, as shown in Figure 4.7. What is the maximum horizontal distance travelled by the projectile?

Solution: We begin by determining the time required for the vertical movement of the projectile. The projectile will, of course, be back on the ground at its maximum horizontal distance.

$$y_f = y_i \quad \rightarrow \quad 0 = v_{y,i}\Delta t + \frac{1}{2}(-g)(\Delta t)^2$$

The initial value of the y-axis component of the velocity of the object is found by decomposing the initial velocity vector shown in Figure 4.7 into its x-axis and y-axis components[3].

$$v_{y,i} = v_i \sin\theta$$

$$v_{x,i} = v_i \cos\theta$$

---

3   See Section B-4.

Hence,

$$y_f = y_i \;\rightarrow\; 0 = \left(v_i \sin\theta\right)\Delta t + \frac{1}{2}\left(-g\right)\left(\Delta t\right)^2 \;\rightarrow\; 0 = \left(v_i \sin\theta\right) + \frac{1}{2}\left(-g\right)\left(\Delta t\right)$$

$$\Delta t = \frac{2v_i \sin\theta}{g}$$

Substitution of this solution into the equation for the horizontal position of the object yields

$$x_f = x_i + \left(v_i \cos\theta\right)\left(\frac{2v_i \sin\theta}{g}\right) \;\rightarrow\; \Delta x = \frac{2v_i^2 \sin\theta\cos\theta}{g}$$

This equation can be simplified through an addition trigonometric substitution.

$$2\sin\theta\cos\theta = \sin\left(2\theta\right) \;\rightarrow\; \Delta x = \frac{v_i^2 \sin\left(2\theta\right)}{g}$$

This equation is frequently referred to as the range equation for projectile motion. It is not, necessarily, generally applicable, however, since the equation assumes that the initial and final vertical positions of the projectile are the same, and since it also ignores air resistance.

Example 4-5:

Problem: A projectile is launched from the ground with an initial speed v at an angle θ relative to the ground, as shown in Figure 4.7. What horizontal distance will be covered by the projectile when it has reached its maximum vertical position?

Solution: We begin by determining the time required for the vertical movement of the projectile. The vertical component of the projectile's velocity will be zero when the projectile is at its maximum vertical position.

$$v_{y,f} = v_{y,i} + \left(-g\right)\Delta t \;\rightarrow\; 0 = v_{y,i} + \left(-g\right)\Delta t \;\rightarrow\; v_{y,i} = g\Delta t$$

$$v_{y,i} = v_i \sin\theta \;\rightarrow\; \Delta t = \frac{v_i \sin\theta}{g}$$

Substitution of this solution into the equation for the horizontal position of the object yields

$$x_f = x_i + \left(v_i \cos\theta\right)\left(\frac{v_i \sin\theta}{g}\right) \quad \rightarrow \quad \Delta x = \frac{v_i^2 \sin\theta \cos\theta}{g}$$

We immediately see that this distance corresponds to one half of the range of the projectile. This occurs because the time required for the projectile to move from the ground to its maximum vertical position is the same as the time required for the projectile to move from its maximum vertical position back to the ground.

4-5 Multiple Objects Moving Together

The approach presented in Section 4-3 can also be used to calculate the acceleration of a system that consists of multiple objects moving together. Let's consider the system shown in Figure 4.9 that consists of two blocks, A and B, which are connected to each other by a massless rope that passes over a massless pulley. The horizontal surface along which block A slides is frictionless. The blocks are initially held in place, and then released from rest. What is the subsequent acceleration of block B?

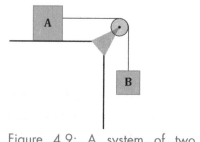

Figure 4.9: A system of two blocks, a rope, and a pulley.

In this problem, the system consists of the two blocks, the rope, and the pulley, and, hence, the energy of this system is the sum of the kinetic and potential energies of these objects.

We immediately notice that both of the blocks are moving in 1-dimension but along different coordinate axes. As discussed previously in Section 2-7, we can describe the positions and velocities of the blocks using two separate 1-dimensional coordinate axes. The 1-dimensional coordinate axis for the horizontal position and velocity of block A, which we will denote as the x-axis, will be parallel to the horizontal surface on which block A moves and has a positive direction pointing from block A to the pulley (*i.e.*, to the right in Figure 4.9). We can define an origin for the x-axis ($x = 0$) on this surface and then denote the position of block A as x_A with respect to this origin, as shown in Figure 4.10. For block B, the 1-dimensional axis will be the vertical direction in Figure 4.9, which we refer to as the y-axis. Furthermore, we can specify the floor or the ground to be the origin of the y-axis ($y = 0$) and denote the position of block B as y_B with respect to this origin, as shown in Figure 4.10. The vertical position of block A, which is required to determine the gravitational potential energy of block A, will be denoted as y_A and measured

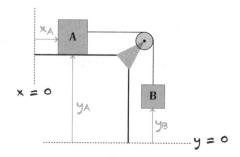

Figure 4.10: Definitions of the x and y axes for the motion of the blocks in Figure 4.9.

with respect to the same 1-dimensional coordinate axis as is used for the vertical position and velocity of block B.

With these definitions of the coordinate axes, we can write the expression for the energy of this system as

$$E = \frac{1}{2}m_A v_{A,x}^2 + m_A g y_A + \frac{1}{2}m_B v_{B,y}^2 + m_B g y_B$$

For this equation, we have defined the zero point of the gravitational potential energy to be the ground (*i.e.*, at $y = 0$). The variable $v_{A,x}$ is the speed of block A along the *x*-axis, and the variable $v_{B,y}$ is the speed of block B along the *y*-axis. There are no kinetic or gravitational potential energies associated with rope and the pulley since these objects have no mass. However, because the rope connects the two blocks, there is a relationship between the speeds of the two blocks (Section 1-6). Specifically, these speeds must be equal[4], and, therefore, the square of these speeds must also be equal.

$$v_{A,x}^2 = v_{B,y}^2$$

We know from Section 4-3 that we can differentiate the equation for the energy of a system to determine the acceleration of that system or of any object in that system. In order to simplify this calculation, we should always write this equation for the energy using as few variables as possible. In this particular case, since we are interested in determining the acceleration of block B, we can use the relationship between the speeds of the blocks to eliminate $v_{A,x}$ from the equation for the energy of the system.

$$v_{A,x}^2 = v_{B,y}^2 \quad \rightarrow \quad E = \frac{1}{2}\left(m_A + m_B\right)v_{B,y}^2 + m_A g y_A + m_B g y_B$$

The first term in this equation, which we obtained by combining the translational kinetic energy of block A with the translational kinetic energy of block B, can be thought of as the *effective translational kinetic energy* for this system for its motion[5].

$$K_{effective} = \frac{1}{2}\left(m_A + m_B\right)v_{B,y}^2$$

Since there is no friction present, the energy of the system will be constant as the blocks move (*i.e.*, the system is isolated). We can express this condition mathematically in terms of a derivative of the energy of the system with respect to a number of variables.

$$\frac{dE}{dt} = 0 \qquad \frac{dE}{dv_{B,y}} = 0 \qquad \frac{dE}{dy_A} = 0 \qquad \frac{dE}{dy_B} = 0$$

---

4   The velocities are, of course, not equal since they are in different directions.
5   We will discuss this idea further in Section 5-8 and then again in Section 12-6.

The simplest of these derivatives to apply is either of the two derivatives of energy with respect to position. There are two main reasons why this is the case:

(i) As we have seen in previous examples, the derivative of the translational kinetic energy with respect to position is directly proportional to the acceleration.

$$\frac{d}{dx}\left(\frac{1}{2}mv_x^2\right) = ma_x$$

(ii) The relative positions of the objects within a system are often easier to relate than the speeds or velocities of the objects.

Therefore, we will determine the acceleration of block B by differentiating the energy of the system with respect to the position of block B.

$$\frac{dE}{dy_B} = 0 \quad \rightarrow \quad \left(m_A + m_B\right)a_{B,y} + m_A g\frac{dy_A}{dy_B} + m_B g = 0$$

Since block A is sliding across a horizontal surface, its vertical position will not change as the vertical position of block B changes.

$$\frac{dy_A}{dy_B} = 0$$

Hence,

$$\left(m_A + m_B\right)a_{B,y} + m_B g = 0 \quad \rightarrow \quad a_{B,y} = -\left(\frac{m_B}{m_A + m_B}\right)g$$

The negative sign in the solution indicates that block B will fall when the blocks are released from rest[6]. The acceleration is also constant, which we could have anticipated since the translational kinetic energy of the system is linearly dependent upon the vertical position of block B.

It is interesting to note that the magnitude of the acceleration is less than it would be if block B was in free-fall (as in Section 4-3). This occurs because this system distributes energy differently from the free-fall system. Specifically, during free-fall, the gravitational potential energy of the falling block is converted into the translational kinetic energy of the falling block. In this system, however, the gravitational potential energy of block B is being converted into the translational kinetic energy of block B *and* the translational kinetic energy of block A. Since the gravitational potential energy

---

6   Recall from Section 4-3 that a (±) sign convention for vertical motion is implicit in the formula for gravitational potential energy.

for block B is being divided, or *partitioned,* into multiple translational kinetic energies, each of these translational kinetic energies will, therefore, receive less than the total converted gravitational potential energy. The change in the translational kinetic energy of block B associated with its vertical movement is, therefore, less than it would be had the block been in free-fall. Since translational kinetic energy is proportional to speed, a smaller rate of change of translational kinetic energy corresponds to a smaller rate of change of speed and, therefore, to a smaller acceleration[7].

Lastly, it is worth recognizing that the total mass of the system appears in the denominator of the expression for the acceleration of the system. We will revisit the generality of this result for other moving systems in Chapter 5 and Chapter 6 and will discuss it in more detail in Chapter 12.

Example 4-6:

Problem: Two blocks, A and B, are connected to each other by a massless rope that passes over a massless pulley (see Figure 4.9). The horizontal surface along which block A slides is frictionless. What is the acceleration of block A?

Solution: Again, in this problem the system consists of the two blocks, the rope, and the pulley. Following our previous solution, we can write the equation for the energy of this system as

$$E = \frac{1}{2}m_A v_{A,x}^2 + m_A g y_A + \frac{1}{2}m_B v_{B,y}^2 + m_B g y_B$$

For this equation, we have defined the zero point of the gravitational potential energy to be the ground. Since we want to determine the acceleration of block A, we can eliminate $v_{B,y}$ from our equation for the energy of the system.

$$v_{B,y}^2 = v_{A,x}^2 \;\;\rightarrow\;\; E = \frac{1}{2}\left(m_A + m_B\right)v_{A,x}^2 + m_A g y_A + m_B g y_B$$

Finally, because there is no friction, the energy of the system is constant.

$$\frac{dE}{dx_A} = 0 \;\;\rightarrow\;\; \left(m_A + m_B\right)a_{A,x} + m_A g \frac{dy_A}{dx_A} + m_B g \frac{dy_B}{dx_A} = 0$$

---

7   Indeed, since the magnitude of the slope of translational kinetic energy versus displacement has decreased, the magnitude of the acceleration must have also decreased (see Section 4-2).

Since block A is sliding across a horizontal surface and, consequently, has no motion along the y-axis, we know that $\frac{dy_A}{dx_A} = 0$. For block B, we see from Figure 4.10 that as x_A increases, y_B must decrease. Hence,

$$\frac{dy_B}{dx_A} = -1$$

The substitution of these relationships then yields

$$\left(m_A + m_B\right)a_{A,x} + m_B g\left(-1\right) = 0 \quad \rightarrow \quad a_{A,x} = \left(\frac{m_B}{m_A + m_B}\right)g$$

The positive direction for the acceleration, based upon our definition of the positive direction for the x-axis, is consistent with our expectations for the motion of the block; specifically, block A will move to the right when the system is released from rest. Furthermore, as expected, the magnitude of the acceleration of block A is equal to the magnitude of the acceleration of block B since the two blocks are connected by a rope and, hence, move together.

Although we would have obtained the same solution in Example 4-6 by differentiating the equation for the energy of the system with respect to time or the velocity of block A, we will always prefer to differentiate with respect to the position of an object in the system. Indeed, as we will see in the next section, differentiating the equation for the energy of the system with respect to position will also be the approach we employ when working with non-isolated systems.

4-6 Energy Dissipation by Friction

Friction arises when two surfaces move past each other, such as when you drag a box along the floor or rub your hands together vigorously. As discussed in Section 3-6, the effect of friction acting on a system is the dissipation of energy from the system. In Example 3-8, we modeled friction as negative work done on a 4 kg block sliding across a horizontal surface. Now, let's calculate the acceleration of that block.

In this problem, the system consists of the block only, and, consequently, the energy of the system is the sum of the kinetic and potential energies of the block. Let's denote the 1-dimensional axis for the motion of the block as the x-axis and define the positive direction for the x-axis to point in the same direction as the initial velocity of the block.

$$E = K + U_g \quad \rightarrow \quad E = \frac{1}{2}mv_x^2 + mgy$$

In this equation, we have defined the zero point of the gravitational potential energy to be the horizontal surface along which the block slides. We have included the subscript "*x*" to denote that the velocity is directed along the *x*-axis. The energy of this system will decrease linearly with the distance travelled by the block along the *x*-axis at a constant rate of 2.5 J/m due to energy dissipation by friction. We can mathematically express the dissipation of energy due to friction as

$$\frac{dE}{dx} = -2.5\frac{J}{m}$$

The negative sign is required since the energy of the system is decreasing as the block slides in the positive *x*-axis direction; recall that the work done by friction is always negative (Section 3-6). Taking the derivative of the equation for the energy of the system with respect to *x* yields

$$\frac{dE}{dx} = ma_x + mg\frac{dy}{dx}$$

We now have an expression that we can relate to our equation for the rate of energy dissipation due to friction. Since the surface is horizontal, we also know that

$$\frac{dy}{dx} = 0$$

Therefore,

$$\frac{dE}{dx} = ma_x \quad \rightarrow \quad -2.5\frac{J}{m} = \left(4\,\text{kg}\right)a_x \quad \rightarrow \quad a_x = -0.625\frac{m}{s^2}$$

The acceleration is constant and in the negative direction, which, according to our definition, is opposite the direction of the initial velocity of the block. As expected, this acceleration will cause the speed of the block to decrease. Of course, we could have anticipated that the acceleration of the block would be constant since friction caused the translational kinetic energy to decrease linearly with the position of the block (*i.e.*, in this problem the translational kinetic energy is linearly dependent upon the position of the block).

We can now use this acceleration to solve the kinematics question posed in Example 3-8: How far does the block slide before stopping? Since acceleration is constant, we can use the constant acceleration kinematics equations (Section 2-5) to relate the initial velocity, the final velocity, the acceleration, and the displacement of the block.

$$v_{f,x}^2 = v_{i,x}^2 + 2a_x\Delta x \quad \rightarrow \quad \Delta x = \frac{v_{f,x}^2 - v_{i,x}^2}{2a_x}$$

$$\Delta x = \frac{0 - \left(5\frac{m}{s}\right)^2}{2\left(-0.625\frac{m}{s^2}\right)} \quad \rightarrow \quad \Delta x = 20\,\text{m}$$

As expected, this is the same answer we obtained before (Example 3-8). Another way we could have arrived at this solution would be from our initial expression for the effect of friction on the energy of the system.

$$\frac{dE}{dx} = -2.5\frac{J}{m} \quad \rightarrow \quad dE = \left(-2.5\frac{J}{m}\right)dx \quad \rightarrow \quad \int_{E_i}^{E_f} dE = \int_{x_i}^{x_f}\left(-2.5\frac{J}{m}\right)dx$$

In this integration we will define the block to have energy E_i at time t_i, and energy E_f at time t_f. The rate of energy dissipation is constant, so both integrals are straightforward.

$$\Delta E = \left(-2.5\frac{J}{m}\right)\Delta x$$

Since the surface along which the block slides is horizontal

$$\Delta y = 0 \quad \rightarrow \quad \Delta U_g = 0 \quad \rightarrow \quad \Delta E = \Delta K$$

Thus,

$$\Delta x = \frac{\Delta K}{-2.5\frac{J}{m}} \quad \rightarrow \quad \Delta x = \frac{0 - \frac{1}{2}(4\,\text{kg})\left(5\frac{m}{s}\right)^2}{-2.5\frac{J}{m}} \quad \rightarrow \quad \Delta x = 20\,\text{m}$$

It is important to remember that the effect of friction acting on a system is always a decrease in the energy of the system. Therefore, the particular equation we use to relate energy dissipation by friction to a rate of change of a system's energy depends upon how we have defined the positive direction for the displacement of the objects in the system. For a constant rate of energy dissipation, we have

$$\Delta E = \left(\frac{dE}{dx}\right)\Delta x$$

Thus, if the displacement Δx is negative, $\frac{dE}{dx}$ must be positive so that ΔE is negative. Similarly, if the displacement Δx is positive, $\frac{dE}{dx}$ must be negative so that ΔE is negative.

Example 4-7:

Problem: A 4 kg block is sliding down a ramp, as shown in Figure 4.11. Because of friction, energy will be dissipated from this system at a constant rate of 2 J/m. What is the acceleration of the block?

Solution: The system in this problem consists of the block only. Following the solution of Example 4-3, we can write the equation for the energy of this system as

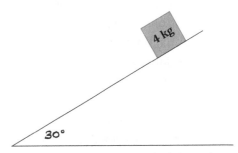

Figure 4.11: A 4 kg block sliding down a 30° ramp in Example 4-7.

$$E = \frac{1}{2}mv_s^2 + mg\left(s\sin\theta\right)$$

The definition of the s-axis in this equation is identical to the definition of the s-axis in Example 4-3. Differentiation of the energy of the system with respect to the position of the block along the s-axis yields

$$\frac{dE}{ds} = ma_s + mg\sin\theta \quad \rightarrow \quad \frac{dE}{ds} = m\left(a_s + g\sin\theta\right)$$

Therefore,

$$m\left(a_s + g\sin\theta\right) = \frac{dE}{ds} \quad \rightarrow \quad a_s = -g\sin\theta + \frac{\dfrac{dE}{ds}}{m}$$

In order to determine the ($\pm$) sign associated with $\frac{dE}{ds}$, we must consider the direction of the displacement of the block as it slides. Since we have defined the positive direction for the s-axis to point up the ramp[8], we know that the displacement of the block will be negative as the block slides down the ramp. Therefore, for this problem, $\frac{dE}{ds}$ must be positive so that energy is dissipated from the system as the block slides down the ramp.

$$\frac{dE}{ds} = 2\frac{J}{m} \quad \rightarrow \quad a_s = -\left(9.8\frac{m}{s^2}\right)\left(\frac{1}{2}\right) + \frac{2\dfrac{J}{m}}{4\,kg} \quad \rightarrow \quad a_s = -4.4\frac{m}{s^2}$$

---

8   See Example 4-3.

As we noted in the previous example, if no friction was present, then the acceleration of the block would be -4.9 m/s². The magnitude of the acceleration has decreased because now there is not a simple conversion of gravitational potential energy into translational kinetic energy as the block slides down the ramp[9]. This is because some of the gravitational potential energy is dissipated from the system by friction. Since not all of the gravitational potential energy is converted into translational kinetic energy, the block has correspondingly less translational kinetic energy as it slides down the ramp than it had when no friction was present. Since translational kinetic energy is proportional to speed, a smaller rate of change of translational kinetic energy corresponds to a smaller rate of change of speed and, therefore, to a smaller acceleration[10].

We can, of course, also apply this same approach to more complicated mechanisms of energy dissipation where the rate of energy decrease is not constant. For example, let's consider an object moving in 1-dimension along a horizontal surface; we will denote the horizontal axis for the motion of the block as the x-axis. The equation for the energy of this system is

$$E = \frac{1}{2}mv_x^2$$

In this equation, we have defined the zero point for the gravitational potential energy to be the horizontal surface along which the object is sliding; since the surface is horizontal, the gravitational potential energy of the object is always zero. The object is initially moving in the positive x-axis direction, and the rate of energy decrease of the object is proportional to its speed.

$$\frac{dE}{dx} = -\eta v_x$$

In this equation, η is a constant. The acceleration of this system can be found through differentiation.

$$E = \frac{1}{2}mv_x^2 \quad \rightarrow \quad \frac{dE}{dx} = ma_x \quad \rightarrow \quad ma_x = -\eta v_x \quad \rightarrow \quad a_x = -\frac{\eta}{m}v_x$$

As expected, the acceleration of the object is not constant but rather depends upon the speed of the object. We can determine the change in the speed of the object by integrating this acceleration.

$$\frac{dv_x}{dt} = -\frac{\eta}{m}v_x \quad \rightarrow \quad \frac{dv_x}{v_x} = -\frac{\eta}{m}dt \quad \rightarrow \quad \int_{v_{x,i}}^{v_{x,f}} \frac{dv_x}{v_x} = \int_{t_i}^{t_f} \left(-\frac{\eta}{m}\right)dt$$

---

9   Had we chosen $\frac{dE}{ds}$ to be negative, the magnitude of the acceleration would have increased in the presence of friction, which is not possible.

10   Since the magnitude of the slope of translational kinetic energy versus displacement has decreased, the magnitude of the acceleration must have also decreased (see Section 4-2).

In this integration, we will define the object to have velocity v_i at time t_i and velocity v_f at time t_f. Performing the integration gives us

$$\ln\left(\frac{v_{x,f}}{v_{x,i}}\right) = -\frac{\eta}{m}\Delta t \quad \rightarrow \quad v_{x,f} = v_{x,i}e^{-\frac{\eta}{m}\Delta t}$$

The speed of the object decreases exponentially due to the dissipation of energy.

Example 4-8:

Problem: A 10 kg object is moving in 1-dimension along a horizontal surface; we will denote the horizontal axis for the motion of the block as the x-axis. The object is initially moving in the positive x-axis direction with a rate of energy decrease given by the equation:

$$\frac{dE}{dx} = -\left(2\frac{kg}{s}\right)v_x$$

At time $t = 0$ s, the object is at $x = 2$ m and moving with speed of 6 m/s. What is the position of the object at $t = 4$ s?

Solution: As derived previously, the equation for the speed of the object as a function of time is

$$v_{x,f} = v_{x,i}e^{-\frac{\eta}{m}\Delta t} \quad \rightarrow \quad v_{x,f} = \left(6\frac{m}{s}\right)e^{-\left(\frac{2\frac{kg}{s}}{10kg}\right)(t_f-0)} \quad \rightarrow \quad v_{x,f} = \left(6\frac{m}{s}\right)e^{-\left(0.2\frac{1}{s}\right)t_f}$$

The position of the object can be found through integration.

$$v_{x,f} = \frac{dx}{dt_f} \quad \rightarrow \quad \frac{dx}{dt_f} = \left(6\frac{m}{s}\right)e^{-\left(0.2\frac{1}{s}\right)t_f} \quad \rightarrow \quad dx = \left(6\frac{m}{s}\right)e^{-\left(0.2\frac{1}{s}\right)t_f}dt_f$$

$$\int_{2m}^{x_f} dx = \int_{0s}^{4s}\left(6\frac{m}{s}\right)e^{-\left(0.2\frac{kg}{s}\right)t_f}dt_f \quad \rightarrow \quad x_f - 2m = -\left(\frac{6\frac{m}{s}}{0.2\frac{kg}{s}}\right)\left(e^{-\left(0.2\frac{kg}{s}\right)(0s)} - e^{-\left(0.2\frac{kg}{s}\right)(4s)}\right)$$

$$x_f - 2m = 16.5m \quad \rightarrow \quad x_f = 18.5m$$

4-7 Power

The rate at which energy is converted or transferred with respect to time is called **power**.

Power: The rate of change of energy with respect to time.

The unit of power is the watt, named for James Watt, and is denoted by W.

$$1\,W = 1\frac{J}{s}$$

Example 4-9:

Problem: How much energy is converted by a 100 W light bulb that is left on all day?

Solution:

$$\left(100\frac{J}{s}\right)\left(\frac{60\,s}{1\,min}\right)\left(\frac{60\,min}{1\,hr}\right)(24\,hr)$$

$$8.64\,MJ$$

If you have ever paid an electric bill you know that you are charged for the number of kilowatt-hours (kWh) that you have "*consumed*" during a given billing period. Looking at these units, we can tell that this is a measure of energy since it is the product of power (kilowatts) and time (hours); the specific conversion is 1 kWh equals 3.6 MJ. This means that the power company is actually charging you for the energy you convert (into light, into making the light bulb warmer, *etc.*).

We can describe the rate of energy change in terms of the average power (Equation 4-1) or the instantaneous power (Equation 4-2), each having units of J/s.

$$P_{avg} = \frac{\Delta E}{\Delta t} \qquad\qquad (4\text{-}1)$$

$$P = \frac{dE}{dt} \qquad\qquad (4\text{-}2)$$

Example 4-10:

Problem: An elevator motor lifts a 1000 kg elevator car a height of 100 m in 20 seconds at constant speed. What average power does the motor supply?

Solution: The system in this problem consists of the elevator car only. The equation for the energy of this system is

$$E = \frac{1}{2}mv_y^2 + mgy$$

In this equation we have defined the zero point for the gravitational potential energy to be at the bottom of the elevator shaft and the variable y to be the distance from the bottom of the elevator shaft to the elevator car. Since the speed of the elevator car is constant, the translational kinetic energy is constant, and only the gravitational potential energy of the elevator car will change during the time interval. This gives us

$$P_{avg} = \frac{\Delta E}{\Delta t} \quad \rightarrow \quad P_{avg} = \frac{\Delta U_g}{\Delta t} \quad \rightarrow \quad P_{avg} = mg\frac{\Delta y}{\Delta t}$$

Substitution yields

$$P_{avg} = \left(1000\text{kg}\right)\left(9.8\frac{\text{m}}{\text{s}^2}\right)\left(\frac{100\text{m}}{20\text{s}}\right)$$

$$P_{avg} = 49\text{kW}$$

Naturally, since power denotes the rate of energy change, we can incorporate it into our energy-based kinematics calculations.

Example 4-11:

Problem: A 2400 kg car can accelerate from 0 mph to 60 mph in 4 s. What is the average power supplied by the engine during this acceleration?

Solution: We begin with Equation 4-1 and assume that the only change in the energy of the system is a change in the translational kinetic energy.

$$P_{avg} = \frac{\Delta E}{\Delta t} = \frac{\Delta K}{\Delta t} \quad \rightarrow \quad P_{avg}\Delta t = \Delta K \quad \rightarrow \quad P_{avg} = \frac{K_f - K_i}{t_f - t_i}$$

Since the car starts from rest its initial kinetic energy is zero (*i.e.*, $K_i = 0$). We can further simplify this equation by defining $t_i = 0$ s.

$$P_{avg} = \frac{\frac{1}{2}mv_f^2 - 0}{t_f - 0} \quad \rightarrow \quad P_{avg} = \frac{mv_f^2}{2t_f}$$

Because we use SI units in physics (Section 1-7), the next step is to convert the final speed into the appropriate units:

$$60\frac{\text{miles}}{\text{hr}}\left(\frac{1\,\text{hr}}{60\,\text{min}}\right)\left(\frac{1\,\text{min}}{60\,\text{s}}\right)\left(\frac{1\,\text{km}}{0.62\,\text{mile}}\right)\left(\frac{1000\,\text{m}}{1\,\text{km}}\right) = 26.9\frac{\text{m}}{\text{s}}$$

Substitution then yields

$$P_{avg} = \frac{\left(2400\,\text{kg}\right)\left(26.9\frac{\text{m}}{\text{s}}\right)^2}{2\left(4\,\text{s}\right)} \quad \rightarrow \quad P_{avg} = 217083\,\text{W} \quad \rightarrow \quad P_{avg} = 217\,\text{kW}$$

In the United States, we typically describe the power of an engine using the unit horsepower (hp), defined to be 746 W. We could, therefore, also express the power of the engine in this problem as

$$P_{avg} = \left(217083\,\text{W}\right)\left(\frac{1\,\text{hp}}{746\,\text{W}}\right) \quad \rightarrow \quad P_{avg} = 291\,\text{hp}$$

Of course, this is an underestimate of the *total* power supplied by the engine since we have ignored any energy dissipation from the system due to air resistance or due to friction within the car itself.

Let's assume that the power supplied by an engine to a car is constant as the car accelerates. The relationship between the time and displacement of the car can then be expressed in terms of this power, which we can denote as the average power. Building upon the solution to Example 4-11, we have

$$P_{avg} = \frac{K_f - K_i}{t_f - t_i} \quad \rightarrow \quad P_{avg} = \frac{\frac{1}{2}mv_f^2 - 0}{t_f - 0} \quad \rightarrow \quad P_{avg} = \frac{mv_f^2}{2t_f}$$

$$v_f = \left(\frac{2P_{avg}}{m}\right)^{\frac{1}{2}} t_f^{\frac{1}{2}} \quad \rightarrow \quad \frac{dx}{dt} = \left(\frac{2P_{avg}}{m}\right)^{\frac{1}{2}} t^{\frac{1}{2}} \quad \rightarrow \quad \int_0^x dx = \int_0^t \left(\frac{2P_{avg}}{m}\right)^{\frac{1}{2}} t^{\frac{1}{2}} \, dt$$

$$x = \left(\frac{2P_{avg}}{m}\right)^{\frac{1}{2}} \frac{2}{3} t^{\frac{3}{2}} \quad \rightarrow \quad t = \left(\frac{3}{2}x\right)^{\frac{2}{3}} \left(\frac{m}{2P_{avg}}\right)^{\frac{1}{3}}$$

It is interesting to note that the time required to travel a specific distance decreases as the power increases, but only to the 1/3 power.

4-8 General Problem Solving Strategy

Based upon the solutions to the problems presented in this chapter, we have developed the following general strategy for an energy-based approach for solving kinematics problems.

Step 1: Determine an equation for the energy of the system. The energy of the system is the sum of the translational kinetic and potential energies of each object in the system. We should also be careful to use as many subscripts as necessary to indicate clearly the definition of each term in the equation for the energy of the system.

Step 2: Combine as many translational kinetic energy terms as possible. Often, many objects have the same speed, even if they have different velocities. When this occurs, we should express the associated translational kinetic energies of these objects with a common v^2 term. We can then combine all of these translational kinetic energy terms together into one *effective translational kinetic energy* for the entire system.

Step 3: Differentiate the equation for the energy of the system to determine acceleration. It is always simplest to differentiate with respect to the position of an object in the system to determine the acceleration of that object since the first derivative of translational kinetic energy with respect to position is proportional to the acceleration. For example,

$$\frac{d}{dx}\left(\frac{1}{2}mv_x^2\right) = ma_x$$

Step 4a: If the system is isolated, then the expression resulting from the differentiation in Step 3 is equal to zero. It's now just a matter of algebra to determine the acceleration.

Step 4b: **If the system is not isolated, then the expression resulting from the differentiation in Step 3 is equal to the rate of energy dissipation/addition.** We need to be careful with our ($\pm$) signs to guarantee that energy of the system is correctly decreasing or increasing as a result of its interaction with the outside environment. After that, it's just a matter of algebra to determine the acceleration.

Step 5a: **If the acceleration is constant, then we can use constant acceleration kinematics equations (Section 2-5) to determine the relationships between the position, velocity, and acceleration as a function of time.**

Step 5b: **If the acceleration is not constant, then we can use the general kinematic equations (Section 2-3) to determine the relationships between the position, velocity, and acceleration as a function of time.** This may involve calculus, so be prepared.

Summary

- **If the translational kinetic energy of an object is linearly dependent upon its position, then the acceleration of the object will be constant.** If the translational kinetic energy is linearly dependent upon time, then the acceleration will not be constant.
- **The first derivative of an object's translational kinetic energy with respect to the object's position is equal to the product of the object's mass and acceleration.**

$$\frac{d}{dx}\left(\frac{1}{2}mv_x^2\right) = ma_x$$

- **The acceleration of a system can be determined from the equation for the energy of the system through differentiation.** This differentiation can be with respect to the position of any of the objects in the system, to time, or to the speed of any of the objects in the system.
- **The simplest approach for determining the acceleration of a system is to differentiate the equation for the energy of the system with respect to the position of one of the objects of the system.** The first reason for this is that the differentiation of translational kinetic energy with respect to position is proportional to the acceleration. The second reason for this is that this differentiation requires us to determine how changes in the positions of the objects in the system are related to each other. These relative displacements are, typically, easy to find.
- **Power:** The rate at which energy is converted or transferred.

$$P = \frac{dE}{dt}$$

Problems

1. A 4 kg block is sliding up a 60° ramp with an initial speed of 4 m/s. How far up the ramp will the block slide before coming to a rest? What is the acceleration of the block?

2. A 4 kg block is sliding up a 60° ramp with an initial speed of 4 m/s at the base of the ramp. Because of friction, energy will be dissipated at a constant rate of 2 J/m as the block slides. What is the acceleration of the block? How far up the ramp will the block slide before coming to a rest?

3. The four blocks shown in the figure at right have equal masses and are thrown/pushed with equal speeds from the same height above the ground. The directions of the arrows indicate the directions at which the blocks were thrown/ pushed. The ramp along which block D slides is frictionless. Rank from highest to lowest the speeds of the blocks when they hit the ground. You may assume each block consti- tutes an isolated system.

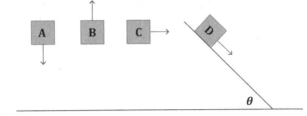

4. An object attached to a spring is moving back and forth on a horizontal frictionless surface. Is the magnitude of the acceleration of this object constant in time?

5. The energy of an object is given by the following equation:

$$E = \left(5\,\text{kg}\right)v_x^2 + \left(10\,\frac{\text{J}}{\text{m}}\right)x$$

   What is the magnitude of the acceleration of the object? You may assume that the object is an isolated system.

6. A 3 kg object is moving along a horizontal surface. The translational kinetic energy of the object is increasing at a constant rate of 6 J/m; that is, the energy increases linearly with the distance travelled. If the object starts from rest, how far has it moved after 4 s?

7. Three blocks are connected by a massless rope that passes over massless pulleys, as shown in the figure at right. The horizontal surface along which block B slides is friction- less. What is the magnitude of the acceleration of block A? What is the direction of this acceleration if the mass of block C is larger than the mass of block A?

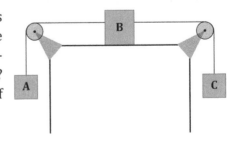

8. Two blocks are connected by a massless rope that passes over massless pulleys, as shown in the figure at right. The horizontal surface along which block A slides is frictionless. What is the magnitude of the acceleration of block A?

9. Two blocks, A and B, are connected by a massless rope that passes over a massless pulley, as shown in the figure at right. Because of friction, energy will be dissipated at a constant rate of 3 J/m as block A slides across the horizontal surface. If the mass of block A is 2 kg and the mass of block B is 3 kg, what is the magnitude of the acceleration of block B? What fraction of the decrease in the gravitational potential energy of the system is converted into the translational kinetic energy of block A?

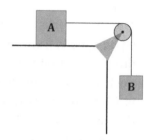

10. Two blocks with masses of 2 kg and 4 kg are connected by a massless rope that passes over a massless pulley, as shown in the figure at right. When the system is released from rest, the 4 kg block is 2 m above the ground. How much time will it take for the 4 kg block to fall to the ground?

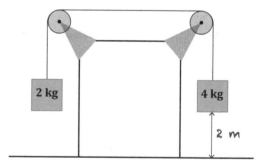

11. The figure below shows 4 different systems of moving blocks. The mass of block A is 4 kg, and the mass of block B is 2 kg. For system A and system B, the blocks are in free-fall. The pulley and rope in both system C and system D are massless. Rank in order from largest to smallest the magnitude of acceleration of systems.

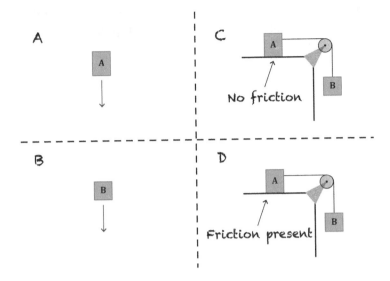

12. The figure below shows 4 different systems of moving masses connected by a massless rope; the pulleys in A, B, and C are massless. The mass of object B is larger than the mass of object A, and all surfaces are frictionless. Rank in order from largest to smallest the magnitude of acceleration of systems.

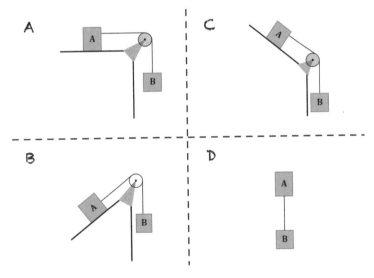

13. An object is moving in 1-dimension along a horizontal surface denoted as the x-axis. The object is initially moving in the positive x-axis direction, and the rate of energy decrease of the object is proportional to the square of its speed.

$$\frac{dE}{dx} = -\lambda v_x^2$$

The variable λ in this equation is a constant with units of kg/m. The speed of the object at $t_0 = 0$ s is v_0. What is the speed of the object as a function of $t > t_0$?

14. A 60 kg person runs up a 30° ramp with a constant acceleration. She starts from rest at the bottom of the ramp and covers a distance of 15 m up the ramp in 5.8 s. What instantaneous power was she exerting at $t = 4$ s?

CHAPTER FIVE
Circular and Rotational Motion

We demonstrated in Chapter 4 how expressions for the energy of a system can be used as a starting point for kinematic calculations. For example, the acceleration of a system can be determined by differentiating the expression for the energy of the system. We can now build upon those results by including an additional energy term: **rotational kinetic energy**. Rotational kinetic energy is the energy that an object possesses because of its circular or rotational motion. As we expect, the inclusion of an additional energy term in the expression for a system's energy affects how that system partitions its energy and, thus, also affects its acceleration.

5-2 Variable Definitions

Consider the system shown in Figure 5.1, which consists of a block moving in a uniform[1] circle of radius R.

The positions of the block along the x and y axes, defined in Figure 5.1, both change as the block moves around the circle. Hence, with respect to this system of coordinate axes, this circular motion is 2-dimensional motion. However, just as for the 2-dimensional motion of a block sliding down a ramp (Example 4-3), the motion along one of these dimensions is coupled to the motion along the other. For the block sliding down the ramp, the horizontal and vertical components of the motion were coupled by the slope of the ramp. For circular motion, the x-axis and y-axis components of the motion are

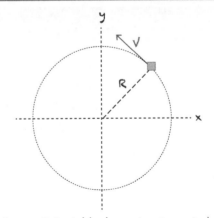

Figure 5.1: A block moving in a circle of radius R. The direction of the velocity of the block is indicated by the arrow.

---

1   A uniform circle is a circle whose radius is constant. Similarly, uniform circular motion is motion around a circle whose radius is constant.

coupled by the radius of the circle. In this way, we can think of circular motion as effectively 1-dimensional motion if we use an appropriate coordinate transformation. There are two common options (Figure 5.2):

(i) Tangential Definition: The position and motion of the object can be described in terms of the object's location along the circumference of the circle. Following the coordinate transform of Example 4-3, we will denote this as the s-axis. The origin of the s-axis will be at the x-axis (see Figure 5.2), and we will define the positive direction for the s-axis to be *counterclockwise* motion around the circle. We refer to this as a tangential definition since the s-axis is always tangent to the circumference of the circle. Keep in mind that the direction of the s-axis will constantly change with respect to the x and y axes as the block moves around the circle.

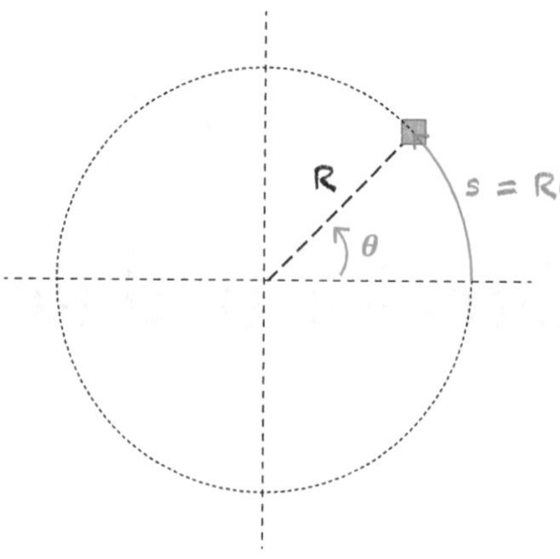

(ii) Angular Definition: The position of the object can be described in terms of the angle of the object using polar coordinates (*i.e.*, in terms of the angle θ in Figure 5.2). Again, *motion of the object counterclockwise around the circle is defined to be in the positive direction*

As shown in Figure 5.2, these two definitions of position are linked by Equation 5-1.

Figure 5.2: Determining the position of an object undergoing circular motion using either an angular description with polar coordinates or a tangential description with the distance along the circumference of the circle.

$$s = R\theta \tag{5-1}$$

It is important to note that Equation 5-1 will be valid only if the angle θ is measured in radians. It is also worth mentioning that since both R and s in Equation 5-1 have units of meters, radians are actually a dimensionless unit. Because of this, the radian unit may come and go freely in our calculations, as we shall see.

5-3 Circular Motion Kinematics

We will begin with an angular description of the position of an object moving in a circle using polar coordinates. Recall that for linear translational motion the first derivative of the position with respect to time is the velocity (Section 2-3). A similar relationship holds in circular motion as well. The first derivative of the angular position of the object with respect to time is the angular velocity, denoted by ω.

$$\omega = \frac{d\theta}{dt} \tag{5-2}$$

Similarly, the first derivative of the angular velocity with respect to time, or the second derivative of angular position with respect to time, is the angular acceleration.

$$\alpha = \frac{d\omega}{dt} = \frac{d^2\theta}{dt^2} \tag{5-3}$$

The direction for the angular velocity and angular acceleration will be denoted using a ($\pm$) sign, following the convention introduced in Section 5-2.

Using Equation 5-1, we can also write down equivalent expressions for the velocity and acceleration of the object with respect to its motion along the circumference of the circle. These are referred to as the tangential velocity and tangential acceleration, respectively.

$$v_t = \frac{ds}{dt} \quad \rightarrow \quad v_t = R\omega \tag{5-4}$$

$$a_t = \frac{dv_t}{dt} = \frac{d^2s}{dt^2} \quad \rightarrow \quad a_t = R\alpha \tag{5-5}$$

Example 5-1:

Problem: The position of an object moving in a uniform circle with a radius of 20 cm is given by the following equation:

$$\theta(t) = \left(2\frac{\text{rad}}{\text{s}}\right)t + \left(4\frac{\text{rad}}{\text{s}^2}\right)t^2$$

What is the angular acceleration of this object? What is the tangential acceleration of the object?

Solution: We determine the angular velocity using Equation 5-3.

$$\omega = \frac{d\theta}{dt} \quad \rightarrow \quad \omega = \frac{d}{dt}\left(\left(2\frac{\text{rad}}{\text{s}}\right)t + \left(4\frac{\text{rad}}{\text{s}^2}\right)t^2\right)$$

$$\omega = 2\frac{\text{rad}}{\text{s}} + \left(8\frac{\text{rad}}{\text{s}^2}\right)t$$

$$\alpha = \frac{d\omega}{dt} \quad \rightarrow \quad \alpha = \frac{d}{dt}\left(2\frac{\text{rad}}{\text{s}} + \left(8\frac{\text{rad}}{\text{s}^2}\right)t\right)$$

$$\alpha = 8\frac{\text{rad}}{\text{s}^2}$$

We can then use Equation 5-5 to determine the tangential acceleration.

$$a_t = R\alpha \quad \rightarrow \quad a_t = (0.2\text{m})\left(8\frac{\text{rad}}{\text{s}^2}\right) \quad \rightarrow \quad a_t = 1.6\frac{\text{m rad}}{\text{s}^2}$$

However, since radians are dimensionless, we can drop them from our final answer.

$$a_t = 1.6 \frac{m}{s^2}$$

Example 5-2:

Problem: The angular velocity as a function of time for an object undergoing circular motion is shown in the Figure 5.3.

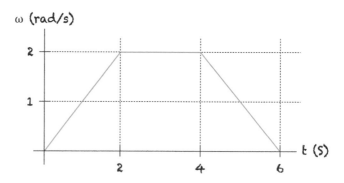

Figure 5.3: A plot of angular velocity versus time for Example 5-2.

What is the change in the angular position of the object from $t = 0$ s to $t = 6$ s?

Solution: We begin with Equation 5-2

$$\omega = \frac{d\theta}{dt} \quad \rightarrow \quad d\theta = \omega\, dt \quad \rightarrow \quad \int_{\theta_i}^{\theta_f} d\theta = \int_{t_i}^{t_f} \omega\, dt \quad \rightarrow \quad \Delta\theta = \int_{t_i}^{t_f} \omega\, dt$$

In this integration, we have defined the object to be angular position θ_i at time t_i and at angular position θ_f at time t_f. The change in the angular position is the integral of the angular velocity with respect to time, which is simply the area under the curve of a plot of angular velocity versus time. For the curve in Figure 5.3, this area is 8 rad. Thus,

$$\Delta\theta = 8\,rad$$

5-4 Constant Angular Acceleration Kinematics

When the angular acceleration of an object is constant, there are three often-used equations to relate the angular position and angular velocity of the object.

$$\Delta\omega = \alpha\Delta t$$

$$\Delta\theta = \omega_i \Delta t + \frac{1}{2}\alpha(\Delta t)^2$$

$$\omega_f^2 = \omega_i^2 + 2\alpha\Delta\theta$$

We notice that these equations are reminiscent of those presented in Section 2-5 for 1-dimensional translational motion with constant acceleration. The only difference is a change in the symbol used for the variables. Similarly, as shown in Figure 5.4, these equations indicate that when angular acceleration is constant, the angular velocity will change linearly with time, and the angular position will change quadratically with time.

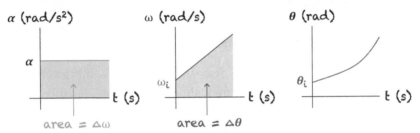

Figure 5.4: Plots of angular acceleration, angular velocity, and angular position as a function of time for circular motion with constant and positive angular acceleration. The initial angular velocity and angular position are denoted by ω_i and θ_i, respectively. The area under the curve of angular acceleration versus time is the change in the angular velocity, and the area under the curve of angular velocity versus time is the angular displacement.

Example 5-3:

Problem: A model train moves along a circular track with a radius of 0.5 m. Starting from rest, the train accelerates at 0.2 m/s². Through what total angle has the train travelled after 10 s?

Solution: Since the acceleration is constant, we can use the constant acceleration angular acceleration kinematics equations to relate the time interval to an angular displacement. We recognize that the acceleration given in the problem must be the tangential acceleration since it has units of m/s². Thus, our first step is to convert this into an angular acceleration.

$$\alpha = \frac{a_t}{R} \quad \rightarrow \quad \alpha = \frac{0.2\frac{m}{s^2}}{0.5m} \quad \rightarrow \quad \alpha = 0.4\frac{rad}{s^2}$$

$$\Delta\theta = \omega_i \Delta t + \frac{1}{2}\alpha(\Delta t)^2 \quad \rightarrow \quad \Delta\theta = 0 + \frac{1}{2}\left(0.4\frac{rad}{s^2}\right)(10s)^2$$

$$\Delta\theta = 20\,rad$$

Alternative Solution: We could, instead, have solved first for the change in the tangential position of the train.

$$\Delta s = v_{i,s}\Delta t + \frac{1}{2}a_s\left(\Delta t\right)^2 \quad \rightarrow \quad \Delta s = 0 + \frac{1}{2}\left(0.2\frac{m}{s^2}\right)\left(10s\right)^2 \quad \rightarrow \quad \Delta s = 10m$$

Now, using Equation 5-1 we can determine the corresponding change in angle.

$$\Delta\theta = \frac{\Delta s}{R} \quad \rightarrow \quad \Delta\theta = \frac{10m}{0.5m} \quad \rightarrow \quad \Delta\theta = 20\,rad$$

5-5 Rotational Motion, Rotational Kinetic Energy, and Moment of Inertia

It is straightforward to extend the preceding discussion of circular motion to the rotational motion of solid objects. Consider, for example, the system shown in Figure 5.5, which consists of a solid disk rotating around an axis that passes through the center of the disk and that is oriented perpendicular to the plane of the disk.

We can use Equation and 5-2 and Equation 5-3 to describe the rotation of the disk in terms of the change in its angular position. For solid objects, the unit *revolution* (typically denoted by rev) is often used rather than radians in expressions of angular position and angular velocity. A revolution denotes a complete circle completed by the object undergoing the rotational motion. Hence,

$$1\,rev = 2\pi\,rad$$

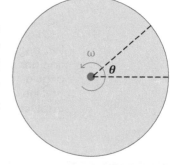

Figure 5.5: A disk rotating at a constant angular velocity around an axis, denoted by the red circle, oriented perpendicular to the plane of the disk and passing through the center of the disk.

Example 5-4:

Problem: What is the angular velocity in rad/s of the solid disk in Figure 5.5 if it is rotating at 45 revolutions per minute (rpm)?

Solution:

$$45\frac{rev}{min}\left(\frac{1\,min}{60\,sec}\right)\left(\frac{2\pi\,rad}{1\,rev}\right)$$

$$4.7\frac{rad}{s}$$

Notice that the conversion factor from rpm to rad/s is very close to 0.1.

Example 5-5:

Problem: A disk starts from rest and then spins with a constant angular acceleration of 2 rad/s². Through what angle will the disk have moved when its angular velocity is 4 rad/s?

Solution: Since the angular acceleration is constant, we can use the constant angular acceleration kinematics equations

$$\omega_f^2 = \omega_i^2 + 2\alpha\Delta\theta \quad \rightarrow \quad \Delta\theta = \frac{\omega_f^2 - \omega_i^2}{2\alpha}$$

$$\Delta\theta = \frac{\left(4\frac{rad}{s}\right)^2 - 0}{2\left(2\frac{rad}{s^2}\right)} \quad \rightarrow \quad \Delta\theta = 4\,rad$$

If a rotating object has mass, there will be kinetic energy associated with its rotation. Specifically, there will be translational kinetic energy associated with the tangential speed of each "*bit*" of mass that constitutes the object. In order to determine an expression for this kinetic energy, which we will refer to as rotational kinetic energy (denoted by the variable K_{rot}), let's consider the simple system shown in Figure 5.6, which consists of four blocks attached to each other by massless rods and rotating around a fixed point. The angular velocity of the rotation is constant.

The rotational kinetic energy for this system is, simply, the sum of the translational kinetic energies of the blocks.

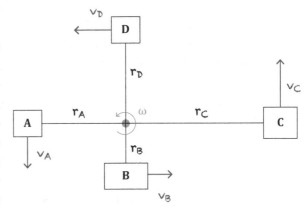

Figure 5.6: A system of four blocks connected by massless rods rotating around a fixed point, denoted by the red circle, oriented perpendicular to the plane in which the objects are moving.

$$K_{rot} = \frac{1}{2}m_A v_{A,t}^2 + \frac{1}{2}m_B v_{B,t}^2 + \frac{1}{2}m_C v_{C,t}^2 + \frac{1}{2}m_D v_{D,t}^2$$

The speeds used in this calculation of the rotational kinetic energy of the system are the tangential speeds of the blocks; the subscript "t" denotes that these are tangential speeds. The blocks all have the same angular velocity since they are rotating together, but they have different tangential velocities and speeds due to their varying distance from the axis of rotation (Equation 5-4).

Thus, it is useful for us to express the rotational kinetic energy of the system in terms of this common angular velocity.

$$K_{rot} = \frac{1}{2}m_A\left(\omega r_A\right)^2 + \frac{1}{2}m_B\left(\omega r_B\right)^2 + \frac{1}{2}m_C\left(\omega r_C\right)^2 + \frac{1}{2}m_D\left(\omega r_D\right)^2$$

$$K_{rot} = \frac{1}{2}\left(m_A r_A^2 + m_B r_B^2 + m_C r_C^2 + m_D r_D^2\right)\omega^2$$

The term within the parentheses is the *moment of inertia* of this system and is denoted by the letter *I*.

$$I = m_A r_A^2 + m_B r_B^2 + m_C r_C^2 + m_D r_D^2$$

For this collection of blocks, which we have treated as point particles, the moment of inertia is the sum of the products of the masses and the square of their distances from the axis of rotation. The rotational kinetic energy of this or any rotating system can, therefore, be expressed as

$$K_{rot} = \frac{1}{2}I\omega^2 \tag{5-6}$$

Indeed, let's now extend this derivation to determine the moment of inertia of a solid object. Consider the rotating disk shown in Figure 5.7. This disk is rotating at a constant angular velocity around an axis that passes through its center and that is oriented perpendicular to the plane of the disk.

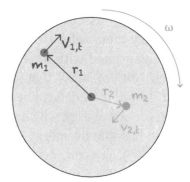

We can model this solid disk as a composite of infinitesimally small "*bits*" of mass moving together. We denote two of these small bits of mass in Figure 5.7 as m_1 and m_2, which are at distances r_1 and r_2 from the axis of rotation, respectively, and moving with tangential speeds $v_{1,t}$ and $v_{2,t}$, respectively. The moment of inertia for the disk is, simply, the sum of the contributions from all of these discrete small bits of mass[2].

Figure 5.7: A solid disk rotating around an axis, denoted by the red circle, oriented perpendicular to the plane of the disk and passing through the center of the disk. The tangential velocities of two constitutive "*bits*" of mass are shown.

$$I = m_1 r_1^2 + m_2 r_2^2 + \ldots = \sum_i m_i r_i^2 \tag{5-7}$$

In the limit that the bits of mass become truly infinitesimally small, we can replace the summation with integration.

$$I = \int r^2\, dm \tag{5-8}$$

---

2 Since the bits are infinitesimally small, we can treat them as point particles. The moment of inertia for a point particle, as derived above, is mr².

An example of using Equation 5-8 to calculate a moment of inertia together with a table of several moments of inertia of common solid objects appear in Appendix D. Equation 5-8 also allows for a qualitative understanding of moment of inertia. Specifically, it is a measure of how the mass of an object is distributed around the axis of rotation. A smaller moment of inertia corresponds to an object's mass being more tightly distributed around the axis of rotation, and a larger moment of inertia corresponds to an object's mass being more widely distributed around the axis of rotation. Furthermore, upon comparing Equation 5-6 with Equation 3-1, we see that the moment of inertia can be interpreted as the circular/rotational motion equivalent of mass. However, unlike mass, which is invariant with respect to the motion of an object, the moment of inertia depends upon the location of the axis of rotation.

Example: 5-6:

Problem: A uniformly dense solid sphere with a mass of 4 kg and a radius of 2 m is free to rotate around an axis that passes through its center. The rotational kinetic energy of the sphere is given by the equation:

$$K_{rot}(\theta) = 25J + \left(16\frac{J}{rad}\right)\theta$$

What is the angular acceleration of the sphere?

Solution: Differentiating Equation 5-6 with respect to θ gives us

$$\frac{d}{d\theta}\left(\frac{1}{2}I\omega^2\right) = I\omega\frac{d\omega}{d\theta} \quad \rightarrow \quad \frac{d}{d\theta}\left(\frac{1}{2}I\omega^2\right) = I\omega\frac{d\omega}{dt}\frac{dt}{d\theta} \quad \rightarrow \quad \frac{d}{d\theta}\left(\frac{1}{2}I\omega^2\right) = I\omega\alpha\frac{1}{\omega}$$

$$\frac{d}{d\theta}\left(\frac{1}{2}I\omega^2\right) = I\alpha$$

Hence, for the solid sphere in this problem

$$\frac{d}{d\theta}\left(25J + \left(16\frac{J}{rad}\right)\theta\right) = I\alpha \quad \rightarrow \quad I\alpha = 16\frac{J}{rad} \quad \rightarrow \quad \alpha = \frac{16\frac{J}{rad}}{I}$$

The moment of inertia for the sphere can be found in Table D-2.

$$I = \frac{2}{5}MR^2 \quad \rightarrow \quad I = \frac{2}{5}(4\,\text{kg})(2\,\text{m})^2 \quad \rightarrow \quad I = 6.4\,\text{kgm}^2$$

Thus,

$$\alpha = \frac{16\dfrac{J}{rad}}{6.4\,kgm^2} \quad \rightarrow \quad \alpha = 2.5\frac{1}{rads^2}$$

Since the rad unit is dimensionless, we can rewrite this solution with the correct units for angular acceleration.

$$\alpha = 2.5\frac{rad}{s^2}$$

Example 5-7:

Problem: Two identical 2 kg point masses are connected by a 3 m long thin massless rod and are rotating with an angular velocity of 3 rad/s around an axis halfway between them. What is the kinetic energy of this rotation?

Solution: The first step in our solution is to determine the moment of inertia of the rotating system. The moment of inertia of a point mass can be found using Equation 5-7. In this equation, the distance between each mass and the axis of rotation is exactly one half the length of the rod that connects them.

$$I = \sum_i m_i r_i^2 \quad \rightarrow \quad I = (2kg)(1.5m)^2 + (2kg)(1.5m)^2$$

$$I = 9\,kg\,m^2$$

The kinetic energy of this rotating system can then be found using Equation 5-6.

$$K_{rot} = \frac{1}{2}I\omega^2 \quad \rightarrow \quad K_{rot} = \frac{1}{2}(9\,kg\,m^2)\left(3\frac{rad}{s}\right)^2$$

$$K_{rot} = 40.5\,J$$

The additional rad² unit is dropped from the final answer since it is dimensionless.

It follows from the definition of moment of inertia in Equation 5-7 and Equation 5-8 that the moment of inertia for a system consisting of many rotating objects is the linear sum of the moments of inertia for each object in the system.

Example 5-8:

Problem: A small 4 kg block is attached at the edge of a uniformly dense solid disk with a mass of 20 kg and radius of 0.25 m, as shown in Figure 5.8.

This system rotates about an axis through the center of the disk and perpendicular to the surface of the disk (the dashed line in Figure 5.8). If the angular speed of the rotation is 6 rad/s, what is the rotational kinetic energy of the system?

Figure 5.8: A system consisting of a small block attached to a disk. The system is rotating around an axis (dashed line) that passes through the center of the disk and that is oriented perpendicular to the plane of the disk.

Solution: The first step in our solution is to determine the moment of inertia of the system. This will be the linear sum of the moments of inertia of the block and the disk.

$$I = I_{block} + I_{disk}$$

We can treat the block as a point particle[3] since it is small. The moment of inertia of the disk can be found in Table D-2. With these assumptions and definitions, the moment of inertia of the system is

$$I = m_{block}R^2_{disk} + \frac{1}{2}m_{disk}R^2_{disk} \quad \rightarrow \quad I = \left(m_{block} + \frac{1}{2}m_{disk} \right)R^2_{disk}$$

The rotational kinetic energy of the system is, therefore,

$$K_{rot} = \frac{1}{2}I\omega^2 \quad \rightarrow \quad K_{rot} = \frac{1}{2}\left(m_{block} + \frac{1}{2}m_{disk} \right)R^2_{disk}\omega^2$$

$$K_{rot} = \frac{1}{2}\left(4\,kg + \frac{1}{2}(20\,kg) \right)(0.25\,m)^2\left(6\frac{rad}{s} \right)^2$$

$$K_{rot} = 15.75\,J$$

If the moment of inertia for a uniformly dense object rotating around an axis passing through its center is known, then the moment of inertia for this object rotating around any parallel axis of rotation can be determined using the parallel axis theorem[4] (Equation 5-9).

$$I = I_{CM} + Md^2 \qquad \qquad \textbf{(5-9)}$$

---

3   Recall that the moment of inertia for a point particle is mr².
4   See Section D-6.

In Equation 5-9, M is the mass of the object, d is the distance between the actual axis of rotation and the parallel axis of rotation passing through the center of the object, and I_{CM} is the moment of inertia for the uniformly dense object rotating around that parallel axis through its center[5].

Consider the system shown in Figure 5.9 that consists of a solid sphere with a mass of 2.5 kg and a radius of 1 m that is attached to a massless rigid rod with a length of 2 m.

The system is initially upright but, after given a small nudge, will rotate around a horizontal axis in the plane of the rod and sphere through the lower end of the rod. The moment of inertia for this system for this rotation is, simply, the sum of the moments of inertia for each object in the system. The rod is massless, and, so, its moment of inertia is zero. The moment of inertia for the sphere for rotating around this axis can be determined using Equation 5-9.

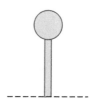

Figure 5.9: A system consisting of a solid sphere attached to a massless rod that is free to rotate around the axis of rotation indicated by the dashed line.

$$I = \frac{2}{5}\left(2.5\,\text{kg}\right)\left(1\,\text{m}\right)^2 + \left(2.5\,\text{kg}\right)\left(1\,\text{m} + 2\,\text{m}\right)^2$$

$$I = 23.5\,\text{kg}\,\text{m}^2$$

It's worth noting that if the distance d in Equation 5-9 is very large compared to the size of the object (*i.e.*, if d is much larger than the object's radius or length), then the Md^2 term in Equation 5-9 will be larger than the I_{CM} term.

$$Md^2 \gg I_{CM} \quad \rightarrow \quad I \approx Md^2$$

In other words, any object can be treated as a point particle if the distance between the object and its axis of rotation is much larger than the physical dimensions (*i.e.*, the size) of the object.

5-6 Systems with Both Rotational Kinetic and Translational Kinetic Energy

Naturally, it is possible for systems to have both rotational and translational movement occurring at the same. For example, consider an object rolling down a ramp or a tossed football spinning in the air. Such systems would, consequently, have both rotational and translational kinetic energy.

Let's consider the system shown in Figure 5.10, which consists of a solid disk of mass M that is both rotating (with angular velocity ω about an axis that passes through its center and oriented perpendicular to the plane of the disk) and moving translationally (at speed v_x) along a 1-dimensional x-axis.

---

5 Technically, I_{CM} is the moment of inertia for the object rotating around an axis through its center of mass. For uniformly dense objects, the center of mass is at the center of the object (Section 10-5). However, Equation 5-9 is valid for all objects, including those that are not uniformly dense, as long as the moment of inertia for an axis of rotation through the center of mass is known.

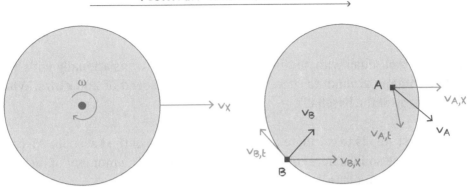

Figure 5.10: A solid disk that is rotating and moving translationally; the axis of rotation, indicated by the red circle, is oriented perpendicular to the plane of the disk and passes through the center of the disk. As shown on the right, the velocities of each bit of mass that constitute the disk can be expressed in terms of a tangential component (denoted by the subscript "*t*") and a translational component (denoted by the subscript "*x*") components.

The total kinetic energy of this system is the sum of the kinetic energies of each bit of mass that constitutes the disk. As shown in Figure 5.10, we can represent the velocities of each bit of mass in terms of translational and tangential components. All of these translational components of velocity will be identical and equal to the translational velocity of the entire disk as long as the disk is not changing its shape as it moves.

$$v_{A,x} = v_{B,x} = v_x$$

The tangential components of the velocities of each bit of mass are related to the position of that bit of mass on the disc and the rotational velocity of the disc as a whole through Equation 5-4.

Because we can make this distinction between the components of velocity, we can also break up the kinetic energy associated with each bit of mass into a translational and rotational component. The total kinetic of the disk is then simply the sum of the translational and rotational kinetic energies of each bit of mass that constitutes the disk. We can use the fact that each bit of mass has the same translational speed and the same angular velocity to simplify these summations.

$$K = \sum_i \frac{1}{2}m_i v_{i,x}^2 \quad \rightarrow \quad K = \frac{1}{2}\left(\sum_i m_i\right)v_x^2 \quad \rightarrow \quad K = \frac{1}{2}Mv_x^2$$

$$K_{rot} = \sum_i \frac{1}{2}m_i v_{i,t}^2 \quad \rightarrow \quad K_{rot} = \frac{1}{2}\sum_i m_i\left(r_i^2\omega^2\right) \quad \rightarrow \quad K_{rot} = \frac{1}{2}\left(\sum_i m_i r_i^2\right)\omega^2$$

$$K_{rot} = \frac{1}{2}I\omega^2$$

$$K_{total} = K + K_{rot} \quad \rightarrow \quad K_{total} = \frac{1}{2}Mv_x^2 + \frac{1}{2}I\omega^2$$

Example 5-9:

Problem: A 145 g baseball with a radius of 4 cm is moving translationally with a speed of 15 m/s while rotating around its center with an angular speed of 200 rad/s. What is the total kinetic energy of the baseball?

Solution: Our first step is to calculate the moment of inertia of the baseball. We can treat it as a uniformly dense solid sphere rotating around its center. The moment of inertia for this object can be found in Table D-2.

$$I = \frac{2}{5}MR^2 \quad \rightarrow \quad I = \frac{2}{5}(0.145\,\text{kg})(0.04\,\text{m})^2$$

$$I = 9.3 \times 10^{-5}\,\text{kg}\,\text{m}^2$$

Thus, the total kinetic energy of the baseball is

$$K_{total} = \frac{1}{2}(0.145\,\text{kg})\left(15\frac{\text{m}}{\text{s}}\right)^2 + \frac{1}{2}(9.3 \times 10^{-5}\,\text{kg}\,\text{m}^2)\left(200\frac{\text{rad}}{\text{s}}\right)^2$$

$$K = 18.2\,\text{J}$$

In this case, the rotational kinetic energy constitutes only 10% of the total kinetic energy of the baseball.

Although it is possible for the translational and rotational movements of an object to be independent of each other, we will primarily focus on instances in which these two movements are coupled. For example, let's consider the system shown in Figure 5.11 that consists of a ball rolling across a horizontal surface.

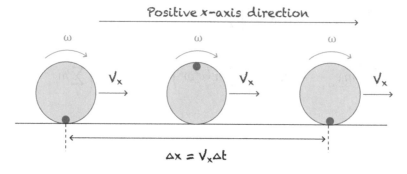

Figure 5.11: A ball rolling across a horizontal surface. The angular velocity of the ball's rotation is ω, and the translational velocity of the ball is v_x.

We say that the ball is *rolling without slipping* across the surface if the rotational and translational movements of the ball are coupled in such a way that the time required for the ball to compete one revolution is the same as the time required for the ball to move translationally a distance equal to its circumference. We can express this requirement mathematically as

$$\Delta t_{rotation} = \Delta t_{translation} \quad \rightarrow \quad \frac{2\pi}{\omega} = \frac{2\pi R}{v_x} \quad \rightarrow \quad v_x = \omega R$$

However, we need to be careful with our positive and negative signs in this expression. Indeed, although we use a fixed convention for the assignment of positive and negative signs for rotational motion (Section 5-2), the choice for which direction corresponds to positive translational motion is arbitrary. Consequently, the best way to express the relationship between angular and translational velocities for rolling without slipping is

$$v = \pm \omega R \qquad\qquad\qquad \textbf{(5-10)}$$

We can also apply this same constraint when ropes move over pulleys without slipping. In this case, the velocity of the rope must be the same as the tangential velocity of the pulley at the point where the rope and pulley are in contact with each other. If we apply Equation 5-4 to this condition, we, once again, obtain Equation 5-10.

5-7 Energy Conservation with Rotational Motion

Let's consider the isolated system shown in Figure 5.12, which consists of an object rolling without slipping down a ramp.

We can solve for the acceleration of the object using the same approach we used in Example 4-3[6].

We begin by writing down an equation for the energy of the system.

$$E = K + K_{rot} + U_g$$

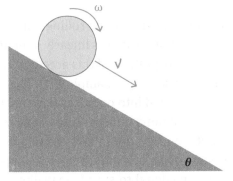

$$E = \frac{1}{2}mv_s^2 + \frac{1}{2}I\omega^2 + mgy \quad \rightarrow \quad E = \frac{1}{2}mv_s^2 + \frac{1}{2}I\omega^2 + mg\left(s\sin\theta\right)$$

Figure 5.12: A system consisting of an object rolling without slipping down a ramp. There is no energy loss due to friction for this system and, thus, this system is isolated.

We have defined the zero point of the gravitational potential energy to be the bottom of the ramp in this equation. We are also defining an s-axis to describe the position and motion of the object. This axis is parallel to the surface of the ramp with

---

6   This approach is also consistent with the general problem-solving strategy outlined in Section 4-8.

the positive direction pointing up the ramp (see Example 4-3). We know from Chapter 4 that we can differentiate this equation for the energy of the system with respect to the position of the rolling object to determine the acceleration of the object. In order to simplify this calculation, we should first rewrite this equation for the energy of the system using as few variables as possible. For example, since the object rolls without slipping, we can use Equation 5-9 to relate the translational and angular velocities.

$$\omega = \pm\frac{v_s}{R} \quad \rightarrow \quad E = \frac{1}{2}mv_s^2 + \frac{1}{2}I\left(\pm\frac{v_s}{R}\right)^2 + mg\left(s\sin\theta\right)$$

$$E = \frac{1}{2}\left(m+\frac{I}{R^2}\right)v_s^2 + mg\left(s\sin\theta\right)$$

Notice that since the kinetic energy depends upon the square of the speed (*i.e.,* on the magnitude of the velocity), the ($\pm$) sign in Equation 5-10 need not be determined.

Since the system is isolated, its energy is constant as the object rolls down the ramp.

$$\frac{dE}{ds} = 0 \quad \rightarrow \quad \left(m+\frac{I}{R^2}\right)a_s + mg\sin\theta = 0$$

$$\left(\frac{mR^2+I}{R^2}\right)a_s = -mg\sin\theta \quad \rightarrow \quad a_s = -\left(\frac{mR^2}{mR^2+I}\right)g\sin\theta$$

The acceleration of the rolling object is constant, which we could have anticipated since the kinetic energy of the system is linearly dependent upon the position of the object. It is also important to note that the magnitude of this acceleration is less than the magnitude of the acceleration of a block sliding down a ramp (Example 4-3). This occurs because the gravitational potential energy of this object is partitioned into both translational kinetic energy and rotational kinetic energy as the object rolls down the ramp. Indeed, since some of the gravitational potential energy is converted into rotational kinetic energy, the rate of change of translational kinetic energy of this system is less than for the system of a block sliding down a ramp (Figure 5.13). It follows that since translational kinetic energy is proportional to speed, a smaller rate of change in translational kinetic energy corresponds to a smaller rate of change in speed and, hence, to a smaller acceleration.

As shown in Figure 5.13, the translational kinetic energy in this system is always a linear function of the position of the object, but the magnitude of that dependence (*i.e.,* the slope of the translational kinetic energy as a function of position) is smaller if the object is also rotating. Since the acceleration of the system is proportional to this slope (Section 4-2), the magnitude of the acceleration is smaller when the object is also rotating.

Lastly, we also notice that the acceleration is inversely proportional to the moment of inertia of the object. This, too, can be understood from how energy is partitioned in this system. As shown in Equation 5-6, a larger moment of inertia corresponds to a larger rotational kinetic energy for a given angular velocity. Consequently, as the moment of inertia is increased, an accordingly larger fraction of the gravitational potential energy must be converted into rotational kinetic energy in order to maintain the rolling-without-slipping requirement (Equation 5-10). Therefore, increasing the moment of inertia of the system results in less gravitational potential energy being converted into translational kinetic energy and, hence, a smaller acceleration of the system.

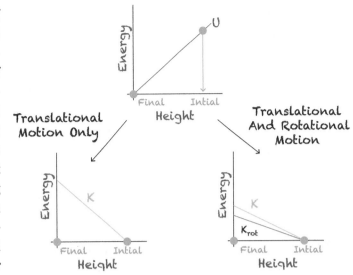

Figure 5.13: Differences in the partitioning of energy for an object sliding down a ramp (translational motion only) and an object that rolls down a ramp without slipping (translational and rotational motion).

Example 5-10:

Problem: Consider the system shown in Figure 5.14, that consists of two blocks, A and B, which are connected to each other by a massless rope that moves over a pulley without slipping. The pulley can be modeled as a uniformly dense solid cylinder with a mass and radius of m_p and R_p, respectively, and an axis of rotation passing through its center. What is the acceleration of block B?

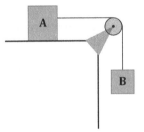

Figure 5.14: A system of two blocks, a rope, and a pulley.

Solution: The system in this problem consists of the two blocks, the rope, and the pulley. The energy of this system is the sum of the kinetic and potential energies of these objects. Following the solution presented in Section 4-5[7], we can write the equation for the energy of this system as

$$E = \frac{1}{2}m_A v_{A,x}^2 + m_A g y_A + \frac{1}{2}m_B v_{B,y}^2 + m_B g y_B + \frac{1}{2}I_p \omega_p^2 + m_p g y_p$$

In this expression for the energy, we have defined the zero point of the gravitational potential energy to be the ground (see Figure 4.10). There are no kinetic or potential

---

7   This approach is also consistent with the general problem-solving strategy outlined in Section 4-8.

energies associated with rope since it has no mass. The two blocks must have the same speed since they are connected by a rope.

$$v_{A,x}^2 = v_{B,y}^2$$

Also, since the rope moves over the pulley without slipping, we can apply Equation 5-9 to relate the angular speed of the pulley to the translational speeds of the blocks.

$$v_{A,x}^2 = v_{B,y}^2 = R_P^2 \omega_P^2$$

Finally, the moment of inertia for the pulley can be found in Table D-2.

$$I_P = \frac{1}{2} m_P R_P^2$$

Substitution of these parameters into our equation for the energy of the system yields

$$E = \frac{1}{2}\left(m_A + m_B\right)v_{B,y}^2 + m_A g y_A + m_B g y_B + \frac{1}{2}\left(\frac{1}{2}m_P R_P^2\right)\left(\frac{v_{B,y}^2}{R_P^2}\right) + m_P g y_P$$

Algebraically combining terms together gives us the following expression.

$$E = \frac{1}{2}\left(m_A + m_B + \frac{1}{2}m_P\right)v_{B,y}^2 + m_A g y_A + m_B g y_B + m_P g y_P$$

The effective translational kinetic energy of this system[8] is

$$K_{effective} = \frac{1}{2}\left(m_A + m_B + \frac{1}{2}m_P\right)v_{B,y}^2$$

This effective translational kinetic energy is larger than that of the system in Example 4-5 since the pulley now has mass and, thus, possesses rotational kinetic energy. Indeed, the rotational kinetic energy of the pulley contributes to the effective translational kinetic energy of the system since the rotational motion of the pulley is coupled to the translational motion of the blocks.

---

8   See Section 4-5.

The system is isolated since there is no friction present. Consequently, the energy will be constant as the masses move.

$$\frac{dE}{dy_B} = 0 \;\;\rightarrow\;\; \left(m_A + m_B + \frac{1}{2}m_P\right)a_B + m_A g\frac{dy_A}{dy_B} + m_B g + m_P g\frac{dy_P}{dy_B} = 0$$

Since

$$\frac{dy_A}{dy_B} = 0 \qquad \frac{dy_P}{dy_B} = 0$$

we have

$$\left(m_A + m_B + \frac{1}{2}m_P\right)a_B + m_B g = 0 \;\;\rightarrow\;\; a_B = -\left(\frac{m_B}{m_A + m_B + \frac{1}{2}m_P}\right)g$$

The acceleration for block B in Example 5-10 is negative since block B will fall when the blocks are released at rest. The acceleration is also constant, which we could have anticipated since the kinetic energy of this system is linearly dependent upon the vertical position of block B. We also notice that if we set the mass of the pulley to be zero, we recover our previous solution for the acceleration of this system (Section 4-5)[9]. Lastly, we recognize that the magnitude of the acceleration has decreased as a result of the pulley having mass. Now, as the system moves, the change in the gravitational potential energy of the system is being divided three ways. It is partitioned into: (i) the translational kinetic energy of block A; (ii) the translational kinetic energy of block B; and (iii) the rotational kinetic energy of the pulley[10]. As discussed previously, this increase in the partitioning of the energy results in a smaller magnitude for the system's acceleration.

5-8 Effective Mass

We recognized in Section 4-5 that the total mass of a system appears in the denominator of expressions for the acceleration of the system. We now see that a more precise statement is that the denominator in expressions for the acceleration of a system is dependent upon the effective translational kinetic energy[11] of the system[12]. Indeed, for the two systems discussed in Section 5-7, the

---

9   As mentioned previously, it is always best to check your solutions in a few limiting cases.
10 In other words, the effective translational kinetic energy of the system has increased.
11 Section 4-5.
12 Similarly, the numerator in expressions for the acceleration of a system is dependent upon the potential energy of the system. We'll discuss this further in Chapter 6.

denominator is not the total mass since the effective translational kinetic energy of these systems is not simply translational kinetic energy, but also includes rotational kinetic energy. Thus, we should interpret the denominator in expressions for the acceleration of a system as the *effective mass* of the system for its motion, which includes contributions from both the mass of the objects in the system (from their translational kinetic energies) and the moments of inertia[13] of the objects in the system (from their rotational kinetic energies). If a system has only translational kinetic energy, such as the system in Section 4-5, then the effective mass of the system is simply the total mass of the system. However, if a system has only rotational kinetic energy or translational and rotational kinetic energy, then the effective mass of the system will include contributions from the moments of inertia of the rotating objects in the system. For example, the effective mass for the system in Example 5-10 is

$$m_{effective} = m_A + m_B + \frac{I_P}{R_P^2} \quad \rightarrow \quad m_{effective} = m_A + m_B + \frac{1}{2}m_P$$

Since the origin of the effective mass is the effective translational kinetic energy of the system, the expression for the effective mass of the system reflects the relative energetic contributions of the motion(s)[14] of each object in the system to the overall motion of the system. Consider, for example, the effective masses of a block sliding down a ramp (Example 4-3) and an object rolling down a ramp (Section 5-7). For the sliding block, the effective mass is simply the mass of the block, but for the rolling object, the effective mass is

$$m_{effective} = m + \frac{I}{R^2}$$

By allowing the object to roll down the ramp rather than to simply slide down the ramp, we have increased the effective mass of the system. This increase in the effective mass of the system and the corresponding decrease in the acceleration of the system both reflect the changes in the partitioning of energy in this system. By allowing the object to roll down the ramp, we have added an additional kinetic energy term to the equation for the energy of the system and, thus, increased the partitioning of the change in the gravitational potential energy of the object associated with its movement down the ramp. This increase in the partitioning of energy results in a smaller magnitude for the acceleration of the object.

---

13   Recall from Section 5-5 that the moment of inertia can be interpreted as the circular/rotational motion equivalent of mass.

14   Some objects might have both rotational and translational motion, such as the object rolling down the ramp in Section 5-7.

Example 5-11:

Problem: Consider the system shown in Figure 5.15 that consists of three blocks—A, B, and C—which are connected to each other by two massless ropes that move over two pulleys without slipping. The pulleys can each be modeled as a uniformly dense solid cylinder with a mass of m_p and an axis of rotation passing through its center. What is the effective mass of this system?

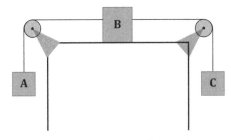

Figure 5.15: A system of three blocks, two ropes, and two pulleys.

Solution: The effective mass of this system is

$$m_{effective} = m_A + m_B + m_C + \frac{1}{2}m_P + \frac{1}{2}m_P$$

$$m_{effective} = m_A + m_B + m_C + m_P$$

Summary

- **The position, velocity, and acceleration of an object moving in a circle can be described using either a 1-dimensional tangential coordinate axis or a 1-dimensional angular coordinate axis.** These descriptions are related by the following equations:

$$s = R\theta \qquad v_t = R\omega \qquad a_t = R\alpha$$

- **Angular velocity:** The rate of change of angular position for either circular or rotational motion. Specifically, it is the first derivative of angular position with respect to time.

$$\omega = \frac{d\theta}{dt}$$

- **Angular acceleration:** The rate of change of angular velocity. Specifically, it is the first derivative of angular velocity with respect to time or the second derivative of angular position with respect to time.

$$\alpha = \frac{d\omega}{dt} = \frac{d^2\theta}{dt^2}$$

- **Equations for constant angular acceleration kinematics**. The following equations can be used to relate the angular position, angular velocity, and angular acceleration of an object moving in a circle (or rotating) with constant angular acceleration.

$$\Delta\omega = \alpha\Delta t$$

$$\Delta\theta = \omega_i\Delta t + \frac{1}{2}\alpha\left(\Delta t\right)^2$$

$$\omega_f^2 = \omega_i^2 + 2\alpha\Delta\theta$$

- **The moment of inertia of an object is a measure of how the mass of the object is distributed around a particular axis of rotation.** Unlike the mass of an object, which is the same for all axes of rotation, the moment of inertia of an object may be different for different axes of rotation. The moment of inertia for a point particle is

$$I = mr^2$$

And the moment of inertia for a distribution of mass is

$$I = \int r^2 \, dm$$

- **Rotational kinetic energy:** Energy associated with the rotational motion of an object.

$$K_{rot} = \frac{1}{2}I\omega^2$$

- **The first derivative of rotational kinetic energy with respect to angular position is the product of the moment of inertia and the angular acceleration**

$$\frac{d}{d\theta}\left(\frac{1}{2}I\omega^2\right) = I\alpha$$

- **The condition for an object to roll without slipping or for a rope to move over a pulley without slipping is**

$$v = \pm\omega R$$

- **The effective mass of a system includes contributions from both the mass of the objects in the system (from their translational kinetic energies) and the moments of inertia of the objects in the system (from their rotational kinetic energies).**

Problems

1. A uniformly dense solid sphere is rolling without slipping down a ramp. As the sphere rolls, gravitational potential energy is being converted into translational kinetic energy and rotational kinetic energy. What fraction of the potential energy is converted into rotational kinetic energy?

2. A uniformly dense disk with a mass of 4 kg and a radius of 2 m is free to rotate around an axis that passes through the center of the disk and is oriented perpendicular to the plane of the disk. The rotational kinetic energy of the disk is increasing at 20 J/s. If the disk starts from rest, through what angular displacement will it have rotated after 5 s?

3. The rotational kinetic energy of a uniformly dense rigid rod with a length of 0.5 m and a mass of 6 kg rotating around an axis through its center is given by the following equation:

$$K_{rot}(t) = \left(5J^{\frac{1}{2}} + \left(8\frac{J^{\frac{1}{2}}}{s} \right) t \right)^2$$

How many revolutions does the rod complete between $t = 1$ s and $t = 3$ s?

4. The block, solid cylinder, solid sphere, and hollow sphere in the figure below all have the same mass. The cylinder and spheres also have the same radii. Rank in order from largest to smallest the accelerations of the objects as they move down the ramp. The cylinder and the spheres all roll without slipping, and the angle of each ramp is the same.

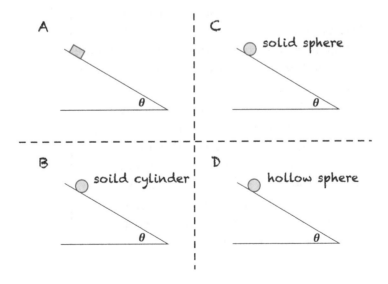

5. Each of the four systems shown in the figure at right consists of two blocks, A and B, that are connected to each other by a massless rope that moves without slipping over a frictionless pulley. The pulley in each system can be modeled as a uniformly dense solid cylinder that rotates around an axis through its center. Rank in order from largest to smallest the magnitude of the acceleration of block B in these systems.

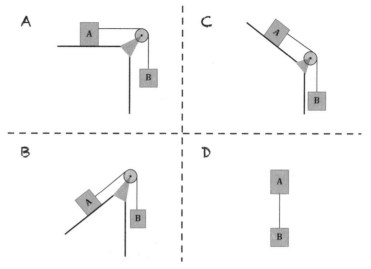

6. Two blocks, A and B, are connected by a massless rope that moves over a pulley, as shown in the figure at right. The pulley can be modeled as a uniformly dense solid cylinder with a mass of 1.5 kg and a radius of 5 cm that rotates around an axis through its center. The rope moves over the pulley without slipping. Because of friction, energy will be lost at a constant rate of 3 J/m as block A slides across the horizontal surface. If the mass of block A is 2 kg, and the mass of block B is 3 kg, what is the magnitude of the acceleration of block B?

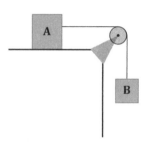

7. Three blocks are connected by a massless rope that moves over two pulleys, as shown in the figure at right. Each pulley can be modeled as a uniformly dense solid cylinder with a mass of 1.5 kg and a radius of 5 that rotates around an axis through its center. The ropes move over the pulleys without slipping. The horizontal surface along which block B slides is frictionless. What is the magnitude of the acceleration of block A? What is the direction of this acceleration if the mass of block C is larger than the mass of block A? What fraction of the kinetic energy of this system is the rotational kinetic energy of the pulleys?

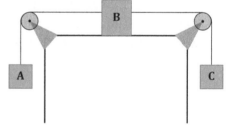

8. Three blocks are connected by a massless rope that moves over two pulleys, as shown in the figure at right. Each pulley can be modeled as a uniformly dense solid cylinder with a mass of 1.5 kg and a radius of 5 that rotates around an axis through its center. The ropes move over the pulleys without slipping. Because of friction, energy will be lost at a constant rate of 2 J/m as block B slides across the horizontal surface. What is the magnitude of the acceleration of block A?

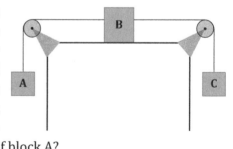

9. Two blocks are connected by a massless rope that moves over two pulleys, as shown in the figure at right. Each pulley can be modeled as a uniformly dense solid cylinder with a mass of 1.5 kg and a radius of 5 that can rotate around an axis through its center. The rope moves over the pulleys without slipping. The horizontal surface along which block A slides is frictionless. What is the magnitude of the acceleration of block A?

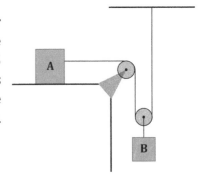

10. Two blocks are connected by a massless rope that moves over two pulleys, as shown in the figure at right. Each pulley can be modeled as a uniformly dense solid cylinder with a mass of 1.5 kg and a radius of 5 that can rotate around an axis through its center. The rope moves over the pulleys without slipping. Because of friction, energy will be lost at a constant rate of 3 J/m as block A slides across the horizontal surface. If the mass of block A is 2 kg, and the mass of block B is 3 kg, what is the magnitude of the acceleration of block B?

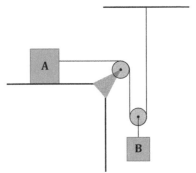

11. Consider the system shown in the figure at right that consists of a solid sphere with a mass of 2.5 kg and a radius of 1 m that is attached to a massless rigid rod with a length of 2 m. The system is initially upright but, after given a small nudge, will rotate around a horizontal axis in the plane of the rod and sphere through the lower end of the rod. What is the angular speed about the rotation axis when the assembly passes through the inverted position? You may assume that the initial energy associated with the nudge is insignificant.

12. Two blocks are attached to one another by a rope that moves over a frictionless pulley, as shown in the figure at right. The pulley can be modeled as a uniformly dense solid cylinder with a mass of 2 kg and a radius of 10 cm that rotates around an axis through its center. The rope moves over the pulley without slipping. As the 4 kg block slides up the ramp, energy will be dissipated at a rate of 7 J/m due to friction. What is the magnitude of the acceleration of the 3 kg block?

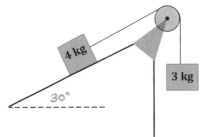

CHAPTER SIX
Oscillatory Motion

6-1 Introduction

The topic of oscillatory motion is introduced in this chapter. Oscillatory motion is the term given to the back and forth motion of an object between two turning points (see Section 3-7). We will initially focus on systems in which the oscillatory motion is caused by the action of a spring and then extend our discussion to include pendula. The goals of this chapter are to learn the terms associated with oscillatory motion and to develop the skills necessary to derive the equations of motion of oscillating systems.

6-2 A Simple Oscillating System

Consider the system shown in Figure 6.1 that consists of a block attached to a horizontally-mounted spring. We will assume that the horizontal surface along which the block moves is frictionless. Let's define a 1-dimensional axis to describe both the length of the spring and the position of the block. The origin of this axis will be where the spring contacts the vertical support, and the positive direction will point toward the block. We will denote this axis as 'l' and define the stable equilibrium position of this system to be when $l = l_0$; the length l_0 is, hence, also the normal (or unstretched) length of the spring[1]. If we initially displace this system from its equilibrium position by extending or compressing the spring, the block will oscillate back and forth across the horizontal surface. What equation describes the subsequent position of the block as a function of time?

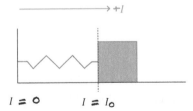

Figure 6.1: A system consisting of a block attached to a horizontally-mounted spring. The horizontal surface is frictionless, and the normal length of the spring is denoted by the dashed line.

---

1   See Section 3-4.

We will follow the general problem-solving strategy outlined in Section 4-8 and begin with an equation for the energy of this system. In this case, the energy of the system is a sum of the translational kinetic energy of the block and the potential energy of the spring.

$$E = \frac{1}{2}mv_l^2 + \frac{1}{2}k(l-l_0)^2$$

In this equation, we have defined the zero point of the gravitational potential energy to be the horizontal surface; this means that the gravitational potential energy of the block is always zero regardless of its position on the horizontal surface. We have included an additional subscript "l" for the speed in the translational kinetic energy term to remind us that the translational kinetic energy of the block results from its movement along the l-axis. A plot of the potential energy for this system as a function of the position of the block is shown in Figure 6.2.

Because the system is isolated, its energy will be constant as a function of the position of the block, as shown in Figure 6.2. Accordingly, the block will oscillate back and forth between the two turning points, l_1 and l_2.

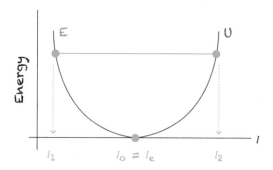

Figure 6.2: The total potential energy of the system in Figure 6.1 as a function of the position of the block. The total energy (red) is constant since the system is isolated. The turning points, l_1 and l_2, as well as the stable equilibrium point, l_e, are also indicated.

The next step in our general problem solving strategy is to determine the acceleration of the system through differentiation of the equation for the energy of the system with respect to the position of the block. Since energy is constant for isolated systems, we have

$$\frac{dE}{dl} = 0 \quad \rightarrow \quad ma_l + k(l-l_0) = 0$$

$$a_l = -\frac{k}{m}(l-l_0) \quad \rightarrow \quad \frac{d^2l}{dt^2} = -\frac{k}{m}(l-l_0)$$

We can see that the acceleration of this system is not constant but, instead, depends upon the position of the block. This is expected because the kinetic energy of the system is not linearly dependent upon the position of the object but, instead, depends upon the square of the position[2]. A non-constant acceleration is also consistent with the back and forth oscillation of the block, as indicated by Figure 6.2.

Let's now define a new variable, w, called the angular frequency of the oscillation.

$$\omega = \sqrt{\frac{k}{m}}$$

---

2   See Section 4-2.

The angular frequency is a measure of how quickly the block moves back and forth across the horizontal surface; angular frequency is always a positive scalar. Using this definition for angular frequency, we can write the kinematic equation for the motion of our block as

$$\frac{d^2 l}{dt^2} = -\omega^2 \left(l - l_0 \right)$$

You can verify that a solution to this equation is

$$l(t) = l_0 + C_1 \sin(\omega t) + C_2 \cos(\omega t)$$

The values of the constants, C_1 and C_2, can be determined from the initial position and initial velocity of the oscillating block. As expected, the position of the block oscillates around l_0, which corresponds to the stable equilibrium point of the potential energy curve of this system (Figure 6.2). Let's denote this equilibrium position in the oscillation as l_e. The equation of motion for this system is, thus,

$$l(t) = l_e + C_1 \sin(\omega t) + C_2 \cos(\omega t) \tag{6-1}$$

Example 6-1:

Problem: A 4 kg block is attached to a horizontally-mounted spring with a spring constant of 400 J/m², as shown in Figure 6.3. The spring is initially extended by 10 cm from its normal length of 20 cm. The block is then released from rest. The horizontal surface along which the block moves is frictionless. What is the angular frequency of the resulting oscillation of the block? What is the equation for the position of the block as a function of time following its release?

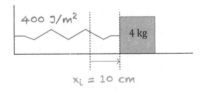

Figure 6.3: A system consisting of a block attached to a horizontally-mounted spring. The spring is initially stretched by 10 cm from its normal length.

Solution: The angular frequency of the oscillation is

$$\omega = \sqrt{\frac{k}{m}} \quad \rightarrow \quad \omega = \sqrt{\frac{400\,\dfrac{J}{m^2}}{4\,kg}} \quad \rightarrow \quad \omega = \sqrt{100\,\dfrac{1}{s^2}} \quad \rightarrow \quad \omega = 10\,\dfrac{rad}{s}$$

Notice that the units of angular frequency, rad/s, are the same as the units for angular velocity[3]. Hence, not only is the symbol for angular frequency the same as the symbol for angular velocity but the two variables also have the same units. *C'est la vie.*

To determine the equation for the position of the block, we begin with Equation 6-1. The derivative of this equation with respect to time gives us

$$v(t) = \frac{d}{dt} l(t) \quad \rightarrow \quad v(t) = C_1 \omega \cos(\omega t) - C_2 \omega \sin(\omega t)$$

If we then substitute the values for the initial position and velocity of the block at $t = 0$, we have

$$l(t=0) = 30\,\text{cm} \quad \rightarrow \quad 30\,\text{cm} = l_e + C_2 \quad \rightarrow \quad C_2 = 30\,\text{cm} - 20\,\text{cm} = 10\,\text{cm}$$

$$v(t=0) = 0 \quad \rightarrow \quad 0 = C_1 \omega \quad \rightarrow \quad C_1 = 0$$

Hence, the position of the block is given by the equation:

$$l(t) = 20\,\text{cm} + (10\,\text{cm})\cos\left(\left(10\frac{\text{rad}}{\text{s}}\right)t\right)$$

A plot of the position of the block in Example 6.1 as a function of time is shown in Figure 6.4. Note that the length of the spring oscillates around the equilibrium length of 20 cm, which corresponds to a stable equilibrium point in the potential energy of the system.

What happens to the energy of an oscillating system? Let's consider an oscillating system consisting of a mass and horizontally-mounted spring, such as the system in Figure 6.1. From Figure 6.2, we see that as the system oscillates back and forth between the turning points, l_1 and l_2, the energy of the system will be continuously converted back and forth between spring potential energy and translational kinetic energy. The equations for these energies as a function of time can be determined using Equation 6-1.

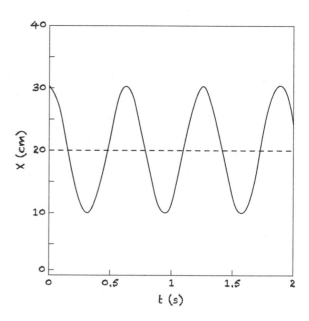

Figure 6.4: The position of the block in the oscillating system shown in Figure 6.3: The dashed line denotes the equilibrium length of the spring.

---

3   Recall that radian is a dimensionless unit.

We begin with the spring potential energy. The substitution of Equation 6-1 into Equation 3-4 yields

$$U_s(t) = \frac{1}{2}k\left(l_e + C_1\sin(\omega t) + C_2\cos(\omega t) - l_e\right)^2$$

$$U_s(t) = \frac{1}{2}k\left(C_1\sin(\omega t) + C_2\cos(\omega t)\right)^2$$

Similarly, we can solve for the kinetic energy of the block from the equation for its velocity (derived in Example 6-1).

$$K(t) = \frac{1}{2}mv^2 \quad \rightarrow \quad K(t) = \frac{1}{2}m\left(C_1\omega\cos(\omega t) - C_2\omega\sin(\omega t)\right)^2$$

$$K(t) = \frac{1}{2}m\omega^2\left(C_1\cos(\omega t) - C_2\sin(\omega t)\right)^2$$

When we substitute $\omega^2 = \dfrac{k}{m}$ into this expression, we obtain

$$K(t) = \frac{1}{2}k\left(C_1\cos(\omega t) - C_2\sin(\omega t)\right)^2$$

The time dependence of the partitioning of the energy in this system between kinetic and potential energy is shown in Figure 6.5.

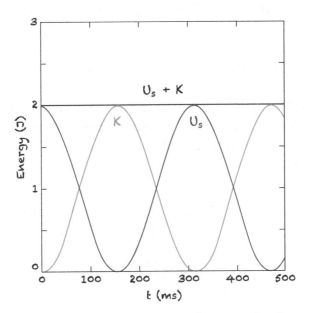

Figure 6.5: The partitioning of energy for the oscillating system in Example 6-1.

The total energy of the system is

$$U_s(t)+K(t)=\frac{1}{2}k\left(\left(C_1\sin(\omega t)+C_2\cos(\omega t)\right)^2+\left(C_1\cos(\omega t)-C_2\sin(\omega t)\right)^2\right)$$

Simplifying this expression gives us

$$U_s(t)+K(t)=\frac{1}{2}k\left(C_1^2+C_2^2\right)\left(\sin^2(\omega t)+\cos^2(\omega t)\right)$$

$$U_s(t)+K(t)=\frac{1}{2}k\left(C_1^2+C_2^2\right)$$

The sum of the potential and kinetic energy is, therefore, constant in time, as expected for an isolated system. The magnitude of this total energy depends upon the initial conditions of the system (*i.e.*, on the values of C_1 and C_2, which are determined from the initial velocity and position of the system).

Example 6-2:

Problem: A system consisting of a block and a horizontally-mounted spring (Figure 6.1) oscillates with simple harmonic motion. The normal length of the spring is 3 cm, and the position of the block as a function of time varies according to the following equation:

$$l(t)=3\,\text{cm}+(2\,\text{cm})\sin\left(\left(\frac{\pi}{2}\frac{\text{rad}}{\text{s}}\right)t+\frac{\pi}{4}\text{rad}\right)$$

At what time after $t = 0$ s is the translational kinetic energy of the system first at a maximum?

Solution: Because the translational kinetic energy of the system is dependent on the square of the speed of the block, it will reach a maximum when the speed of the block is at an extremum. We can solve for the velocity and, thus, the speed of the block from the equation for the block's position.

$$v(t)=\frac{d}{dt}l(t)\quad\rightarrow\quad v(t)=(2\,\text{cm})\left(\frac{\pi}{2}\frac{\text{rad}}{\text{s}}\right)\cos\left(\left(\frac{\pi}{2}\frac{\text{rad}}{\text{s}}\right)t+\frac{\pi}{4}\text{rad}\right)$$

$$v(t)=\left(\pi\frac{\text{cm}}{\text{s}}\right)\cos\left(\left(\frac{\pi}{2}\frac{\text{rad}}{\text{s}}\right)t+\frac{\pi}{4}\text{rad}\right)$$

To find the extrema, we differentiate

$$\frac{dv}{dt} = 0 \quad \rightarrow \quad -\left(\pi\,\frac{cm}{s}\right)\sin\left(\left(\frac{\pi}{2}\,\frac{rad}{s}\right)t + \frac{\pi}{4}\,rad\right)\left(\frac{\pi}{2}\,\frac{rad}{s}\right) = 0$$

$$\sin\left(\left(\frac{\pi}{2}\,\frac{rad}{s}\right)t + \frac{\pi}{4}\,rad\right) = 0 \quad \rightarrow \quad \left(\frac{\pi}{2}\,\frac{rad}{s}\right)t + \frac{\pi}{4}\,rad = n\pi \quad n = 0,1,2,\ldots$$

$$t = -\frac{1}{2}s, \frac{3}{2}s, \frac{7}{2}s, \ldots$$

The first solution that satisfies the condition of the problem (*i.e.*, $t > 0$ s) is

$$t = \frac{3}{2}s$$

Of course, during its oscillations, the block's kinetic and potential energies are continuously converted back and forth between each other. Thus, the maximum kinetic energy corresponds to the minimum potential energy. Since the minimum potential energy occurs when the spring is neither compressed nor extended, the maximum kinetic energy must occur when the length of the spring is its normal length. Hence, maximum kinetic energy occurs when

$$3cm + (2cm)\sin\left(\left(\frac{\pi}{2}\,\frac{rad}{s}\right)t + \frac{\pi}{4}\,rad\right) = 3cm$$

$$(2cm)\sin\left(\left(\frac{\pi}{2}\,\frac{rad}{s}\right)t + \frac{\pi}{4}\,rad\right) = 0 \quad \rightarrow \quad \sin\left(\left(\frac{\pi}{2}\,\frac{rad}{s}\right)t + \frac{\pi}{4}\,rad\right) = 0$$

As expected, we have derived the same condition as previously.

6-3 Simple Harmonic Motion

We used the length of the spring to denote the coordinate axis for the motion of the block in our preceding derivation of the equations associated with the oscillations of a block attached to a horizontally-mounted spring. Since displacements are independent of the origin of the coordinate system (Section 2-2), we should anticipate that we could have defined a different origin for this axis[4].

---

4   Indeed, since the potential energy of the spring depends upon the displacement of the spring from its normal length, the potential energy of the spring is independent of the origin of the coordinate system used to describe the length of the spring.

For example, let's use a coordinate transformation (Section 2-6) to define an x-axis for the position of the block; the origin of the x-axis is where the spring is at its normal length (Figure 6.6). In terms of this coordinate axis, the energy of the system is

$$E = \frac{1}{2}mv_x^2 + \frac{1}{2}k(x-0)^2$$

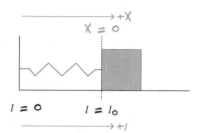

Figure 6.6: A system consisting of a block attached to a horizontally-mounted spring. The horizontal surface is frictionless, and the normal length of the spring is denoted by the dashed line.

In this equation, we have defined the zero point of the gravitational potential energy to be the horizontal surface, and, hence, the gravitational potential energy of the block is always zero regardless of its position on the x-axis. We have also included the subscript "x" for the speed in the translational kinetic energy term to remind us that this translational kinetic energy is associated with the movement of the block along the x-axis. We can now determine the acceleration of the block by differentiating the equation for the energy of the system with respect to the position of the block.

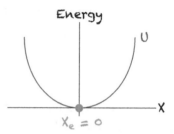

Figure 6.7: The potential energy of the system shown in Figure 6.6 as a function of the position of the block along the x-axis. The stable equilibrium point is at x = 0.

$$\frac{dE}{dx} = 0 \;\rightarrow\; ma_x + kx = 0 \;\rightarrow\; a_x = -\frac{k}{m}x$$

If we substitute into this equation our definition for the angular frequency of the oscillation (Section 6-2), we obtain

$$\frac{d^2x}{dt^2} = -\omega^2 x \qquad\qquad (6\text{-}2)$$

This is the basic equation that we will use to describe oscillatory motion in this book. We will refer to oscillatory motion that can be described by Equation 6-2 as **simple harmonic motion**.

Simple Harmonic Motion (SHM): Oscillatory motion in which the acceleration of the system is linearly proportional to the displacement of the system from equilibrium. SHM occurs for systems in which the translational kinetic energy is proportional to the square of the displacement of the system from its equilibrium point.

As shown previously, a simple solution to Equation 6-2 is a sum of a sine and a cosine term

$$x(t) = C_1 \sin(\omega t) + C_2 \cos(\omega t) \qquad\qquad (6\text{-}3)$$

Equation 6-3 is also frequently written as[5]

$$x(t) = A\sin(\omega t + \phi_0)$$ (6-4)

In Equation 6-4, the variable A denotes the **amplitude** of the oscillation, and ϕ_0 is **the phase constant** of the oscillation (see Figure 6.8).

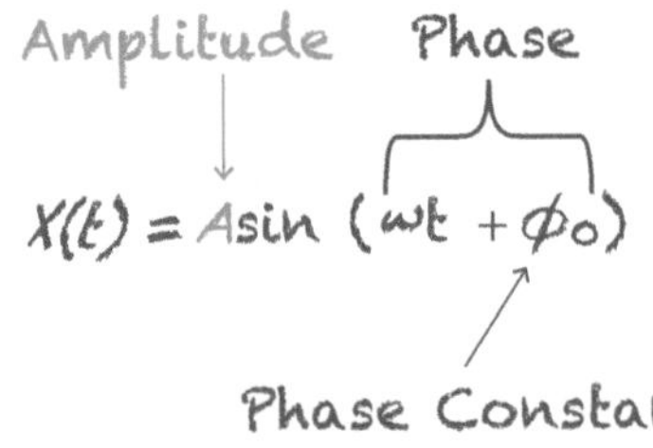

> *Amplitude: The maximum displacement of an oscillating system from its equilibrium position. The amplitude of an oscillation is always positive.*
>
> *Phase: The portion of an oscillating function that varies with position or time. For simple harmonic motion, the phase is equal to $\omega t + \phi_0$.*
>
> *Phase constant: The portion of the phase that is constant in time. It is determined from the initial conditions of the system. The phase constant is measured in radians.*

Figure 6.8: Definition of the amplitude, phase, and phase constant.

By comparing Equation 6-3 and Equation 6-4, we see that

$$A = \sqrt{C_1^2 + C_2^2} \quad \text{and} \quad \phi_0 = \tan^{-1}\left(\frac{C_2}{C_1}\right)$$

The relationship between the amplitude and the total energy of the oscillation can be seen from our discussion following Example 6-1.

$$U_s(t) + K(t) = \frac{1}{2}k\left(C_1^2 + C_2^2\right) \quad \rightarrow \quad U_s(t) + K(t) = \frac{1}{2}kA^2$$

Specifically, the sum of the translational kinetic energy and the spring potential energy (*i.e.*, the total energy of the system) is proportional to the square of the amplitude of the oscillation.

Example 6-3:

Problem: An object oscillates in one dimension with an amplitude of 10 cm. At $t = 0$ s, its position is $x = 5$ cm, and it is moving with a velocity of -2 cm/s. What is the angular frequency of the oscillation?

---

5   Of course, $x(t) = A\cos(\omega t + \phi_0)$ is also a solution since the sine and cosine function are related by a constant phase change of $\pi/2$.

Solution: We can solve the problem using the given information to construct the equation for the position of the object as a function of time. We begin with Equation 6-4.

$$x(t) = A\sin(\omega t + \phi_0) \rightarrow v(t) = A\omega\cos(\omega t + \phi_0)$$

At $t = 0$, we have

$$5\text{cm} = (10\text{cm})\sin(\phi_0) \rightarrow \sin(\phi_0) = \frac{1}{2}$$

There are two solutions for this equation: $\phi_0 = 0.52$ rad and $\phi_0 = 2.62$ rad. We can determine which value is correct from the initial velocity of block. Since the direction of the initial velocity is negative, the cosine of the phase angle must also be negative[6]. Only the phase angle 2.62 rad satisfies this condition, so it must be the correct solution.

$$v(t=0) < 0 \rightarrow \cos(\phi_0) < 0 \rightarrow \phi_0 = 2.62\text{rad}$$

Thus,

$$v(t=0) = -2\frac{\text{cm}}{\text{s}} \rightarrow -2\frac{\text{cm}}{\text{s}} = (10\text{cm})\omega\cos(2.62\text{rad})$$

$$\omega = 0.23\frac{\text{rad}}{\text{s}}$$

Example 6-4:

Problem: A 0.5 kg block is attached to a horizontally-mounted spring with a spring constant of 800 J/m², as shown in Figure 6.9. The spring is extended by 8 cm from its normal length, and the block is then released with an additional pull that imparts an initial velocity of 240 cm/s. What is the amplitude of the resulting oscillation?

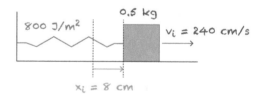

Figure 6.9: A block attached to a horizontally-mounted spring. At time $t = 0$, the spring is extended by 8 cm, and the block is moving with a speed of 240 cm/s.

---

6   Recall that amplitude and angular frequency are both always positive scalars.

Solution: Our first step is to determine the angular frequency of the oscillation.

$$\omega = \sqrt{\frac{k}{m}} \rightarrow \omega = \sqrt{\frac{800\frac{J}{m^2}}{0.5kg}} \rightarrow \omega = \sqrt{1600\frac{1}{s^2}} \rightarrow \omega = 40\frac{rad}{s}$$

Next, according to Equation 6-4, we have

$$x(t) = A\sin\left(\omega t + \phi_0\right) \rightarrow x(0) = A\sin\left(\phi_0\right)$$

$$v(t) = \frac{d}{dt}x(t) \rightarrow v(t) = A\omega\cos\left(\omega t + \phi_0\right) \rightarrow v(0) = A\omega\cos\left(\phi_0\right)$$

We can now determine φ_0 by combining the equations for the initial position and velocity of the oscillator.

$$\frac{x(0)}{v(0)} = \frac{A\sin\left(\phi_0\right)}{A\omega\cos\left(\phi_0\right)} \rightarrow \frac{x(0)}{v(0)} = \frac{\tan\left(\phi_0\right)}{\omega} \rightarrow \frac{8cm}{240\frac{cm}{s}} = \frac{\tan\left(\phi_0\right)}{40\frac{rad}{s}}$$

$$\tan\left(\phi_0\right) = 1.33$$

There are, of course, two solutions for the phase angle: $\phi_0 = 0.93$ rad and $\phi_0 = 4.07$ rad. To determine which value is correct, we must examine the initial conditions of the problem. Initially, the direction of the position and the direction of the velocity are the same (both are directed to the right in Figure 6.9). Therefore, both the sine and the cosine of the phase angle must have the same ($\pm$) sign (in this case, positive). Only the phase angle 0.93 rad satisfies this condition, so it must be the correct solution.

$$\phi_0 = 0.93rad$$

Having determined the phase angle, we can solve for the amplitude.

$$A = \frac{x(0)}{\sin\left(\phi_0\right)} \rightarrow A = \frac{8cm}{\sin\left(0.93rad\right)} \rightarrow A = 10cm$$

Alternative Solution: We could, instead, have chosen the following equation for the position of the oscillator:

$$x(t) = A\cos(\omega t + \phi_0) \;\rightarrow\; x(0) = A\cos(\phi_0)$$

$$v(t) = \frac{d}{dt}x(t) \;\rightarrow\; v(t) = -A\omega\sin(\omega t + \phi_0) \;\rightarrow\; v(0) = -A\omega\sin(\phi_0)$$

Following the same approach as in the previous solution gives us

$$\frac{x(0)}{v(0)} = \frac{A\cos(\phi_0)}{-A\omega\sin(\phi_0)} \;\rightarrow\; \frac{x(0)}{v(0)} = \frac{-1}{\omega\tan(\phi_0)} \;\rightarrow\; \frac{8\,\text{cm}}{240\,\dfrac{\text{cm}}{\text{s}}} = \frac{-1}{\left(40\,\dfrac{\text{rad}}{\text{s}}\right)\tan(\phi_0)}$$

$$\tan(\phi_0) = -0.75$$

There are two solutions for the phase angle: $\phi_0 = -0.64$ rad and $\phi_0 = 2.5$ rad, however only $\phi_0 = -0.64$ rad satisfies the initial conditions of the oscillator. The amplitude of the oscillation is, therefore,

$$A = \frac{x(0)}{\cos(\phi_0)} \;\rightarrow\; A = \frac{8\,\text{cm}}{\cos(-0.64\,\text{rad})} \;\rightarrow\; A = 10\,\text{cm}$$

As expected, the solution is independent of whether we choose a sine or cosine term to describe the position of the oscillator.

We conclude this section by noting that simple harmonic motion has the following interesting characteristics:

1. The angular frequency of simple harmonic motion is a function of the physical characteristics of the system. In our previous examples, it was a function of the spring constant and the mass of the system.
2. The angular frequency of simple harmonic motion is independent of the initial conditions of the system. In other words, it is independent of the amplitude of the oscillation.
3. The sum of the kinetic and spring potential energies of a simple harmonic oscillator is constant in time and proportional to the square of the amplitude of the oscillation.

6-4 Kinematics with Simple Harmonic Motion

We can use very similar kinematic equations to those we found in Chapter 2 and Chapter 4 to describe the motion of an oscillating system. For oscillating systems, Equations 6-3 and 6-4 are the equivalent set of equations.

Example 6-5:

Problem: A system consists of a 4 kg block that is attached to a horizontally-mounted spring with a spring constant of 400 J/m² (Figure 6.3). The block is released from rest with the spring extended by 10 cm from its normal length of 20 cm. The horizontal surface along which the block moves is frictionless. How long will it take this system to complete one full oscillation?

Solution: One full oscillation of the system would correspond to the block returning to its initial position. From the solution to Example 6-1, we know that the position of the block as a function of time is given by the equation:

$$x(t) = 20\,cm + (10\,cm)\cos\left(\left(10\frac{rad}{s}\right)t\right)$$

Thus, the time to complete one full oscillation is equal to

$$30\,cm = 20\,cm + (10\,cm)\cos\left(\left(10\frac{rad}{s}\right)t\right) \quad \rightarrow \quad \cos\left(\left(10\frac{rad}{s}\right)t\right) = 1$$

This equation has an infinite number of solutions

$$\left(10\frac{rad}{s}\right)t = 2\pi\,rad \quad n = 0,1,2,\ldots$$

$$t = n\left(\frac{\pi}{5}s\right) \quad n = 0,1,2,\ldots \quad \rightarrow \quad t = 0\,s,\, 0.63\,s,\, 1.26\,s,\ldots$$

The first solution, $t = 0$, corresponds to the initial release of the system. The subsequent solutions reflect the oscillation of the system and occur at regular intervals of 0.63 s. This means 0.63 s must be the time required for the system to complete each full oscillation.

We denote the time required to complete one full oscillation as the **period** of the system.

Period: The time required for an oscillating system to complete one full oscillation (or cycle of its oscillation). Period is denoted by the variable T.

From the solution to the previous example, we can define the period in terms of the angular frequency of the oscillation.

$$T = \frac{2\pi}{\omega} \qquad (6\text{-}5)$$

Similarly, we can define the **frequency** of the oscillation, denoted by f, as the number of full oscillations completed by the system in one second. Hence, the units of frequency are $1/s$ (s^{-1} or Hz).

> *Frequency: The number of full oscillations (or cycles) completed by an oscillating system in one second. Frequency is denoted by the variable f.*

From this, we have the following relationship:

$$\omega = 2\pi f = \frac{2\pi}{T} \qquad (6\text{-}6)$$

It is important to realize that we can express the position of a system undergoing simple harmonic motion either in terms of its location along a coordinate axis or in terms of the phase of oscillation. This is analogous to our ability to describe circular motion either in terms of tangential motion along the circumference of the circle or in terms of angular displacements (Chapter 5). An angular description of motion for oscillating systems tends to be best because the phase changes linearly with time (Figure 6.8), whereas the position varies sinusoidally with time (Equation 6-4 and Figure 6-4).

Example 6-6:

Problem: A system consists of a 3 kg block that is attached to a horizontally-mounted spring with a spring constant of 27 J/m². The block is released from rest with the spring extended by 10 cm from its normal length of 20 cm. The horizontal surface along which the block moves is frictionless. At a later time, the block is back at its equilibrium position and is moving to the right (Figure 6.3). How long will it take from this instant until the spring reaches its maximum compression?

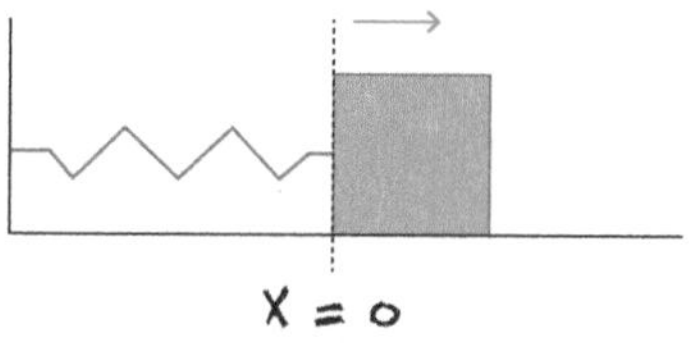

Figure 6.11: The system consisting of a block and horizontally-mounted spring in Example 6-6.

Solution: Moving from this instant to the point of maximum spring compression corresponds to 3/4 of a full oscillation of the system, which corresponds to a change in phase of

$$\Delta\phi = \frac{3}{4}\left(2\pi\,\text{rad}\right) \quad \rightarrow \quad \Delta\phi = \frac{3\pi}{2}\,\text{rad}$$

The time required for this change in phase can be determined from the angular frequency of the oscillation.

$$\omega = \sqrt{\frac{k}{m}} \quad \rightarrow \quad \omega = \sqrt{\frac{27\frac{\text{J}}{\text{m}^2}}{3\text{kg}}} \quad \rightarrow \quad \omega = 3\frac{\text{rad}}{\text{s}}$$

Thus,

$$\Delta\phi = \omega\Delta t \quad \rightarrow \quad \Delta t = \frac{\Delta\phi}{\omega} \quad \rightarrow \quad \Delta t = \frac{\frac{3\pi}{2}\text{rad}}{3\frac{\text{rad}}{\text{s}}} \quad \rightarrow \quad \Delta t = \frac{\pi}{2}\text{s}$$

The analogy between angular descriptions of simple harmonic motion and circular/rotational motion for one complete oscillation or revolution is summarized in Table 6-1.

6-5 Vertically-Mounted Springs

Now, let's consider the isolated system shown in Figure 6.12 that consists of a block on top of a vertically-mounted massless spring; the spring is initially compressed by the block due to gravity. The block is then pushed down further (*i.e.*, the spring is compressed further) and released from rest. What is the period of the subsequent oscillations of this system?

We begin by writing down an equation for the energy of the system.

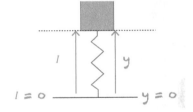

Figure 6.12: A block on top of a vertically-mounted spring. The variable y denotes the vertical position of the block and is equal to the length of the spring, denoted by the variable l.

$$E = \frac{1}{2}mv_y^2 + mgy + \frac{1}{2}k\left(l - l_0\right)^2$$

For this equation, we have defined the zero point of the gravitational potential energy to correspond to the horizontal surface on which the spring is mounted (*i.e.*, at $y = l = 0$) and have included an additional subscript "y" for the speed in the translational kinetic energy term to remind us that the translational kinetic energy of the block results from its movement along the y-axis. It is worth noting that in previous examples we have been able to ignore the gravitational potential energy term because the object did not move in the vertical direction with respect to the surface of the Earth. However, because the direction for the motion of the block in this this system is vertical, we must include the effects of changes in the gravitational potential energy of the system in our calculation.

We begin by recognizing from Figure 6.12 that the length of the spring is the same as the vertical position of the mass.

Number of Oscillations	Oscillation	$\Delta\phi$ Change in Phase / $\Delta\phi$ Angular Displacement	Rotation	Number of Revolutions	Time Required
0		$0\,\mathrm{rad}$		0	0
$\dfrac{1}{4}$		$\dfrac{\pi}{2}\,\mathrm{rad}$		$\dfrac{1}{4}$	$\dfrac{\pi}{2\omega}$
$\dfrac{1}{2}$		$\pi\,\mathrm{rad}$		$\dfrac{1}{2}$	$\dfrac{\pi}{\omega}$
$\dfrac{3}{4}$		$\dfrac{3\pi}{2}\,\mathrm{rad}$		$\dfrac{3}{4}$	$\dfrac{3\pi}{2\omega}$
1		$2\pi\,\mathrm{rad}$		1	$\dfrac{2\pi}{\omega}$
n		$n(2\pi)\,\mathrm{rad}$		n	$\dfrac{n(2\pi)}{\omega}$

Hence, we can simplify our equation for the energy of the system.

$$E = \frac{1}{2}mv_y^2 + mgy + \frac{1}{2}k\left(y - l_0\right)^2$$

Because the system is isolated, we know that energy will be conserved.

$$\frac{dE}{dy} = 0 \quad \rightarrow \quad ma_y + mg + k\left(y - l_0\right) = 0$$

$$a_y = \frac{d^2y}{dt^2} = -\frac{k}{m}\left(y - l_0\right) - g$$

You can verify that a solution to this equation is

$$y\left(t\right) = A\sin\left(\omega t + \phi_0\right) + \left(l_0 - \frac{mg}{k}\right)$$

where $\omega^2 = \frac{k}{m}$, as before. Through comparison with Equation 6-1 and Equation 6-4, we see that the equilibrium length of the spring in this oscillating system is given by

$$l_e = l_0 - \frac{mg}{k}$$

As expected, this system will not oscillate around the normal length of the spring but rather, around a compressed length. Nevertheless, the angular frequency of the oscillation is the same regardless of the orientation of the system.

6-6 Simple Pendula

We can now discuss other oscillating systems that are not based on the motion on a spring but still exhibit harmonic motion. An example of such a system is the *simple pendulum*, which consists of a small object of mass m (called the bob) suspended from a horizontal surface by a massless rope of length L (Figure 6.13). The radius of the bob is much smaller than the length of the string so that the bob may be treated as a point particle (Equation 5-9).

As the bob swings back and forth, the energy of the system will be continuously converted back and forth between rotational kinetic energy and gravitational potential energy.

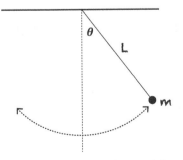

Figure 6.13: A simple pendulum.

To determine the equation of motion that describes the oscillation of the bob, we start with an equation for the energy of this system.

$$E = \frac{1}{2}I\omega^2 + mgy$$

When written in this form, the equation for the energy of the system is a combination of angular descriptions of motion (*i.e.,* the angular velocity ω) and translational descriptions of motion (*i.e.,* the position along the *y*-axis). The subsequent differentiation and algebra required to determine the angular frequency of the oscillations of the pendulum can be simplified if instead, we express the energy in terms of only one description of motion. For pendula, it is simplest if we choose an angular description of the motion.

Let's define the origin of the *y*-axis and the zero point of the gravitational potential energy of the system to both be at the horizontal surface to which the string is attached (Figure 6.14).

As shown in Figure 6.14, the equation that relates the vertical position of the bob to its angular position is

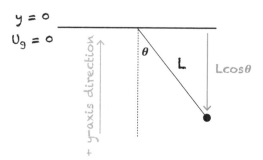

Figure 6.14: Parameter definitions for a simple pendulum.

$$y = -L\cos\theta$$

Hence,

$$E = \frac{1}{2}I\omega^2 - mgL\cos\theta$$

We can determine the acceleration of the bob by differentiating this equation for the energy of the system with respect to the position of the bob (*i.e.,* with respect to θ). Since the system is isolated, we have

$$\frac{dE}{d\theta} = 0 \quad \rightarrow \quad I\alpha + mgL\sin\theta = 0 \quad \rightarrow \quad \alpha = -\frac{mgL}{I}\sin\theta$$

Because the bob is a point particle, its moment of inertia is

$$I = mL^2$$

Thus,

$$\alpha = -\frac{mgL}{mL^2}\sin\theta \quad \rightarrow \quad \alpha = -\frac{g}{L}\sin\theta$$

This is an equation for oscillatory motion, but it is not simple harmonic motion because it does not meet the definition of simple harmonic motion (Section 6-3). Specifically, the acceleration of this system does not depend linearly on its displacement from equilibrium. However, if the amplitude of the oscillation is small, simple pendula do behave as simple harmonic oscillators.

To understand why this is true, let's expand the trigonometric function in the equation for the gravitational potential energy of the pendulum using a Taylor series.

$$U_g = -mgL\cos\theta \;\; \rightarrow \;\; U_g = -mgL\left(1 - \frac{\theta^2}{2!} + \frac{\theta^4}{4!} - \frac{\theta^6}{6!} + \dots\right)$$

If we limit the oscillation to only small angles, this equation can be approximated as

$$U_g \approx -mgL\left(1 - \frac{\theta^2}{2!}\right) \;\; \rightarrow \;\; E = \frac{1}{2}I\omega^2 - mgL\left(1 - \frac{\theta^2}{2}\right)$$

$$E = \frac{1}{2}I\omega^2 - mgL + \frac{mgL\theta^2}{2} \;\; \rightarrow \;\; \frac{d}{d\theta}\left(\frac{1}{2}I\omega^2 - mgL + \frac{mgL\theta^2}{2}\right) = 0$$

$$I\alpha + mgL\theta = 0 \;\; \rightarrow \;\; \alpha = -\frac{mgL}{I}\theta \;\; \rightarrow \;\; \alpha = -\frac{mgL}{mL^2}\theta$$

$$\alpha = \frac{d^2\theta}{dt^2} = -\frac{g}{L}\theta \qquad\qquad (6\text{-}7)$$

This is commonly referred to as the small angle approximation[7]. Similarly, in the limit of small angles, the Taylor series expansion of the equation for the angular acceleration of the pendulum can be written as

$$\alpha = -\frac{g}{L}\left(\theta - \frac{\theta^3}{3!} + \frac{\theta^5}{5!} - \frac{\theta^7}{7!} + \dots\right) \;\; \rightarrow \;\; \alpha \approx -\frac{g}{L}\theta$$

This solution is, as expected, identical to Equation 6-7. More significantly, we see that Equation 6-7 is an equation for simple harmonic motion and, furthermore (upon comparison to Equation 6-2), that the angular frequency of this oscillation is

$$\omega = \sqrt{\frac{g}{L}}$$

---

7   The small angle approximation is frequently written as $\sin\theta \sim \theta$ and $\cos\theta \sim 1$.

Example 6-7:

Problem: A simple pendulum consists of a 0.2 kg bob and a 0.5 m massless rope. What is the period of small amplitude oscillations of this system about its equilibrium point?

Solution: We start with calculating the angular frequency of the oscillations. Since we are able to use the small angle approximation, we have

$$\omega^2 = \frac{g}{L} \quad \rightarrow \quad \omega^2 = \frac{9.8 \frac{m}{s^2}}{0.5m} \quad \rightarrow \quad \omega^2 = 19.6 \frac{rad^2}{s^2}$$

Therefore, the period of the oscillations (Equation 6-5) is

$$T = \frac{2\pi}{\omega} \quad \rightarrow \quad T = \frac{2\pi \, rad}{\sqrt{19.6 \frac{rad^2}{s^2}}} \quad \rightarrow \quad T = 1.42s$$

6-7 Effective Mass and Effective Spring Constant for Oscillating Systems

Because of the generality of our energy-based approach to kinematics, we can readily expand our previous derivations to include more complicated systems that undergo simple harmonic oscillation. Consider the isolated system shown in Figure 6.15 that consists of two blocks connected by a massless rope that passes over a massless pulley. One of the blocks is connected to a horizontally-mounted spring. Because of the existance of a spring in the system, when the blocks are displaced slightly from their equilbirium positions, this system will also undergo simple harmonic motion.

To determine the angular frequency of this oscillation, we begin, as always, by writing down an equation for the energy of the system. The system in this problem consists of the two blocks, the rope, the pulley, and the spring. Following the solution presented in Section 4-5[8],

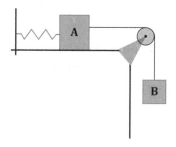

Figure 6.15: A system consisting of two blocks, A and B, connected by a massless rope that passes over a massless pulley. Block A is also attached to a horizontally-mounted spring.

---

8   This approach is also consistent with the general problem-solving strategy outlined in Section 4-8.

we can describe the positions of the blocks and the spring using two separate 1-dimensional coordinate axes, as shown in Figure 6.16.

With these definitions of the coordinate axes, the length of the spring is equal to the position of block A, and, thus, our expression for the energy of this system is

$$E = \frac{1}{2}m_A v_{A,x}^2 + m_A g y_A + \frac{1}{2}m_B v_{B,y}^2 + m_B g y_B + \frac{1}{2}k\left(x_A - l_0\right)^2$$

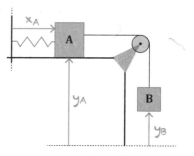

Figure 6.16: The definitions of the x-axis and y-axis for the system in Figure 6.15.

In this equation, we have defined the zero point of the gravitational potential energy to be on the ground (*i.e.*, at $y_B = 0$). From our solution to Example 4-6, we know that

$$v_{A,x}^2 = v_{B,y}^2$$

Hence,

$$E = \frac{1}{2}\left(m_A + m_B\right)v_{A,x}^2 + m_A g y_A + m_B g y_B + \frac{1}{2}k\left(x_A - l_0\right)^2$$

We can now determine the acceleration of block A by differentiating this equation for the energy of the system with respect to the position of block A. Since the system is isolated,

$$\frac{dE}{dx_A} = 0 \quad \rightarrow \quad \left(m_A + m_B\right)a_{A,x} + m_A g \frac{dy_A}{dx_A} + m_B g \frac{dy_B}{dx_A} + k\left(x_A - l_0\right) = 0$$

The following two relationships we know from inspection of Figure 6.16:

$$\frac{dy_A}{dx_A} = 0 \qquad \frac{dy_B}{dx_A} = -1$$

Putting it all together we have

$$\left(m_A + m_B\right)a_{A,x} - m_B g + k\left(x_A - l_0\right) = 0$$

$$a_{A,x} = \frac{d^2 x_A}{dt^2} = -\frac{k}{m_A + m_B}\left(x_A - l_0\right) + \frac{m_B}{m_A + m_B}g$$

You can verify that a solution for this equation is

$$x_A(t) = l_e + A\sin(\omega t + \phi_0)$$

Therefore, block A will undergo simple harmonic motion with an angular frequency and equilibrium spring length of

$$\omega = \sqrt{\frac{k}{m_A + m_B}} \qquad l_e = l_0 + \frac{m_B g}{k}$$

As expected, the spring is stretched initially.

We could have guessed that this would be the angular frequency for this oscillation by comparing this system to the system consisting of a single block attached to a spring (Section 6-2 and Section 6-5). The only difference here is that the total mass of the oscillating system in this example has increased through the addition of the second block.

This result can also be readily understood in terms of the effective mass of the oscillating system (Section 5-8). Indeed, a general expression for the angular frequency of oscillation for a system undergoing simple harmonic motion can be written as

$$\omega^2 = \frac{k_{effective}}{m_{effective}} \qquad\qquad (6\text{-}8)$$

In Equation 6-8, $k_{effective}$ denotes the *effective spring constant* of the system. As we shall see, the number of springs (or effective springs like pendula) in a system, their associated spring constants, and their location to the axis of rotation all contribute to the value of $k_{effective}$. We can also consider the effective spring constant to be a measure of the steepness of the total potential energy of the system as a function of the position of the oscillating object; the steeper the curve, the larger the value of $k_{effective}$.

Example 6-8:

Problem: A spring with a spring constant of 288 J/ m² is attached to a uniformly dense solid cylinder with a mass of 3 kg that rolls without slipping across a horizontal surface around an axis through its center, as shown in Figure 6.17. What is the period of simple harmonic oscillations of this system about its equilibrium position?

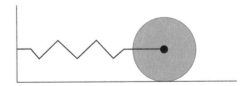

Figure 6.17: The oscillating system in Example 6-8.

Solution: We begin by writing down an equation for the energy of the system.

$$E = \frac{1}{2}I\omega^2 + \frac{1}{2}mv_x^2 + \frac{1}{2}kx^2$$

In this equation, we have defined the zero point of the gravitational potential energy to be the horizontal surface and the zero point of the x-axis to be the normal length of the spring. Due to the constraint that the cylinder rolls without slipping, we know that the angular and translational velocities of the cylinder are related to each other by the radius of the cylinder (Equation 5-10).

$$\omega^2 R^2 = v_x^2$$

Substitution yields

$$E = \frac{1}{2}I\left(\frac{v_x^2}{R^2}\right) + \frac{1}{2}mv_x^2 + \frac{1}{2}kx^2 \quad \rightarrow \quad E = \frac{1}{2}\left(\frac{I}{R^2} + m\right)v_x^2 + \frac{1}{2}kx^2$$

Because the system is isolated, we know its energy will be constant

$$\frac{dE}{dx}\bigg|_A = 0 \quad \rightarrow \quad \left(\frac{I}{R^2} + m\right)a_x + kx = 0 \quad \rightarrow \quad m_{effective}a_x + kx = 0$$

$$a_x = \frac{d^2x}{dt^2} = -\left(\frac{k}{m_{effective}}\right)x$$

Using Equation 6-2, we see that the angular frequency of the oscillation is

$$\omega = \sqrt{\frac{k}{m_{effective}}} \quad \rightarrow \quad \omega = \sqrt{\frac{k}{\frac{I}{R^2} + m}} \quad \rightarrow \quad \omega = \sqrt{\frac{R^2 k}{I + mR^2}}$$

As expected, the angular frequency of this oscillation is less than that of a block attached to a spring (Section 6-2) since the *effective mass* of this oscillator is larger. The period of oscillations of this system is

$$T = \frac{2\pi}{\omega} \quad \rightarrow \quad T = 2\pi\sqrt{\frac{I + mR^2}{R^2 k}}$$

The moment of inertia for the cylinder can be found in Table D-2.

$$T = 2\pi \sqrt{\frac{\frac{1}{2}mR^2 + mR^2}{R^2 k}} \quad \rightarrow \quad T = 2\pi \sqrt{\frac{\frac{3}{2}m}{k}}$$

Substitution of the values for the mass and the spring constant yields

$$T = 2\pi \sqrt{\frac{\frac{3}{2}(3\text{kg})}{288 \frac{\text{J}}{\text{m}^2}}} \quad \rightarrow \quad T = 0.79\text{s}$$

Example 6-9:

Problem: A 5 kg bob is connected to a thin massless but rigid rod of length $L = 1.3$ m to form a simple pendulum, as shown in Figure 6.18. The bob is also connected to a nearby vertical wall by a spring with spring constant $k = 75$ J/m². What is the angular frequency of small amplitude oscillations of this isolated system? When the spring is at its equilibrium position, $\theta = 0$.

Solution: We begin by writing down an equation for the energy of the system.

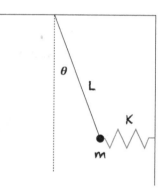

Figure 6.18: The oscillating system in Example 6-9.

$$E = \frac{1}{2}I\omega^2 + \frac{1}{2}kx^2 + mgy$$

As discussed earlier, it is simplest if the equation for the energy of the pendulum is written in terms of angular descriptions of motion only. If we define the zero point of the y-axis to be at the horizontal surface of the system as before (Figure 6.14), we have

$$E = \frac{1}{2}I\omega^2 + \frac{1}{2}kx^2 - mgL\cos\theta$$

As shown in Figure 6.19, if the amplitude of the oscillation is small, the displacement of the spring can be related to the angle of the oscillation by

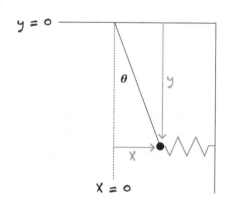

Figure 6.19: The relationship between x and θ for the system in Figure 6.18.

$$x = L\sin\theta$$

Substitution of this expression gives us

$$E = \frac{1}{2}I\omega^2 + \frac{1}{2}kL^2\sin^2\theta - mgL\cos\theta$$

Since the system is isolated, this energy must be constant.

$$\frac{dE}{d\theta} = 0 \quad \rightarrow \quad I\alpha + kL^2\sin\theta\cos\theta + mgL\sin\theta = 0$$

$$\alpha = -\frac{kL^2\sin\theta\cos\theta + mgL\sin\theta}{I} \quad \rightarrow \quad \alpha = -\left(\frac{kL^2\cos\theta + mgL}{I}\right)\sin\theta$$

Because we are interested in small amplitude oscillations, we can apply the small angle approximation to this equation.

$$\alpha = \frac{d^2\theta}{dt^2} = -\left(\frac{kL^2 + mgL}{I}\right)\theta \quad \rightarrow \quad \omega = \sqrt{\frac{kL^2 + mgL}{I}}$$

Substitution of the moment of inertia for a point particle gives us

$$\omega = \sqrt{\frac{kL^2 + mgL}{mL^2}} \quad \rightarrow \quad \omega = \sqrt{\frac{kL + mg}{mL}}$$

Hence, for our system

$$\omega = \sqrt{\frac{\left(75\frac{J}{m^2}\right)(1.3m) + (5kg)\left(9.8\frac{m}{s^2}\right)}{(5kg)(1.3m)}} \quad \rightarrow \quad \omega = 4.75\frac{rad}{s}$$

The solution to Example 6-9 identifies another conclusion about simple harmonic oscillators. The angular frequency for small amplitude oscillations of the system in Figure 6.18 can be written as

$$\omega^2 = \frac{kL + mg}{mL} \quad \rightarrow \quad \omega^2 = \frac{kL}{mL} + \frac{mg}{mL} \quad \rightarrow \quad \omega^2 = \frac{k}{m} + \frac{g}{L}$$

$$\omega^2 = \omega^2_{spring} + \omega^2_{pendulum}$$

In other words, the value for ω^2 for a system is the sum of the individual values of ω^2 corresponding to the different oscillating elements in the system. This is true since ω^2 is determined from the acceleration of the system, which is determined from the equation for the energy of the system (Section 4-8). Since we can linearly sum the energies of the objects in a system to determine the equation for the energy of the system, it follows that we can linearly sum the values of ω^2 for the individual oscillating elements in a system to determine the value of ω^2 for the entire system[9].

6-8 General Simple Harmonic Oscillator Approximation

As discussed in Section 1-5, stable equilibrium points of a system occur where the system's potential energy curve is concave. Because of this curvature, systems can undergo oscillations around stable equilibrium points. Depending upon the specific shape of the potential energy curve, these oscillations may or may not be simple harmonic oscillations. However, as with the case of simple pendula, if the amplitude of these oscillations is small, then the oscillations can be approximated as simple harmonic motion.

To understand why this occurs, let's consider a system whose potential energy is a function of the position of an object along the x-axis. The minimum of this potential energy occurs when the object is at $x = x_0$. We can write an equation for this potential energy as a function of position relative to x_0 using a Taylor series expansion.

$$U(x) = U(x_0) + \left(\frac{dU}{dx} \bigg|_{x=x_0} \right)(x - x_0) + \frac{1}{2!} \left(\frac{d^2U}{dx^2} \bigg|_{x=x_0} \right)(x - x_0)^2 + \dots$$

The potential energy is a minimum when $x = x_0$.

$$\frac{dU}{dx} \bigg|_{x=x_0} = 0$$

Hence,

$$U(x) = U(x_0) + \frac{1}{2!} \left(\frac{d^2U}{dx^2} \bigg|_{x=x_0} \right)(x - x_0)^2 + \dots$$

---

9 Although this approach will work for the simple oscillating systems in this book, it is not universally valid and cannot be applied to more complex oscillating systems (such as coupled oscillators). Please be inspired to take additional physics classes to learn why this is true.

If we limit ourselves to only small amplitude oscillations (*i.e.*, oscillations in which *x* is always very close to x_0), we can ignore all higher order terms in this expansion, thus, leaving us with

$$U(x) \approx U(x_0) + \frac{1}{2!}\left(\frac{d^2U}{dx^2}\bigg|_{x=x_0}\right)(x-x_0)^2$$

Therefore, under these conditions, the potential energy will depend upon the square of the displacement of the system from its equilibrium position. Because of this, the associated oscillations will be simple harmonic (Section 6-3). This leads to a very powerful conclusion.

Small amplitude oscillations of any system near stable equilibrium points can be modeled as simple harmonic oscillations.

Furthermore, the effective spring constant for these oscillations is dependent upon the curvature (*i.e.*, the steepness) of the potential energy function near the equilibrium point.

$$k_{effective} = \frac{d^2U}{dx^2}\bigg|_{x=x_0}$$

This is consistent with the discussion in Section 6-6.

Example 6-10:

Problem: An isolated system consists of a 1.5 kg mass moving in the presence of the following potential energy function.

$$U(x) = \left(1\frac{J}{m^5}\right)x^5 - \left(1\frac{J}{m^2}\right)x^2$$

What is the period of small amplitude oscillations of this system about its stable equilibrium point?

Solution: We begin by determining the location of the equilibrium points of the potential energy function.

$$\frac{dU}{dx} = 0 \ \rightarrow \ \left(5\frac{J}{m^5}\right)x^4 - \left(2\frac{J}{m^2}\right)x = 0 \ \rightarrow \ x = 0\,\text{m}, \left(\frac{2}{5}\right)^{\frac{1}{3}}\text{m}$$

We ignore the additional complex roots since they are not physically relevant. We can determine if the remaining real roots correspond to stable or unstable equilibrium points by determining the value of the second derivative of the potential energy function at those locations.

$$\left.\frac{d^2U}{dx^2}\right|_{x=0\text{m}} = \left.\left(\left(20\frac{\text{J}}{\text{m}^5}\right)x^3 - \left(2\frac{\text{J}}{\text{m}^2}\right)\right)\right|_{x=0\text{m}} = -2\frac{\text{J}}{\text{m}^2} \quad \text{unstable}$$

$$\left.\frac{d^2U}{dx^2}\right|_{x=\left(\frac{2}{5}\right)^{\frac{1}{3}}\text{m}} = \left.\left(\left(20\frac{\text{J}}{\text{m}^5}\right)x^3 - \left(2\frac{\text{J}}{\text{m}^2}\right)\right)\right|_{x=\left(\frac{2}{5}\right)^{\frac{1}{3}}\text{m}} = 6\frac{\text{J}}{\text{m}^2} \quad \text{stable}$$

The effective spring constant for small amplitude oscillations around the stable equilibrium point is, therefore,

$$k_{effective} = \left.\frac{d^2U}{dx^2}\right|_{x=\left(\frac{2}{5}\right)^{\frac{1}{3}}\text{m}} \quad \rightarrow \quad k_{effective} = 6\frac{\text{J}}{\text{m}^2}$$

The period of oscillations is, thus,

$$T = \frac{2\pi}{\omega} \quad \rightarrow \quad T = \frac{2\pi}{\sqrt{\dfrac{k_{effective}}{m_{effective}}}} \quad \rightarrow \quad T = \frac{2\pi}{\sqrt{\dfrac{6\dfrac{\text{J}}{\text{m}^2}}{1.5\text{kg}}}} \quad \rightarrow \quad T = \pi \text{ s}$$

6-9 Oscillations of Non-Isolated Systems

We recognize from Section 6-3 that if the energy of an oscillating system changes (*i.e.*, if the system is not isolated), then the amplitude of the oscillation also changes; this is also consistent with Figure 3.8 and the associated discussion in Section 3-7. We refer to an oscillating system in which energy is dissipated from the system (*i.e.*, a system for which the amplitude of the oscillation decreases over time) as a *damped* oscillating system. A common damping mechanism to consider is one in which the rate of energy dissipation is proportional to the speed of the oscillating object[10]

$$\frac{dE}{dx} = -\eta v_x$$

---

10   We first encountered this energy dissipation mechanism in Section 4-6.

Let's consider as our damped oscillating system the system shown in Figure 6.6 that consists of a block attached to a horizontally mounted spring. The equation for the energy of this system is

$$E = \frac{1}{2}mv_x^2 + \frac{1}{2}kx^2$$

In this equation, we have defined the zero point of the gravitational potential energy to be the horizontal surface along which the block oscillates. Differentiating this equation for the energy of the system with respect to the position of the block gives us

$$\frac{dE}{dx} = -\eta v_x \quad \rightarrow \quad ma_x + kx = -\eta v_x \quad \rightarrow \quad ma_x + \eta v_x + kx = 0$$

$$m\frac{d^2x}{dt^2} + \eta\frac{dx}{dt} + kx = 0$$

You can verify that a solution to this equation is

$$x(t) = Ae^{-\left(\frac{\eta}{2m}\right)t}\sin\left(\omega t + \phi_0\right)$$

In this equation, w is the angular frequency of the damped oscillation and is given by

$$\omega = \sqrt{\frac{k}{m} - \frac{\eta^2}{4m^2}} \quad \rightarrow \quad \omega^2 = \frac{k}{m} - \frac{\eta^2}{4m^2} \quad \rightarrow \quad \omega^2 = \omega_{spring}^2 - \left(\frac{\eta}{2m}\right)^2$$

Following the discussion at the end of Section 6-6, we can identify the term $\left(\frac{\eta}{2m}\right)^2$ in this equation as the value of ω^2 corresponding to the oscillating energy loss in the system. Recall that since the rate of energy loss in this system is proportional to the speed of the block, the rate of energy loss will oscillate just as the position and speed of the block oscillate. Furthermore, since the $\left(\frac{\eta}{2m}\right)^2$ term is associated with dissipation of energy of the system, it should decrease the angular frequency of oscillation for the system (i.e., it should appear with a negative sign in the equation for ω^2). This is analogous to how the presence of friction decreased the magnitude of the acceleration of a block sliding down a ramp (Example 4-7).

Example 6-11:

Problem: A block with a mass of 2 kg is attached to a horizontally-mounted spring with a spring constant of 200 J/m², as shown in Figure 6.6.

The surface along which the block oscillates is perfectly horizontal. As the block oscillates, it dissipates energy at a rate of

$$\frac{dE}{dx} = -\eta v_x$$

What value of η will result in a 50% reduction in the angular frequency of oscillation of the system?

Solution: According to our previous derivation, we have

$$\omega^2 = \frac{k}{m} - \frac{\eta^2}{4m^2} \quad \rightarrow \quad \frac{\left(\frac{k}{m}\right)}{2} = \frac{k}{m} - \frac{\eta^2}{4m^2} \quad \rightarrow \quad \frac{\eta^2}{4m^2} = \frac{k}{2m}$$

$$\eta = \sqrt{2mk} \quad \rightarrow \quad \eta = \sqrt{2(2\text{kg})\left(200\frac{\text{J}}{\text{m}^2}\right)}$$

$$\eta = 28.3\frac{\text{kg}}{\text{s}}$$

We refer to an oscillating system in which energy is continually added as a *driven* oscillating system. Let's, again, consider as a model the oscillating system shown in Figure 6.6. The equation for the energy of this system is

$$E = \frac{1}{2}mv_x^2 + \frac{1}{2}kx^2$$

We will describe the addition of energy to this system using the time dependent sinusoidal function

$$\frac{dE}{dx} = \varepsilon \cos\left(\omega_D t\right)$$

In this equation, the variable ε (with units of J/m) is the small rate of energy addition that has an angular frequency of ω_D. Differentiating the equation for the energy of the system with respect to the position of the block gives us

$$\frac{dE}{dx} = ma_x + kx \quad \rightarrow \quad ma_x + kx = \varepsilon \cos\left(\omega_D t\right)$$

$$m\frac{d^2x}{dt^2} + kx = \varepsilon \cos\left(\omega_D t\right)$$

You can verify that a solution to this equation is

$$x(t) = A\sin\left(\left(\sqrt{\frac{k}{m}}\right)t + \phi_0\right) + \frac{\varepsilon\cos(\omega_D t)}{m\left(\dfrac{k}{m} - \omega_D^2\right)}$$

$$x(t) = A\sin\left(\omega_{spring}t + \phi_0\right) + \frac{\varepsilon\cos(\omega_D t)}{m\left(\omega_{spring}^2 - \omega_D^2\right)}$$

The second term in this equation results from the periodic addition of energy to the system. As expected, the magnitude of this term depends upon the difference between the angular frequency of the mass-spring oscillator (ω_{spring}) and the angular frequency of the energy addition (ω_D); it will be largest when $\omega_{spring} = \omega_D$. If these two angular frequencies are identical, we say that the frequency of energy addition is in *resonance* with the *natural* frequency of the system. As an example of a driven oscillator in resonance, consider a parent pushing her child on a swing. The parent must synchronize her pushing to the swinging motion of her child in order to increase the amplitude of each swing.

For our model system, we see that during resonance (*i.e.*, when $\omega_{spring} = \omega_D$), the amplitude of the oscillation becomes infinite. There is, of course, always some energy dissipation present in all oscillating systems, and, thus, it is not be possible to achieve an infinite amplitude oscillation. Indeed, a more realistic equation to describe a driven oscillating system would be

$$m\frac{d^2x}{dt^2} + \eta\frac{dx}{dt} + kx = \varepsilon\cos(\omega_D t)$$

A solution to this equation is

$$x(t) = Ae^{-\left(\frac{\eta}{2m}\right)t}\sin(\omega t + \phi_0) + \frac{\varepsilon\left(\left(k - m\omega_D^2\right)\cos(\omega_D t) + \eta\omega_D\sin(\omega_D t)\right)}{\eta^2\omega_D^2 + \left(k - m\omega_D^2\right)^2}$$

The position of the block is, therefore, described by a combination of two terms. The first term is the solution that we previously derived for the position of a damped harmonic oscillator. The angular frequency for the sinusoidal component of this term is also the same as what we derived previously.

$$\omega = \sqrt{\frac{k}{m} - \frac{\eta^2}{4m^2}} \;\rightarrow\; \omega^2 = \frac{k}{m} - \frac{\eta^2}{4m^2} \;\rightarrow\; \omega^2 = \omega_{spring}^2 - \left(\frac{\eta}{2m}\right)^2$$

Eventually, after sufficient time has passed, the contribution of this first term to the position of the block will become insignificant due to the exponential decay it contains. After this first term has become sufficiently small, we can rewrite the equation for the position of the block in terms of the second term only.

$$x(t) = \frac{\varepsilon\left(\left(k - m\omega_D^2\right)\cos\left(\omega_D t\right) + \eta\omega_D \sin\left(\omega_D t\right)\right)}{\eta^2\omega_D^2 + \left(k - m\omega_D^2\right)^2} \;\rightarrow\; x(t) = A\sin\left(\omega_D t + \phi_0\right)$$

The amplitude and phase constant for this oscillation are

$$A = \frac{\varepsilon}{\sqrt{\eta^2\omega_D^2 + \left(k - m\omega_D^2\right)^2}} \qquad \phi_0 = \tan^{-1}\left(\frac{k - m\omega_D^2}{\eta\omega_D}\right)$$

The resonance frequency for this oscillation (*i.e.,* the frequency corresponding to the largest amplitude of the oscillation) is, thus,

$$\omega_D^2 = \frac{k}{m} - \frac{\eta^2}{2m^2} \;\rightarrow\; \omega_D^2 = \omega_{spring}^2 - 2\left(\frac{\eta}{2m}\right)^2$$

It is interesting to note that the resonance frequency is not the natural frequency of oscillation for the damped oscillator but rather is slighter smaller. This compensates for the dissipation of the additional added energy resulting from the damping.

Summary

- **Simple Harmonic Motion (SHM):** Oscillatory motion that occurs when the acceleration of the system is linearly proportional to the displacement of the system from equilibrium. The proportionality constant is the square of the angular frequency of the oscillation.

$$a_x = \frac{d^2 x}{dt^2} = -\omega^2 x$$

SHM occurs for systems in which the potential energy is proportional to the square of the displacement of the system from its equilibrium point.
- **Angular frequency:** A measure of the rate of oscillation. Angular frequency is denoted by the variable ω.
- **Period:** The time required for a system to complete a full oscillation. Period is denoted by the variable T.

- **Frequency:** The number of full oscillations completed by the system in one second. The frequency of an oscillation is the inverse of the period of the oscillation. Frequency, period, and angular frequency are related by the following equation.

$$\omega = 2\pi f = \frac{2\pi}{T}$$

- **Amplitude:** The maximum displacement of an oscillation. The amplitude is always positive and is proportional to the total energy of the oscillating system. For isolated simple harmonic oscillations, the energy is proportional to the square of the amplitude.

$$E = \frac{1}{2}kA^2$$

- **The angular frequency for simple harmonic motion can be determined from the effective spring constant and effective mass of the oscillating system.**

$$\omega^2 = \frac{k_{effective}}{m_{effective}}$$

- **The small amplitude oscillations of any system around a stable equilibrium point can be described as simple harmonic motion.**
- **The angular frequency of a damped oscillator is smaller than the angular frequency of an otherwise equivalent un-damped oscillator.**
- **A driven oscillator is said to be in resonance when the amplitude of the oscillation is maximum.**

Problems

1. A system consisting of a block attached to a horizontally-mounted spring is undergoing simple harmonic motion along a horizontal x-axis with an amplitude of 10 cm. At $t = 0$ s, the block is $x = -5$ cm and moving with a velocity of $+2$ cm/s. What is the position of the block at $t = 25$ s? What is the velocity of the block at $t = 25$ s?

2. A system consists of a block attached to two horizontally-mounted springs, as shown in the figure is to the right. The horizontal surface across which the block slides is frictionless. What is the angular frequency of the oscillations of this system? Express your answer in terms of the mass of the block (m) and the spring constant of the spring (k).

3. A system consists of a block oscillating with a spring on an inclined plane, as shown in the figure at right. The surface across which the block slides is frictionless. What is the angular

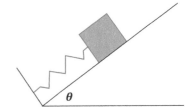

frequency of the oscillations of this system? Express your answer in terms of the mass of the block (m) and the spring constant of the spring (k).

4. The figure below shows 4 different oscillating systems. The mass of the block and the value of the spring constant are the same for all the systems. Rank in order from largest to smallest the period of the oscillations of the systems.

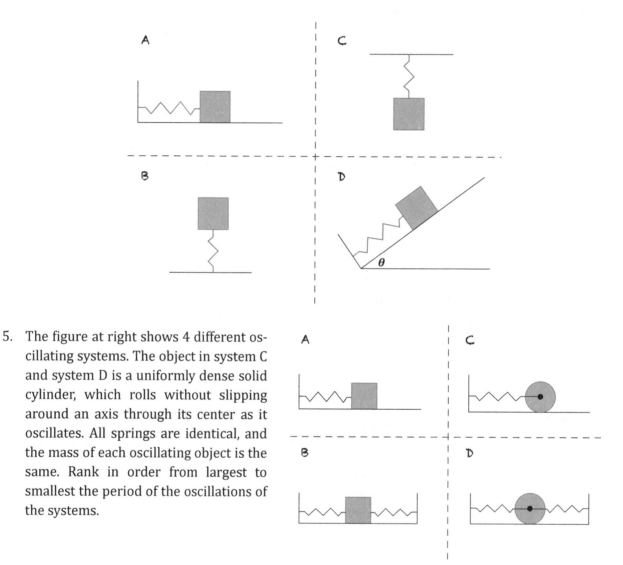

5. The figure at right shows 4 different oscillating systems. The object in system C and system D is a uniformly dense solid cylinder, which rolls without slipping around an axis through its center as it oscillates. All springs are identical, and the mass of each oscillating object is the same. Rank in order from largest to smallest the period of the oscillations of the systems.

6. Four different springs have been compressed from their equilibrium position at $x = 0$ cm. Two of the springs have spring constant k, and two of the springs have spring constant $2k$. The springs are also attached to blocks with masses of m or $2m$. When released from this initial position, all of the blocks will undergo simple harmonic motion. You can assume that the horizontal surfaces along which the blocks oscillate are all frictionless. Rank in order from highest to lowest the angular frequency of these oscillations. Rank in order from highest to lowest the maximum speed of these blocks during the oscillations.

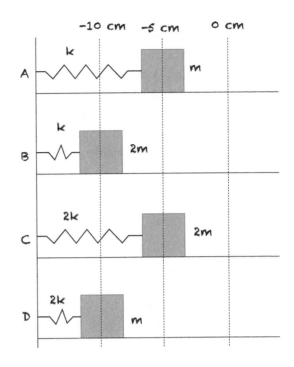

7. A system consists of two blocks, A and B, connected by a massless rope that moves over a pulley without slipping, as shown in the figure at right. Block A is also connected to a horizontally-mounted spring. The pulley can be modeled as a uniformly dense solid cylinder with a mass of m_p and an axis of rotation passing through its center. What are the effective mass and spring constant for this system? What is the period of oscillations of this system?

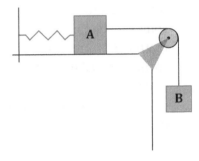

8. A torsion pendulum is created by attaching a uniformly dense rigid rod of mass 0.4 kg and length 0.5 m to a massless string, as shown in the figure at right; the rod is suspended from its midpoint. Rotating the rod through an angle θ results in elastic potential energy being stored in the string; the equation for this energy is $U = \frac{1}{2}k\theta^2$. The "spring constant," k, for this energy storage is 7.5 J. What is the angular frequency of simple harmonic oscillations of this oscillator?

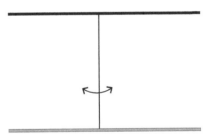

9. A 5 kg bob is connected to a thin massless but rigid rod of length $L = 1.3$ m to form a simple pendulum, as shown in the figure at right. The bob is also connected to two nearby vertical walls by identical springs; each spring has a spring constant $k = 75$ J/m². What is the angular frequency of small amplitude oscillations of this isolated system? Each spring is at its normal length when the bob is hanging straight down.

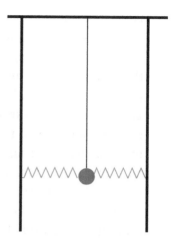

10. A system consists of a block with a mass of 0.5 kg attached to a horizontally-mounted spring with a spring constant of 100 J/m². The surface along which the block oscillates is perfectly horizontal. Because of friction, energy is dissipated from this system at a rate of 0.1 J for every meter travelled by the block. The spring is initially extended 20 cm from its normal length when the block is released from rest. What is the total distance travelled by the block before it comes to a rest?

11. Notice that for a damped harmonic oscillator, if $\frac{\eta^2}{4m^2} > \frac{k}{m}$, the angular frequency of oscillation becomes imaginary. Under these conditions, the system will no longer undergo simple harmonic motion, but rather the position of the block will exponentially decrease until the length of the spring is equal to the normal length. What is the exponential equation for the length of the spring under these conditions?

12. What is the phase constant for a damped and driven harmonic oscillator in resonance when $\eta = 0$? What is the phase constant for a damped and driven harmonic oscillator in resonance when $\eta = \infty$?

CHAPTER SEVEN
Forces

7-1 Introduction

Previously in this book, we relied upon energy-based descriptions of systems as the starting point for kinematic calculations. An alternative approach focuses on the mechanical interactions responsible for the changes in energy (*i.e.*, on the work done by these interactions). We use the term *force* to describe such an interaction, and, over the next few chapters, we will develop and present a formulation of mechanics based upon forces. This framework is called Newtonian mechanics after Sir Isaac Newton who introduced it. As we shall see, Newtonian mechanics is simply another approach for solving the problems we have already solved using our energy-based approach. In fact, we will motivate it using an energy-based calculation.

7-2 Equilibrium Conditions

From the principle of minimum potential energy (Section 1-4), we know that systems will always arrange themselves to minimize their total potential energy. Because of this, the stable equilibrium arrangement of a system must correspond to a minimum potential energy for the system[1].

The total potential energy of a system is at a minimum at equilibrium.

We can use this constraint to determine the conditions corresponding to the equilibrium arrangement of systems. For example, consider the system shown in Figure 7.1 that consists of a 5 kg block on top of a vertically-mounted massless spring with a spring constant of 490 J/m^2

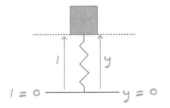

Figure 7.1: A block on top of a vertically-mounted spring. The variable y denotes the vertical position of the block and is equal to the length of the spring, denoted by the variable l.

---

1 This may be either a local or a global minimum of the energy of a system (Section 1-5).

and a normal length of 30 cm. The spring was at its normal length when the block was placed on top of it. When released from rest, this system will oscillate back and forth until eventually coming to a stop due to energy dissipation by friction. What is the position of the block at this final equilibrium?

The block and spring will move in order to minimize the total potential energy of the system, which is described by the following equation.

$$U_{total} = U_g + U_s \quad \rightarrow \quad U_{total} = mgy + \frac{1}{2}k(\Delta l)^2 \quad \rightarrow \quad U_{total} = mgy + \frac{1}{2}k(l-l_0)^2$$

In this equation, we have defined the zero point of the gravitational potential energy to be the horizontal surface on which the spring is mounted (*i.e.*, at $y = 0$). Since the length of the spring is the same as the vertical position of the mass, we can further simplify this equation.

$$U_{total} = mgy + \frac{1}{2}k(y-l_0)^2$$

A plot of the gravitational potential energy and the spring potential energy as a function of the position of the block (y) is shown in Figure 7.2.

As shown in Figure 7.2, when the spring is compressed from its normal length, the gravitational potential energy of the system decreases and the spring potential energy of the system increases. Initially, the total potential energy of the system decreases since the slope of the gravitational potential energy curve is larger than the slope of the spring potential energy curve. However, the slope of the spring potential energy curve continues to increase as the spring is compressed and, eventually, becomes larger than the slope of the gravitational potential energy curve, which remains constant. At this point, the total potential energy of the system begins to increase as the spring continues to be compressed. The final equilibrium position of the block occurs at this transition point when the total potential energy of the system is a minimum.

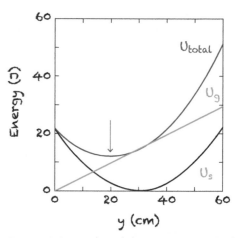

Figure 7.2: A plot of the spring potential energy (black), the gravitational potential energy (red), and the total potential energy (blue) of the system shown in Figure 7.1: The minimum in the total potential energy is indicated by the arrow.

$$\frac{dU_{total}}{dy} = 0 \quad \rightarrow \quad \frac{dU_g}{dy} + \frac{dU_s}{dy} = 0 \quad \rightarrow \quad mg + k(y-l_0) = 0$$

Solving yields

$$y = l_0 - \frac{mg}{k}$$

We recognize this as the same equilibrium length determined in Section 6-5 for the oscillations of this system.

$$l_e = l_0 - \frac{mg}{k}$$

Substitution of the values of our system gives

$$l_e = 0.3\,\text{m} - \frac{(5\,\text{kg})\left(9.8\,\dfrac{\text{m}}{\text{s}^2}\right)}{490\,\dfrac{\text{J}}{\text{m}^2}} \;\rightarrow\; l_e = 0.2\,\text{m}$$

We can confirm that this is, in fact, a stable equilibrium point by taking the second derivative of the total potential energy.

$$\frac{d^2U_{total}}{dy^2} = k \;\rightarrow\; \frac{d^2U_{total}}{dy^2} = 490\,\frac{\text{J}}{\text{m}^2} \;\rightarrow\; \frac{d^2U_{total}}{dy^2} > 0$$

Since the second derivative of the total potential is positive, we know that we have determined a minimum and, thus, l_e corresponds to a stable equilibrium point.

In general, a system is in equilibrium with respect to its location along a particular coordinate axis when the sum of the derivatives of the potential energies of the system with respect to that axis is zero. For example, for 1-dimensional motion along the x-axis, the equilibrium condition would be

$$\frac{dU_{total}}{dx} = 0 \;\rightarrow\; \sum_i \frac{dU_i}{dx} = 0$$

This expression allows us to define a new quantity: force (F).

$$F_i = -\frac{dU_i}{dx} \tag{7-1}$$

Force: The negative of the derivative of potential energy with respect to position. Force is, thus, related to the slope of the potential energy curve.

We interpret the negative sign in Equation 7-1 to indicate that forces always act to reduce their associated potential energies. Our equilibrium condition can now be expressed as

$$\sum_i \frac{dU_i}{dx} = 0 \;\rightarrow\; \sum_i \left(-F_i\right) = 0 \;\rightarrow\; -\sum_i F_i = 0 \;\rightarrow\; -F_{net} = 0$$

$$\text{Equilibrium} \;\rightarrow\; F_{net} = 0 \tag{7-2}$$

In Equation 7-2, we have defined the net force acting on a system as a sum of all the forces acting on the system.

The net force is the sum of all of the forces acting on the system.

Furthermore,

The net force acting on a system must equal zero when the system is at equilibrium.

The unit of force is the newton, named for Sir Isaac Newton, and is denoted by N. The newton is defined to be

$$1\,N = 1\frac{J}{m} = 1\frac{kg\,m}{s^2}$$

7-3 What is a Force?

In addition to Equation 7-1, we can use the following operational definition for a force. A force ...

(i) is a push or a pull.
(ii) has an agent that does the pushing or pulling. There must be an identifiable "*source*" of the force.
(iii) acts on an object.
(iv) is a vector. There is a direction along which the force is pushing or pulling.
(v) results either from the contact between objects (in Figure 7.1 the spring is exerting a force on the block through its contact with the block) or from a long range interaction (in Figure 7.1 the Earth is exerting a gravitational force on the block without touching it).

An interaction must satisfy these criteria to be considered a force.

7-4 Conservative and Non-Conservative Forces

Any force that is associated with a potential energy function is referred to as a *conservative force*. For example, the gravitational force is a conservative force because it is derived from the gravitational potential energy (Section 3-3).

$$U_g = -G\frac{m_1 m_2}{r} \quad \rightarrow \quad F_g = -\frac{d}{dr}\left(-G\frac{m_1 m_2}{r}\right)$$

$$F_g = -G\frac{m_1 m_2}{r^2} \tag{7-3}$$

Equation 7-3 is referred to as Newton's law of gravity; the negative sign in Equation 7-3 denotes that the force of gravity always acts to bring the two objects together. We can derive a similar expression using our approximation for the gravitational potential energy function for objects near the surface of the Earth.

$$U_g = mgy + \left(U_g\right)_0 \quad \rightarrow \quad F_g = -\frac{d}{dy}\left(mgy + \left(U_g\right)_0\right)$$

$$F_g = -mg \tag{7-4}$$

The negative sign in Equation 7-4 denotes that the force of gravity is always directed in the negative direction (*i.e.*, the force of gravity is directed down toward the ground, specifically toward the center of the Earth).

The spring force is derived from the spring potential energy (Section 3-3).

$$U_s = \frac{1}{2}k\left(l - l_0\right)^2 \quad \rightarrow \quad F_s = -\frac{d}{dl}\left(\frac{1}{2}k\left(l - l_0\right)^2\right)$$

$$F_s = -k\left(l - l_0\right) \tag{7-5}$$

Equation 7-5 is referred to as Hooke's Law. We see from Equation 7-5 that if the length of the spring is larger than its normal length, the spring force will be negative, meaning that it will act to decrease the length of the spring. Similarly, if the length of the spring is less than the normal length, the spring force will be positive, meaning that it will act to increase the length of the spring. Incidentally, the spring constant is usually expressed in terms of newtons rather than Joules.

$$1\frac{J}{m^2} = 1\frac{N}{m}$$

Non-conservative forces are forces that are not associated with potential energy functions; these forces cannot be determined using Equation 7-1. There are four non-conservative forces that we will encounter in this course:

(i) External Pushes and Pulls.

(ii) Tension. Tension is the force that exists within ropes (and cables, strings, *etc.*). It exists when the rope is taut and is directed along the length of the rope.

(iii) Normal Force. The normal force is a force that acts between the surfaces of interacting objects. For example, if a book is lying on a table, then the table and book exert normal forces on each other. The normal force arises from the electrostatic repulsion of the atoms that constitute matter and is directed perpendicular (*i.e.*, normal) to the surfaces.

(iv) Friction. Friction forces also arise from the interaction between surfaces. Static friction is the force of friction that opposes the start of motion and is directed in order to satisfy that requirement. Kinetic friction is the force of friction that opposes the continuing motion of an object and, thus, is always directed opposite the direction of the velocity of the object. Because of this, the direction of the force of kinetic friction is always opposite the direction of the displacement of the object.

7-5 Forces Do Work

In Section 3-6, we defined **work** to be a change in energy associated with a mechanical interaction (*i.e.*, with a push or a pull that we now call a force). For 1-dimensional motion, we can mathematically express this relationship between work and force as

$$W = \int F_x \, dx \qquad \text{(7-6)}$$

Work done by a force: The integral of the force with respect to the displacement of the force's object.

In Equation 7-6, we have included the subscript "*x*" to indicate that the force is directed along the *x*-axis, which is the axis for the displacement of the force's object.

Since for 1-dimensional motion ($\pm$) signs denote the directions of force and displacement, it is possible for the work done by the force to be positive or negative.

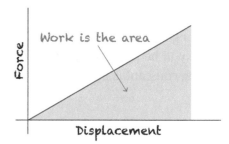

Figure 7.3: The relationship between force, displacement, and work.

The work done by a force is positive if the force and the displacement of the force's object have the same direction. The work done by a force is negative if the force and the displacement of the force's object have opposite directions.

This makes sense. If we are pushing on an object in the same direction that the object is already moving, then we would expect the speed of the object to increase. In this case, the change in the kinetic energy of the system would be positive, and the work done on the object would be positive (see Section 3-6). This is consistent with Equation 7-6 since, in this case, the direction of the force and the direction of the displacement of the force's object (or the velocity of the force's object) are the same.

Let's consider this further by revisiting Example 3-8.

Example 7-1:

Problem: A block with a mass of 4 kg is sliding across a horizontal surface with an initial speed of 5 m/s. Because of kinetic friction, the energy of this system will decrease linearly with the distance travelled by the block at a constant rate of 2.5 J/m. How much work will be done by the force of kinetic friction during the first 10 m travelled by the block?

Solution: We now recognize the magnitude of the rate of energy lost per distance to kinetic friction (2.5 J/m) as the magnitude of the kinetic friction force (2.5 N). From Equation 7-6, we can determine the work done by this force on the block by integrating the force with respect to the displacement of the block.

Let's denote the direction of the initial velocity of the block to be the positive direction and the magnitude of the force of kinetic friction by the variable f_k (see Figure 7.4). Then, our integral for the work done by the force of kinetic friction becomes

$$W_{f_k} = \int_{x_i}^{x_f} f_k \, dx \quad \rightarrow \quad W_{f_k} = \int_{x_i}^{x_f} (-2.5\,\text{N}) \, dx \quad \rightarrow \quad W_{f_k} = (-2.5\,\text{N}) \int_{x_i}^{x_f} dx$$

$$W_{f_k} = (-2.5\,\text{N}) \Delta x$$

The displacement Δx is independent of the origin of our x-axis[2] and is simply 10 m. Therefore,

$$W_{f_k} = (-2.5\,\text{N})(10\,\text{m}) \quad \rightarrow \quad W_{f_k} = -25\,\text{J}$$

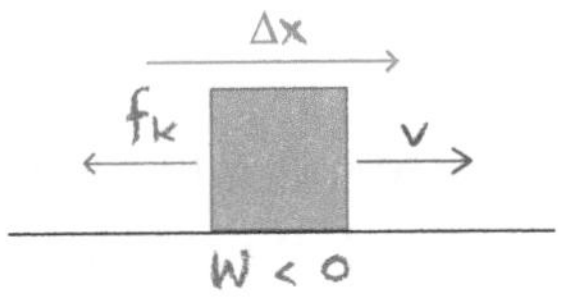

The work done by the force of kinetic friction is negative, consistent with our discussion in Section 3-6[3]. We could also have determined that work is negative based upon the relative orientations of the force of kinetic friction and the displacement, as shown in Figure 7.4.

Figure 7.4: A block sliding across a surface where friction is present. The variable f_k denotes the magnitude of force of kinetic friction.

---

2   See Section 2-2.

3   However, we nevertheless need to refine the discussion in Section 3-6. The work done by the force of kinetic friction will always be negative since the direction of the force of kinetic friction is always opposite the direction of the displacement of the object. The work done the force of static friction is always zero, however, since there is no displacement of the object when the force of static friction is acting (Section 7-4).

Example 7-2:

Problem: The force acting on object as a function of the object's position is shown in Figure 7.5. What is the work done by this force on this object?

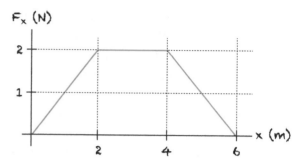

Figure 7.5: The force acting in Example 7-2.

Solution: We begin with Equation 7-6.

$$W = \int F_x \, dx$$

The work done by the force is the integral of the force with respect to the displacement of the object, which is the area under the curve of a plot of force versus the position of the object. For our figure, this area is 8 Nm. Hence, the work done by the force is

$$\int_{0m}^{6m} F_x \, dx = 8 \, \text{Nm} \quad \rightarrow \quad W = 8 \, \text{Nm} \quad \rightarrow \quad W = 8 \, \text{J}$$

Example 7-3:

Problem: A block with a mass of 4 kg is released from rest at a height of 5 m above the ground. What is the work done by the force of gravity as the block falls to the ground? Assume that the system is isolated (*i.e.*, assume that the block is in free-fall).

Solution: As shown in Figure 7.6, we can denote the vertical direction as the y-axis with a positive direction pointing up from the surface of the Earth. Thus, the force of gravity, the velocity of the block, and the displacement are all negative.

The work done by the force of gravity on the block must be positive since the direction of the force of gravity and the direction of the displacement of the block are the same for this system. This also results from the application of Equation 7-4 to this system.

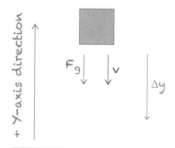

Figure 7.6: A block falling under the influence of the force of gravity alone.

$$W_{F_g} = \int F_g \, dy \quad \rightarrow \quad W_{F_g} = \int (-mg) \, dy$$

$$W_{F_g} = (-mg) \int dy \quad \rightarrow \quad W_{F_g} = (-mg) \Delta y$$

Substitution yields

$$W_{F_g} = -\left(4\,kg\right)\left(9.8\frac{m}{s^2}\right)\left(0\,m - 5\,m\right) \;\rightarrow\; W_{F_g} = 196\,J$$

We note that in the solution for Example 7-3, we determined that the work done by the force of gravity is simply the negative of the change in the gravitational potential energy of the falling object. This is true for any conservative force, as seen from Equation 7-1 and Equation 7-6.

$$F_i = -\frac{dU_i}{dx} \;\rightarrow\; \int_{x_i}^{x_f} F_i\,dx = -\int_{U_i}^{U_f} dU_i$$

In this integration, the object is defined to have potential energy U_i when it is at position x_i and potential energy U_f when it is at position x_f. Hence,

$$W = -\Delta U \tag{7-7}$$

Since the work done by a conservative force is equal to the negative of the change in the associated potential energy, the work done by a conservative force must be independent of the path over which the displacement of the force's object occurs. Consider, for example, the three identical blocks shown in Figure 7.7 that are released from the same height above the ground. The initial speed of each block is identical, but the directions of the velocities of the blocks are different. We will assume that each block is in free-fall. The force of gravity will do work on each block as the block

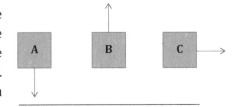

Figure 7.7: Three identical blocks in free fall.

moves from its initial position to the ground. For which block will this work be the largest?

The work done by the force of gravity on each of the blocks is independent of the path over which the displacement of the block occurs and depends upon only the associated change in the gravitational potential energy of the block. Since each block has the same initial position and the same final position, the change in the gravitational potential energy of each block will be the same. Thus, the work done by the force of gravity will be identical for each block.

7-6 Work and Kinetic Energy

The pushing or pulling of a force often changes the speed and/or velocity of the object upon which the force is acting. A change in the speed of an object can be associated with a change in translational kinetic energy of the object. Thus, the work done by a force can be associated with a change in translational kinetic energy. As shown in Equation 7-8, the net work done on a system is equal to the change in the translational kinetic energy of the system.

$$\Delta K = W_{net} \tag{7-8}$$

In Equation 7-8, the net work done on a system is the sum of the work done by all of the forces acting on the system. Equation 7-8 is often referred to as the work-kinetic energy theorem, but it is really just a restatement of energy conservation (see Section 3-6)[4].

Example 7-4:

Problem: A block with a mass of 4 kg is sliding across a horizontal surface with an initial speed of 5 m/s. Because of kinetic friction, the energy of this system will decrease linearly with the distance travelled by the block at a constant rate of 2.5 J/m. How much work will be done by the force of kinetic friction as the block slows to a stop?

Solution: We begin with Equation 7-8.

$$\Delta K = W_{net} \quad \rightarrow \quad \frac{1}{2}mv_f^2 - \frac{1}{2}mv_i^2 = W_{net}$$

Substitution yields

$$0 - \frac{1}{2}\left(4\,\text{kg}\right)\left(5\frac{\text{m}}{\text{s}}\right)^2 = W_{net} \quad \rightarrow \quad W_{net} = -50\,\text{J}$$

This is the net work done on the block by all the forces acting on the block. These forces are: kinetic friction, the normal force, and the force of gravity. Since there is no displacement in the vertical direction (*i.e.*, the block is sliding across a horizontal surface), we know from Equation 7-6 that the work done by the normal force and the force of gravity will be zero. Therefore, the net work done on the system is equal to the work done by kinetic friction.

$$W_{friction} = -50\,\text{J}$$

It is significant that Equation 7-8 describes a relationship between work and change in kinetic energy. Although changes in kinetic energy and displacements of objects can both be measured

---

4   This is also another way of expressing Newton's 2nd law (see Chapter 8).

precisely (*i.e.*, mass, position, and speed can be easily determined to high levels of accuracy), it is not always straightforward or even possible to characterize how the instantaneous force acting on an object varies with the position of the object. However, we can, nevertheless, use Equation 7-6 and Equation 7-8 to estimate the *average net force* associated with a change in kinetic energy.

Let's consider the work done by a net force, $F_{x,net}(x)$, that acts on an object undergoing 1-dimensional motion along the *x*-axis; the magnitude and direction of this force are functions of the position of the object along the *x*-axis. The change in the translational kinetic energy of this object associated with the work done by this force is

$$\Delta K = \int_{x_i}^{x_f} \left(F_{x,net}(x) \right) dx$$

Let's now define the average value of $F_{x,net}(x)$ over the displacement of the object to be $\left(F_{x,net} \right)_{avg}$.

$$\left(F_{x,net} \right)_{avg} = \frac{\int_{x_i}^{x_f} \left(F_{x,net}(x) \right) dx}{\Delta x}$$

Both the magnitude and the direction of the average net force $\left(F_{x,net} \right)_{avg}$ are constant over the displacement of the object. The change in the kinetic energy of the object can now be written as

$$\Delta K = \left(F_{x,net} \right)_{avg} \Delta x \qquad\qquad \textbf{(7-9)}$$

Example 7-5:

Problem: An object is moving along a 1-dimensional axis with a velocity of $+v$. A net force pushes on this object and, thereby, changes its velocity to $-v$. What is the net work done by this force during this process?

Solution: We begin with Equation 7-8.

$$\Delta K = W_{net} \quad \rightarrow \quad \frac{1}{2}mv_f^2 - \frac{1}{2}mv_i^2 = W_{net}$$

$$W_{net} = \frac{1}{2}m(-v)^2 - \frac{1}{2}mv^2 \quad \rightarrow \quad W_{net} = \frac{1}{2}mv^2 - \frac{1}{2}mv^2 \quad \rightarrow \quad W_{net} = 0$$

There is no net work done on the object because the kinetic energy hasn't changed; recall that kinetic energy is dependent upon speed, not velocity, and, thus, is independent of the direction of the velocity. This result seems odd because we feel that the force "*should have done something*" since the motion of the object changed. We can ease this discomfort by determining the net work done by the force as a two-part problem.

First, what is the work done by the force as the object slows to a stop? As shown in Figure 7.8, as the object is slowing, the direction of the force is both opposite the direction of the object's velocity and opposite of the direction of the object's displacement. According to Equation 7-6, the work done by the force for this displacement must be negative.

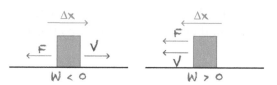

Figure 7.8: The work done by the force in Example 7-5 when the speed of the object is decreasing (left panel) and when the speed of the object is increasing (right panel).

Let's denote the work required to stop the object as $W_{net,1}$. From Equation 7-8, we have

$$\frac{1}{2}m(0)^2 - \frac{1}{2}mv^2 = W_{net,1} \quad \rightarrow \quad W_{net,1} = -\frac{1}{2}mv^2$$

Second, what is the work done by the force as it speeds up the stopped object? As shown in Figure 7.8, as the object is speeding up after being stopped, the force is acting in the same direction as the object's velocity and displacement. According to Equation 7-6, this means the work done by the force must be positive. Let's denote this work as $W_{net,2}$.

$$\frac{1}{2}m(-v) - \frac{1}{2}m(0)^2 = W_{net,2} \quad \rightarrow \quad W_{net,2} = \frac{1}{2}mv^2$$

The net work done by the force during this entire process is the sum of $W_{net,1}$ and $W_{net,2}$.

$$W_{net} = W_{net,1} + W_{net,2} \quad \rightarrow \quad W_{net} = -\frac{1}{2}mv^2 + \frac{1}{2}mv^2 \quad \rightarrow \quad W_{net} = 0$$

Since the positive work done by the force is exactly equal to the negative work done by the force, the net work done by the force is zero.

It is also interesting to note that since the magnitude of the force is not zero, but the work done by the force is zero, the total displacement of the object must be zero (Equation 7-8 and Equation 7-9). In other words, the distance travelled by the object as it slowed to a stop is exactly equal to the distance travelled by the object as it sped back up again. Since these two displacements are in different directions, they differ in the (±) sign used to denote their direction. Thus, since they are two vectors with the same magnitude but different directions, their sum is zero.

The net work done on a system can be expressed as the sum of the net work done by conservative forces and the net work done by non-conservative forces.

$$\Delta K = \left(W_{net}\right)_{conservative} + \left(W_{net}\right)_{non-conservative}$$

But the work done by a conservative force can be written in terms of the change in the associated potential energy (Equation 7-7).

$$\left(W_{net}\right)_{conservative} = \sum_i \left(-\Delta U_i\right)$$

Thus,

$$\Delta K = \left(\sum_i -\Delta U_i\right) + \left(W_{net}\right)_{non-conservative}$$

$$\Delta K + \sum_i \Delta U_i = \left(W_{net}\right)_{non-conservative} \tag{7-10}$$

Example 7-6:

Problem: A block with a mass of 4 kg is sliding across a horizontal surface with an initial speed of 5 m/s when it collides with a horizontally-mounted spring with a spring constant of 49 J/m², as shown in Figure 7.9. As the block, subsequently, compresses the spring, energy will be dissipated at a rate of 6 J/m because of kinetic friction. What is the maximum compression of the spring?

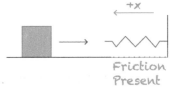

Figure 7.9: The system in Example 7-6.

Solution: We begin with Equation 7-10.

$$\Delta K + \sum_i \Delta U_i = \left(W_{net}\right)_{non-conservative}$$

$$\left(K_f - K_i\right) + mg\Delta y + \left(\frac{1}{2}k\left(\Delta l_f\right)^2 - \frac{1}{2}k\left(\Delta l_i\right)^2\right) = \left(W_{net}\right)_{non-conservative}$$

Let's denote the 1-dimensional axis for the motion of the block as the x-axis with a positive direction oriented opposite the direction of the velocity of the block (Figure 7.9). According to this definition, the displacement of the block will be negative as the spring is compressed.

Since the work done by friction must also be negative, the relationship between the work done by the force of kinetic friction and the displacement would be[5]

$$\left(W_{net}\right)_{non-conservative} = \left(6\frac{J}{m}\right)\Delta x$$

Let's choose as the initial and final points for our energy conservation equation to be before the collision of the block with the spring and when the spring is maximally compressed, respectively. At the maximum compression of the spring, the kinetic energy of the block must be zero.

$$\left(0 - \frac{1}{2}mv_i^2\right) + mg(0) + \left(\frac{1}{2}k\left(\Delta l_f\right)^2 - 0\right) = \left(6\frac{J}{m}\right)\Delta x$$

We recognize from Figure 7.9 that the displacement of the block is equal to the compression of the spring.

$$\Delta x = \Delta l_f$$

Thus,

$$\frac{1}{2}k\left(\Delta l_f\right)^2 - \left(6\frac{J}{m}\right)\Delta l_f - \frac{1}{2}mv_i^2 = 0$$

Substitution of the values for the parameters for this system gives us

$$\frac{1}{2}\left(49\frac{J}{m^2}\right)\left(\Delta l_f\right)^2 - \left(6\frac{J}{m}\right)\Delta l_f - \frac{1}{2}\left(4\,kg\right)\left(5\frac{m}{s}\right)^2 = 0$$

$$\left(24.5\frac{J}{m^2}\right)\left(\Delta l_f\right)^2 - \left(6\frac{J}{m}\right)\Delta l_f - 50J = 0$$

This equation has two solutions

$$\Delta l_f = -1.3\,m \qquad \Delta l_f = 1.6\,m$$

---

5   See Section 4-6.

From our definition of the position direction for the motion of the block, we know that only the negative root is physically real. Thus, the spring reaches a maximum compression of 1.3 m.

We can naturally build upon the derivation of Equation 7-9 to rewrite Equation 7-10 in terms of the average net non-conservative force acting on a system. For a system undergoing 1-dimensional motion, we have

$$\Delta K + \sum_i \Delta U_i = \left(\left(F_{x,net} \right)_{non-conservative} \right)_{avg} \Delta x \qquad \textbf{(7-11)}$$

Example 7-7:

Problem: A 4 kg block is pushed up a frictionless 30° ramp at constant speed, as shown in Figure 7.10. What is the magnitude of the average pushing force if the block is moved 6 m up the ramp?

Solution: There is no change in the block's kinetic energy as it is pushed up the ramp since the block is moving at constant speed. Therefore, from Equation 7-11, we have

$$\Delta K = 0 \quad \rightarrow \quad \sum_i \Delta U_i = \left(\left(F_{s,net} \right)_{non-conservative} \right)_{avg} \Delta s$$

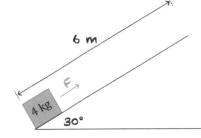

Figure 7.10: A block pushed up a ramp in Example 7-7.

In writing this equation, we have designated a 1-dimensional coordinate axis called the s-axis to be aligned parallel to the surface of the ramp with a positive direction pointing up the ramp[6]. Since the block's only potential energy is gravitational potential energy, this equation becomes

$$\Delta U_g = \left(\left(F_{s,net} \right)_{non-conservative} \right)_{avg} \Delta s \quad \rightarrow \quad mg\Delta y = \left(\left(F_{s,net} \right)_{non-conservative} \right)_{avg} \Delta s$$

The change in the height of the block (Δy) can be related to the change in the position of the block along the ramp (Δs) through trigonometry.

$$\Delta y = \Delta s \sin\left(30°\right) \quad \rightarrow \quad \Delta y = \frac{\Delta s}{2}$$

---

6   See Example 3-7 and Example 4-3.

$$mg\left(\frac{\Delta s}{2}\right) = \left(\left(F_{s,net}\right)_{non-conservative}\right)_{avg}\Delta s \quad \rightarrow \quad \left(\left(F_{s,net}\right)_{non-conservative}\right)_{avg} = \frac{mg}{2}$$

$$\left(\left(F_{s,net}\right)_{non-conservative}\right)_{avg} = \frac{\left(4\,kg\right)\left(9.8\frac{m}{s^2}\right)}{2} \quad \rightarrow \quad \left(\left(F_{s,net}\right)_{non-conservative}\right)_{avg} = 19.6\,N$$

7-7 Simple Machines

It is worth noting that the magnitude of the force required to push the block up the ramp in Example 7-7 is less than the magnitude of the force required to lift the block vertically. The latter can be calculated using Equation 7-11. If we assume that the block is lifted vertically at constant speed, then

$$mg\Delta y = \left(\left(F_{y,net}\right)_{non-conservative}\right)_{avg}\Delta y$$

In writing this equation, we have denoted the vertical direction as the y-axis with a positive direction pointing up from the surface of the Earth. Simplifying this equation gives us

$$\left(\left(F_{y,net}\right)_{non-conservative}\right)_{avg} = mg \quad \rightarrow \quad \left(\left(F_{y,net}\right)_{non-conservative}\right)_{avg} = \left(4\,kg\right)\left(9.8\frac{m}{s^2}\right)$$

$$\left(\left(F_{y,net}\right)_{non-conservative}\right)_{avg} = 39.2\,N$$

$$\left(\left(F_{s,net}\right)_{non-conservative}\right)_{avg} < \left(\left(F_{y,net}\right)_{non-conservative}\right)_{avg}$$

Since the change in the total energy of the block is the same regardless of the path taken by the block[7], we know that the work done by each of these two forces must be the same. Thus, the two forces must act over different displacements of the block.

$$\Delta s > \Delta y$$

---

7   The only energy that is changing is gravitational potential energy, and the change in gravitational potential energy is independent of path (see Section 7-4).

Of course, this result also follows directly from the trigonometric relationship between the s-axis and y-axis[8].

Hence, by requiring that the block be moved over a longer distance, the use of the ramp has decreased the magnitude of the net force required to push the block. The ramp is, therefore, a simple machine.

Simple machine: A device that enables the magnitude of a force necessary to do a certain amount of work to be reduced by increasing the displacement over which the force acts.

Example 7-8:

Problem: Consider the system shown in Figure 7.11 that consists of a 6 kg block being lifted at constant speed by a system of two pulleys.

The block is attached to a pulley by a rigid but massless rod. The two pulleys are connected to each other by a massless rope that moves over the pulleys without slipping. The pulleys are also massless and can be modeled as solid cylinders that rotate around an axis through their centers. What external pulling force (*i.e.*, what tension in the rope) is required to lift the block?

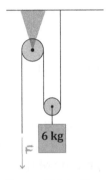

Figure 7.11: The simple machine in Example 7-8.

Solution: There is no change in the block's kinetic energy as it is raised since the block is moving at constant speed. Therefore, from Equation 7-11, we have

$$mg\Delta y_{block} = F\Delta y_F$$

In writing this equation, we have denoted the vertical direction as the y-axis, the displacement of the block as Δy_{block}, and the displacement of the rope as Δy_F. In other words, Δy_F is the length of rope that must be pulled for the change in the position of the block Δy_{block}. Since F and Δy_F are in the same direction it follows that $W_F > 0$. We see immediately from Figure 7.11 that

$$\Delta y_{block} = \frac{1}{2}\Delta y_F$$

Hence,

$$\left(\frac{1}{2}\Delta y_F\right) = F\Delta y_F \quad \rightarrow \quad F = \frac{mg}{2} \quad \rightarrow \quad F = \frac{\left(6\,kg\right)\left(9.8\frac{m}{s^2}\right)}{2}$$

$$F = 29.4\,N$$

---

8   See Example 3-7 and Example 4-3.

We can define the ***mechanical advantage*** of a simple machine as the "*amplification*" of the force obtained by increasing the distance over which the force acts.

> *Mechanical advantage: A measure of the force amplification obtained by using a tool, mechanical device, or machine.*

For the ramp in Example 7-7 and the system of pulleys in Example 7-8, the mechanical advantage is 2. In general, the mechanical advantage of a ramp is equal to the length of the ramp divided by the height of the ramp, and the mechanical advantage of a system of fixed and moving pulleys is equal to twice the number of moving pulleys[9].

Example 7-9:

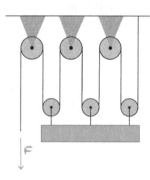

Problem: What is the mechanical advantage of the system of fixed and moving pulleys shown in Figure 7.12?

Solution: Since the system consists of three moving pulleys, the mechanical advantage of this simple machine will be 6. Thus, the magnitude of the external force required to the rope to lift the block in Figure 7.11 would be equal to 1/6 of the magnitude of the force of gravity acting on the block.

Figure 7.11: The simple machine in Example 7-9.

A screw is a simple machine that works as a modified ramp. Indeed, the thread of the screw can be considered to be a ramp that wraps around the shaft of the screw. It follows from the derivation of the mechanical advantage of ramp that the mechanical advantage of a screw would be equal to the ratio of the circumference of the screw to the pitch of the screw (see Figure 7.12).

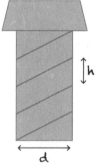

Figure 7.12: A screw with a diameter d and pitch h. The mechanical advantage of the screw is equal to $\frac{\pi d}{h}$.

---

9   This simple calculation assumes that the pulleys are massless and frictionless, and that any ropes are also massless.

7-8 Work, Kinetic Energy, Force, and Acceleration

Using Equation 7-10, we can now define an isolated system as a system upon which no non-conservative forces are acting. Since energy is conserved for isolated systems, we have

$$\frac{dE}{dx} = 0 \quad \rightarrow \quad \frac{d}{dx}\left(K + \sum_i U_i\right) = 0 \quad \rightarrow \quad \frac{dK}{dx} + \sum_i \frac{dU_i}{dx} = 0$$

$$ma_x - \sum_i F_{i,x} = 0 \quad \rightarrow \quad \sum_i F_{i,x} = ma \quad \rightarrow \quad F_{net,x} = ma$$

The sum of all of the conservative forces acting on an isolated system is equal to the product of the mass of the system and the system's acceleration.

Example 7-10:

Problem: An isolated system consists of a block with a mass of 4 kg that is released from rest a height of 5 m above the ground. What is the acceleration of the block as it falls to the ground?

Solution: Since this is an isolated system, the acceleration can be determined from the sum of the conservative forces acting on the system. In this case, the only force is the force of gravity. Let's denote the vertical direction for the acceleration and the force to be y-axis.

$$F_{net,y} = ma_y \quad \rightarrow \quad -mg = ma_y \quad \rightarrow \quad a_y = -g$$

This result is consistent with what we obtained in Section 4-3.

This relationship between the sum of the forces acting on a system and the acceleration of the system is one of Newton's laws of motion that we will discuss in Chapter 8.

Summary

- **A force is:** (i) a push or a pull; (ii) has an agent that does the pushing or pulling; (iii) acts on an object; (iv) is a vector; and (v) results either from the contact between objects or from a long-range interaction.

- **Net force:** The sum of all the forces acting on an object.
- **The work done by a force acting on an object is equal to the integral of the force with respect to the displacement of the object.**

$$W = \int F_x \, dx$$

- **Conservative forces are associated with potential energy functions.**

$$F_i = -\frac{dU_i}{dx}$$

The work done by a conservative force acting on an object is equal to the negative of the change in the associated potential energy of the object.

$$W_{conservative} = -\Delta U$$

Thus, the work done by a conservative force acting on an object is independent of the path of the object's displacement.

- **Non-conservative forces are not associated with potential energy functions.** The work done by a non-conservative force acting on an object depends upon the path of the object's displacement. The most common non-conservative forces are: external pushes and pulls; tension; the normal force; and friction.
- **The total potential energy of a system is a minimum when the system is at equilibrium.** Thus, no net force acts on as system when the system is at equilibrium.
- **The net work done on a system is equal to the change in the kinetic energy of the system.**

$$\Delta K = W_{net}$$

It follows from this equation that

$$\Delta K + \sum_i \Delta U_i = \left(W_{net} \right)_{non-conservative}$$

- **The change in kinetic energy of a system can also be described in terms of the average net force acting on the system.**

$$\Delta K = \left(F_{x,net} \right)_{avg} \Delta x$$

It follows from this equation that

$$\Delta K + \sum_i \Delta U_i = \left(\left(F_{x,net} \right)_{non-conservative} \right)_{avg} \Delta x$$

- **Simple machine:** A device that enables the magnitude of a force necessary to do a certain amount of work to be reduced by increasing the displacement over which the force acts.
- **Mechanical advantage:** A measure of the force amplification obtained by using a tool, mechanical device, or machine.

Problems

1. A block with a mass of 4 kg is sliding across a horizontal surface with an initial speed of 5 m/s. The presence of kinetic friction between the block and the surface results in a constant 4 N force acting on the block. How much work will be done by the force of kinetic friction on the block during the first 8 m travelled by the block?

2. A block with a mass of 4 kg is sliding across a horizontal surface with an initial speed of 5 m/s. Because of kinetic friction, the energy of this system will decrease linearly with the distance travelled by the block. What is the magnitude of the force of kinetic friction acting on the block if the block moves 4 m before coming to a stop?

3. Four identical blocks shown in the figure at right are released from the same height above the ground. The initial speed of each block is identical, but the directions of the velocities of the blocks are different. You can assume that each block is an isolated system. The force of gravity will do work on each block as the block moves from its initial position to the ground. For which block will this work be the largest?

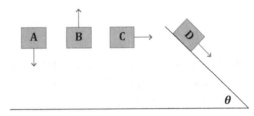

4. Four identical blocks shown in the figure at right are released from the same height above the ground. The initial speeds of block A and block B are identical, but the directions of the velocities of these blocks are different. Block C and block D are released from rest. You can assume that each block is an isolated system. The force of gravity will do work on each block as the block moves from its initial position to the ground. For which block will this work be the largest?

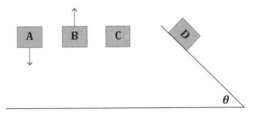

5. A block with a mass of 4 kg is thrown up in the air with an initial speed of 5 m/s. What is the work done by the force of gravity on the block between when it is thrown and when it reaches its maximum height above the ground? You can consider this to be an isolated system so that no energy is dissipated due to air resistance.

6. A 75 g toy rocket blasts off from the ground with a constant acceleration of 10 m/s^2 that persists for the first 3 s of the rocket's flight. Eventually, the rocket falls back down to the ground. What is the work done by the force of gravity on the rocket between blast-off and touchdown? You can consider this to be an isolated system so that no energy is dissipated due to air resistance.

7. A child is able to accelerate a 150 g snowball from rest to a speed of 20 m/s over a horizontal distance of 1.2 m. What is the magnitude of the average force exerted by this child?

8. A block with a mass of 4 kg is released from rest at the top of a 30° ramp, as shown in the figure at right. At the bottom of the ramp is a spring mounted parallel to the surface of the ramp with a spring constant of 49 J/m². As the block compresses the spring, energy will be dissipated at a rate of 6 J/m because of kinetic friction. What is the maximum compression of the spring?

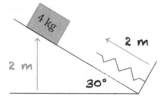

9. What is the mechanical advantage of the simple machine shown in the figure below?

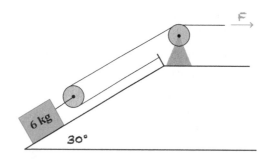

10. A 6 kg block is pulled up a 30° ramp at constant speed, as shown in the figure below. A constant 3 N kinetic friction force acts on the block as it slides up the ramp. What is the magnitude of the external pulling force (*i.e.*, what is the magnitude of the tension in the rope) required to pull the block up the ramp?

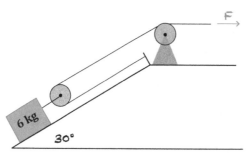

CHAPTER EIGHT
Newtonian Mechanics I

At the end of the Chapter 7, we derived an expression relating the net conservative force acting on an isolated system to the acceleration of that system. The more general relationship between the forces acting on a system and the acceleration of that system is the second of Sir Isaac Newton's three laws of classical mechanics. In this chapter, we will begin our discussion of these laws by demonstrating their use in solving 1-dimensional classical mechanics problems.

In Chapter 2, we introduced the concept of a coordinate system for describing the position, velocity, and acceleration of an object. We then employed similar coordinate systems for all subsequent mechanics calculations. This included the use of coordinate transformations (Section 2-6) to express 2-dimensional motion (blocks sliding on ramps, circular motion, *etc.*) as an equivalent 1-dimensional motion. We will, again, employ coordinate systems and transformations for mechanics calculations using forces, but we need to add an additional caveat to their use. Namely, that the straightforward application of Newton's laws requires that the coordinate system, referred to more generally as the *reference frame*, must not be accelerating. A reference frame that is not accelerating is referred to as an ***inertial reference frame***.

> *Inertial reference frame: A reference frame that is not accelerating. In other words, a reference frame that is at rest or moving at a constant velocity. Newton's laws are valid in only inertial reference frames.*

For example, a system of coordinate axes fixed within a train moving at constant velocity would be an inertial reference frame (Example 2-5), but a system fixed within an accelerating train would be a non-inertial reference frame. Since the Earth is moving around the sun and rotating around its axis, the direction of the velocity of the surface of the Earth is constantly changing. Therefore, the surface of the Earth is, technically, a non-inertial reference frame. However, we will assume (and will show in Chapter 11 and Chapter 14) that corrections to our calculations associated with the circular and rotational motion of the Earth are very small, and, thus, for all practical purposes, we can consider the surface of the Earth to be an inertial reference frame. As we will discover in Section 8-9, fictitious forces (*i.e.*, "*forces*" that do not satisfy the definition of a force in Section 7-3) appear to be acting when we describe the motion of an object using a non-inertial reference frame.

8-3 Newton's 1st Law

Newton's 1st law can be expressed as

An object that is at rest will remain at rest, or an object that is moving will continue to move in a straight line with constant speed if and only if the net force acting on the object is zero.

Newton's 1st law is the origin of the concept of inertia. That is, objects have an inherent tendency to maintain their current state of motion.

8-4 Newton's 2nd Law

Newton's 2nd law can be expressed as

The net force acting on an object is equal to the time rate of change of that object's linear momentum.

Linear momentum like energy is an intrinsic and extensive quantity that objects or collections of objects (*i.e.*, systems) possess. We can define linear momentum as the product of the mass and velocity of an object.

$$p = mv$$

We can, therefore, express Newton's 2nd law mathematically as

$$F_{net} = \frac{dp}{dt} \tag{8-1}$$

If the mass of the system is constant in time, then

$$F_{net} = \frac{d}{dt}(mv) \;\rightarrow\; F_{net} = m\frac{dv}{dt} \;\rightarrow\; F_{net} = ma \tag{8-2}$$

And, we see that we have obtained an expression similar to that derived in Section 7-8. However, Equation 8-2 is more general and can be applied to any system not just isolated systems. We will return to a discussion of linear momentum in Chapter 13, but, for now, we will consider only systems with constant mass and rely upon the simplified expression for Newton's 2nd law given in Equation 8-2.

Example 8-1:

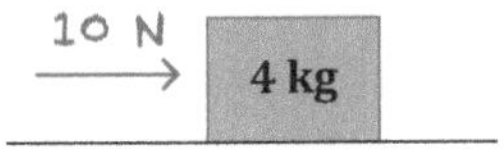

Problem: A block with a mass of 4 kg is at rest on a horizontal and frictionless surface. A constant 10 N force is then applied to the block, as shown Figure 8.1. What is the resulting acceleration of the block?

Figure 8.1: A block on a horizontal surface being pushed by a single horizontal force.

Solution: Since force and acceleration are both vectors, the first step in our solution must be to define the reference frame for our system. Let's define an x-axis to be parallel to the horizontal surface with the positive direction pointing in the same direction as that of the 10 N force, as shown in Figure 8.2.

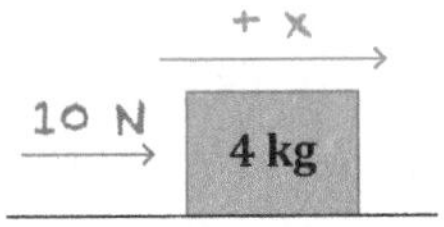

We can then use Newton's 2nd law to determine the acceleration resulting from the force acting on the block. Let's apply Equation 8-2 to the x-axis of the reference frame for the block while using a ($\pm$) sign to denote the direction of the forces. There is only one force acting along the x-axis (the 10 N force), so the component of the net force along the x-axis is equal to the magnitude of that force.

Figure 8.2: The direction for the reference frame (x-axis) in Example 8-1.

$$\left(F_{net}\right)_x = ma_x \quad \rightarrow \quad 10\text{N} = \left(4\,\text{kg}\right)a_x \quad \rightarrow \quad a_x = 2.5\frac{\text{m}}{\text{s}^2}$$

In this equation $\left(F_{net}\right)_x$, denotes the component of the net force acting along the x-axis. The component of the acceleration of the block along the x-axis is, thus, in the positive direction with a magnitude of 2.5 m/s².

Example 8-2:

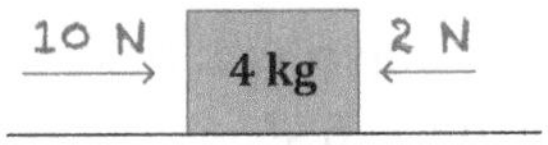

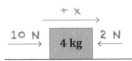

Figure 8.3: A block on a horizontal surface being pushed by a two horizontal forces.

Problem: A block with a mass of 4 kg is at rest on a horizontal and frictionless surface. Two constant forces with magnitudes of 10 N and 2 N, respectively, are then applied to the block, as shown in Figure 8.3. What is the resulting acceleration of the block?

Figure 8.4: The direction for the reference frame (x-axis) in Example 8-2.

Solution: As before, the first step in our solution must be to define the reference frame for our system. Let's define an x-axis to be parallel to the horizontal surface with the positive direction pointing in the same direction as the 10 N force, as shown in Figure 8.4.

We can then use Newton's 2nd law to determine the acceleration resulting from the forces acting on the block. Let's apply Equation 8-2 to the x-axis of the reference frame for the block using a ($\pm$) sign to denote the direction of the forces.

$$\left(F_{net}\right)_x = ma_x \quad \rightarrow \quad 10\,\text{N} - 2\,\text{N} = \left(4\,\text{kg}\right)a_x \quad \rightarrow \quad 8\,\text{N} = \left(4\,\text{kg}\right)a_x$$

$$a_x = 2\frac{\text{m}}{\text{s}^2}$$

The acceleration of the block is, thus, in the positive x-axis direction with a magnitude of 2 m/s^2. The magnitude of the acceleration of the block is smaller here than in Example 8-1 since, in this example, the net force acting on the block has a smaller magnitude.

From Newton's 2nd law, we recognize that *the direction of the net force that acts on an object is the same as the direction of the acceleration of the object.* Or, *the direction of the acceleration of an object is the same as the direction of the net force that acts on the object.* It also important to remember that Newton's 2nd law relates the direction of the net force to the direction of the acceleration not the velocity.

Example 8-3:

Problem: The net force acting on a 2 kg object is given by the following equation:

$$F_{net} = \left(5\frac{\text{N}}{\text{s}}\right)t$$

The object is at rest at $t = 0$ s. What is the change in the velocity of the object between $t = 0$ s and $t = 6$ s?

Solution: We can use Newton's 2nd law to determine the acceleration of the object from the net force acting on the object.

$$F_{net} = ma \quad \rightarrow \quad \left(5\frac{\text{N}}{\text{s}}\right)t = \left(2\,\text{kg}\right)a \quad \rightarrow \quad a = \left(2.5\frac{\text{m}}{\text{s}^3}\right)t$$

The change of the velocity of the object can then be determined using integration.

$$a = \frac{dv}{dt} \quad \rightarrow \quad a\,dt = dv \quad \rightarrow \quad \int a\,dt = \int dv \quad \rightarrow \quad \int a\,dt = \Delta v$$

$$\Delta v = \int_{0s}^{6s} \left(2.5\frac{m}{s^3}\right) t\,dt \quad \rightarrow \quad \Delta v = \left(2.5\frac{m}{s^3}\right) \int_{0s}^{6s} t\,dt \quad \rightarrow \quad \Delta v = \left(2.5\frac{m}{s^3}\right) \frac{t^2}{2}\Bigg|_{0s}^{6s}$$

$$\Delta v = \left(2.5\frac{m}{s^3}\right)\left(\frac{(6s)^2}{2} - \frac{(0s)^2}{2}\right) \quad \rightarrow \quad \Delta v = 45\frac{m}{s}$$

The change in the velocity is in the same direction of the net force acting on the object; specifically, it is in the positive direction.

8-5 Drawing Free Body Diagrams

Newton's laws are powerful and convenient tools for determining the effects of forces acting on systems. However, we require a systematic way of representing the forces acting on a system in order to apply these laws simply and efficiently. To accomplish this, we rely upon pictorial representations of the forces acting on a system known as *free body diagrams*.

Free body diagram: A pictorial representation of the forces that act on a system.

In a free body diagram, the system is represented as the origin of a reference frame (*i.e.*, as the origin of a set of coordinate axes), and the forces are represented by arrows pointing out from the origin. The direction of the arrow denotes the direction of the force. The magnitudes of the forces are represented by the associated variables.

Consider a system that consists of a block at rest on a horizontal surface. The two forces acting on this system are the force of gravity and the normal force. We will use the variables F_g and n to denote the magnitude of the force of gravity and the magnitude of the normal force, respectively. Let's choose the reference frame for this system to consist of a horizontal coordinate axis, called the x-axis, which is parallel to the horizontal surface and a vertical coordinate axis, called the y-axis, which is perpendicular to the x-axis.

The positive direction for the *y*-axis will point up from the horizontal surface. According to this reference frame, the free body diagram for this system is shown in Figure 8.5.

As shown in Figure 8.5, the normal force is pointing in the positive direction along the *y*-axis, and the force of gravity is pointing in the negative direction along the *y*-axis. Since there were no forces acting along the *x*-axis, there was no need to specify the positive direction for the *x*-axis.

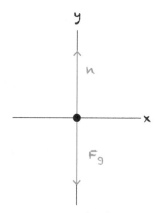

Figure 8.5: The free body diagram for a block at rest on a horizontal surface.

Example 8-4:

Problem: A block with a mass of 4 kg is at rest on a horizontal and frictionless surface. A constant 10 N external force is then applied to the block, as shown Figure 8.1, causing the block to slide. What is the free body diagram for this block?

Solution: Let's define the *x*-axis for the reference frame for this system to be horizontal and parallel to the surface on which the block is sliding. The positive direction of the *x*-axis will point in the same direction as the direction of the external 10 N force. The *y*-axis of the reference frame will be perpendicular to the *x*-axis with a positive direction pointing up from the horizontal surface. We will use the variable F to denote the magnitude of the external 10 N force, the variable n to denote the magnitude of the normal force, and the variable F_g to denote the magnitude of the force of gravity. With these definitions, the free body diagram for the block is shown in Figure 8.6.

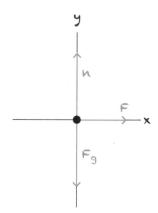

Figure 8.6: The free body diagram for the block in Figure 8.1.

It is important to emphasize that the only forces represented on a free body diagram are the forces that *act on the object* associated with the diagram. Forces for which the object is the agent do not appear on the object's free body diagram. For example, in Example 8-4, the force of the block pushing down on the horizontal surface does not appear in Figure 8.6. This force would appear in the free body diagram for the horizontal surface since the horizontal surface is the object of that force.

8-6 Using Free Body Diagrams

The net force acting along each of the coordinate axes in the reference frame for a system can be easily found from the free body diagram for that system. If the axes are perpendicular to each other (and we will always strive for this to be the case), we can then use Newton's 2nd law to determine independent kinematic equations for the motion of the system along these axes from these net forces. In this way, we have recast our original problem, which might involve forces acting in several directions simultaneously on the system, into a series of 1-dimensional kinematics problems.

In is important to remember that when drawing a free body diagram, we use the direction of the arrow to denote the direction of the associated force. Thus, when applying Newton's 2nd law to these diagrams, we then describe these directions using ($\pm$) signs. Since the variables in these diagrams and associated equations (*e.g.*, n, F_g, and F in Figure 8.6) denote the magnitude of forces, they are always positive scalars.

Example 8-5:

Problem: A block with a mass of 4 kg is at rest on a horizontal and frictionless surface. A constant 10 N external force is then applied to the block, as shown Figure 8.1. What is the acceleration of the block?

Solution: The free body diagram for the block is shown in Figure 8.6. The next step in the solution to this problem is to apply Newton's 2nd law to each of the coordinate axes in this free body diagram.

$$\left(F_{net}\right)_x = ma_x \;\rightarrow\; 10\,\text{N} = \left(4\,\text{kg}\right)a_x \;\rightarrow\; a_x = \frac{10\,\text{N}}{4\,\text{kg}} \;\rightarrow\; a_x = 2.5\frac{\text{m}}{\text{s}^2}$$

$$\left(F_{net}\right)_y = ma_y \;\rightarrow\; n - F_g = ma_y \;\rightarrow\; n - mg = ma_y$$

$$n = m\left(g + a_y\right) \;\rightarrow\; n = \left(4\,\text{kg}\right)\left(g + a_y\right)$$

Although we can immediately determine the acceleration along the *x*-axis, the equation obtained from applying Newton's 2nd law to the *y*-axis results in two unknowns: a_y and n. To proceed further in our solution, we must apply physical intuition. Since the surface is horizontal, the vertical position of the block will not change as the block slides across it. Because of this, we know that the vertical component of the acceleration of the block must be zero. Substitution of $a_y = 0$ into the equation above yields

$$a_y = 0 \;\rightarrow\; n = \left(4\,\text{kg}\right)g \;\rightarrow\; n = \left(4\,\text{kg}\right)\left(9.8\frac{\text{m}}{\text{s}^2}\right) \;\rightarrow\; n = 39.2\,\text{N}$$

We see from the solution to Example 8-5 that the normal force is different from the force of gravity in that its magnitude does not always have the same value but can vary depending upon the acceleration of the system. We will discuss this further in Section 8-9 when we talk about the apparent weight of objects.

8-7 Kinetic and Static Friction

In Section 3-6, we introduced friction as an interaction occurring when two surfaces move past each other. We divided this interaction between surfaces in Section 7-4 into kinetic and static friction, with kinetic friction defined as the force that opposes the continuing motion of an object. The magnitude of the force of kinetic friction depends upon the physical characteristics of the two surfaces that are in contact. For example, we anticipate that the magnitude of the force of kinetic friction will be larger between two rough surfaces than between two smooth surfaces. We can quantify this dependence using a dimensionless quantity known as the coefficient of kinetic friction, denoted as μ_k. The magnitude of the force of kinetic friction, denoted as f_k, can be expressed in terms of μ_k using Equation 8-3.

$$f_k = \mu_k n \tag{8-3}$$

The magnitude of the force of kinetic friction is, thus, directly proportional to the magnitude of the normal force (n).

Example 8-6:

Problem: A block with a mass of 4 kg is at rest on a horizontal surface. A constant 10 N external force is then applied to the block, as shown Figure 8.1. The coefficient of kinetic friction between the block and the surface is $\mu_k = 0.2$. What is the magnitude of the acceleration of the block?

Solution: Let's define the x-axis for the reference frame for this system to be horizontal and parallel to the surface on which the block is sliding. The positive direction of the x-axis will point in the same direction as the direction of the external 10 N force. The y-axis of the reference frame will be perpendicular to the x-axis with a positive direction pointing up from the horizontal surface. In the free body diagram for the block, we will denote the magnitude of the external 10 N force as F, the magnitude of the force of kinetic friction as f_k, the magnitude of the normal force as n, and the magnitude of the force of gravity as F_g. With these definitions, the free body diagram for the block is shown in Figure 8.7.

Applying Newton's 2nd law to each of the coordinate axes in this free body diagram yields the following equations:

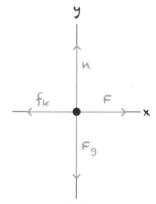

Figure 8.7: The free body diagram for the block in Example 8-6.

$$\left(F_{net}\right)_x = ma_x \;\;\rightarrow\;\; F - f_k = ma_x \;\;\rightarrow\;\; F - \mu_k n = ma_x$$

$$\left(F_{net}\right)_y = ma_y \;\;\rightarrow\;\; n - F_g = ma_y \;\;\rightarrow\;\; n - mg = ma_y$$

Since the block is being pushed across a horizontal surface, we know that the vertical position of the block will not change as the block slides. Because of this, the vertical component of the acceleration of the block must be zero. Substitution of $a_y = 0$ into the equation above yields

$$a_y = 0 \;\;\rightarrow\;\; n - mg = 0 \;\;\rightarrow\;\; n = mg$$

Hence,

$$F - \mu_k mg = ma_x \;\;\rightarrow\;\; a_x = \frac{F}{m} - \mu_k g$$

$$a_x = \frac{10\,\text{N}}{4\,\text{kg}} - \left(0.2\right)\left(9.8\,\frac{\text{m}}{\text{s}^2}\right) \;\;\rightarrow\;\; a_x = 0.54\,\frac{\text{m}}{\text{s}^2}$$

Comparison of this result to that obtained in Example 8-1 demonstrates that the presence of kinetic friction decreases the acceleration of the object. This is consistent with kinetic friction causing dissipation of energy from this system.

The work done by the external 10 N force and the work done by force of kinetic friction acting on the block in Example 8-6 can both be determined from the magnitude of these forces and the displacement of the block using Equation 7-6. Since the magnitudes of these forces are constant as the block slides, this work can be determined from the product of the force and object's displacement. The direction of the external 10 N force is the same as the direction of the displacement of the block, so the work done by this force must be positive.

$$W_F = F\Delta x \;\;\rightarrow\;\; W_F = \left(10\,\text{N}\right)\left(5\,\text{m}\right) \;\;\rightarrow\;\; W_F = 50\,\text{J}$$

The direction of the force of kinetic friction is opposite the direction of the displacement of the block, so the work done by this force must be negative.

$$W_{f_k} = -f_k \Delta x \quad \rightarrow \quad W_{f_k} = -mg\mu_k \Delta x$$

$$W_{f_k} = -(4\,\text{kg})\left(9.8\frac{\text{m}}{\text{s}^2}\right)(0.2)(5\,\text{m}) \quad \rightarrow \quad W_{f_k} = -39.2\,\text{J}$$

Neither the force of gravity nor the normal force do work on the block since there is no displacement of the block along the vertical direction. Thus, the net work done on the block is

$$W_{net} = W_F + W_{f_k} \quad \rightarrow \quad W_{net} = 50\,\text{J} - 39.2\,\text{J} \quad \rightarrow \quad W_{net} = 10.8\,\text{J}$$

We can then relate this net work done on the object to a change in the object's kinetic energy using Equation 7-8.

$$\Delta K = W_{net} \quad \rightarrow \quad \Delta K = 10.8\,\text{J}$$

This change in kinetic energy is consistent with the acceleration we calculated for the block. Indeed, since this acceleration is constant, we can use constant acceleration kinematics equations to relate the position, velocity, and acceleration of the block.

$$v_{f,x}^2 = v_{i,x}^2 + 2a_x \Delta x \quad \rightarrow \quad \frac{1}{2}mv_{f,x}^2 = \frac{1}{2}mv_{i,x}^2 + ma_x \Delta x$$

$$\frac{1}{2}mv_{f,x}^2 - \frac{1}{2}mv_{i,x}^2 = ma_x \Delta x \quad \rightarrow \quad \Delta K = ma_x \Delta x$$

$$\Delta K = (4\,\text{kg})\left(0.54\frac{\text{m}}{\text{s}^2}\right)(5\,\text{m}) \quad \rightarrow \quad \Delta K = 10.8\,\text{J}$$

Of course, we would expect that these two derivations would yield the same result since both are predicated upon the fact that the net force acting on the block (and, hence, the acceleration of the block) is constant[1].

The force of static friction opposes the start of motion and is always directed accordingly. The magnitude of the force of static friction also depends upon the physical characteristics of the two surfaces that are in contact. As with kinetic friction, we can quantify this dependence using a dimensionless quantity. This quantity is known as the coefficient of static friction and is denoted by μ_s. The magnitude of the force of static friction, f_s, can be expressed in terms of μ_s and the magnitude of the normal force (n) acting on the object using Equation 8-4:

---

1   Indeed, these two approaches are simply different ways of applying Newton's 2nd law to this system.

$$f_s \leq \mu_s n \qquad\qquad \textbf{(8-4)}$$

We see, immediately, that the magnitude of the force of static friction is defined by an inequality and, thus, differs from the definition for the magnitude of the force of kinetic friction (Equation 8-3). This inequality exists because static friction acts to oppose the start of motion, and, thus, its magnitude can change as necessary to balance the external forces that seek to cause motion.

Consider a person trying to push a heavy block that is initially at rest across a horizontal surface by applying a horizontally directed force. Let's define the x-axis for the reference frame of the block to be horizontal and parallel to the surface on which the block rests. The positive direction of the x-axis will point in the same direction as the direction of the applied force. The y-axis of the reference frame will be perpendicular to the x-axis with a positive direction pointing up from the horizontal surface. In the free body diagram for the block, we will denote the magnitude of the applied force as F, the magnitude of the force of static friction as f, the magnitude of the normal force as n, and the magnitude of the force of gravity as F_g. With these definitions, the free body diagram for the block is shown in Figure 8.8.

Applying Newton's 2nd law to each of the coordinate axes in this free body diagram yields the following equations:

$$\left(F_{net}\right)_x = ma_x \;\;\rightarrow\;\; F - f_s = ma_x$$

$$\left(F_{net}\right)_y = ma_y \;\;\rightarrow\;\; n - F_g = ma_y \;\;\rightarrow\;\; n - mg = ma_y$$

Let's consider the situation where the block remains at rest as the person pushes on it. In this case, the horizontal component of the acceleration of the block must be zero. The substitution of $a_x = 0$ into our equation above yields

$$a_x = 0 \;\;\rightarrow\;\; f_s = F$$

Thus, in order for the block to remain at rest, the magnitude of the force of static friction must always exactly equal the magnitude of the applied force. If the person pushes with a force of 1 N, then the magnitude of the force of static friction is equal to 1 N. If the person pushes with a force of 10 N, then the magnitude of the force of static friction is equal to 10 N. It is this required variability in the magnitude of the force of static friction that necessitates the use of the inequality in Equation 8-4.

Of course, since there is an upper limit to the magnitude of the force of static friction (Equation 8-4), if the person pushes with a force of sufficient magnitude, she can *overcome* the force of static friction, and the block will start to move. Naturally, when this happens and the block starts to move, it is, then, kinetic friction rather than static friction that acts on the block.

Example 8-7:

Problem: A block with a mass of 400 kg is at rest on a horizontal surface. The coefficient of static friction between the block and the surface is 0.6. What is maximum horizontal force that can be applied to the block without the block starting to move?

Solution: The free body diagram for the block is shown in Figure 8.8. Applying Newton's 2nd law to each of the coordinate axes in this free body diagram yields the following equations:

$$\left(F_{net}\right)_x = ma_x \quad \rightarrow \quad F - f_s = ma_x$$

$$\left(F_{net}\right)_y = ma_y \quad \rightarrow \quad n - F_g = ma_y \quad \rightarrow \quad n - mg = ma_y$$

When working with any force whose magnitude is defined by an inequality, it is always best to solve for the magnitude of that force and then substitute the inequality definition. Thus, the next step in our solution will be to algebraically solve for the magnitude of the force of static friction.

$$f_s = F - ma_x$$

$$f_s \le \mu_s n \quad \rightarrow \quad F - ma_x \le \mu_s n$$

For this problem, the block is initially at rest and will not start moving in either the horizontal or vertical direction. Therefore, both the horizontal and vertical components of the acceleration of the block must be zero. Substitution of $a_x = 0$ and $a_y = 0$ into the equations above gives us

$$a_x = 0 \quad \rightarrow \quad F \le \mu_s n$$

$$a_y = 0 \quad \rightarrow \quad n - mg = 0 \quad \rightarrow \quad n = mg$$

Combining these equations then yields

$$F \le \mu_s mg \quad \rightarrow \quad F \le \left(0.6\right)\left(400\text{kg}\right)\left(9.8\frac{\text{m}}{\text{s}^2}\right)$$

$$F \le 2352\text{N}$$

This equation provides the limit for F that is required for $a_x = 0$ and $a_y = 0$. In other words, it is the condition that is required for those assumptions about the acceleration of the block to be valid. We can determine the maximum value of applied force directly from this inequality.

$$F_{max} = 2352N$$

If the block is pushed with a horizontal force whose magnitude exceeds 2352 N, it will start to move.

8-8 Tension

Tension is the force that exists within taut ropes (and cables, strings, *etc.*). The direction of the tension force is parallel to the rope. Let's consider a system consisting of a block suspended from the ceiling by a single rope, as shown in Figure 8.9.

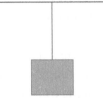

The two forces acting on the block are the force of gravity and the tension in the rope. The force of gravity is pulling the block down toward the surface of the Earth, and the tension is pulling the block up toward the ceiling. Let's

Figure 8.9: A block suspended from the ceiling by a single rope.

define the x-axis for the reference frame for this system to be horizontal and parallel to the ceiling. The positive direction of the x-axis will point to the right in Figure 8.9. The y-axis of the reference frame will be perpendicular to the x-axis and with a positive direction pointing up from the block toward the ceiling. In the free body diagram for the block, we will denote the magnitude of the tension in the rope as T and the magnitude of the force of gravity as F_g. With these definitions, the free body diagram for the block is shown in Figure 8.10.

Applying Newton's 2nd law to each of the coordinate axes in this free body diagram yields the following equations:

$$\left(F_{net}\right)_x = ma_x \;\rightarrow\; 0 = ma_x \;\rightarrow\; a_x = 0$$

$$\left(F_{net}\right)_y = ma_y \;\rightarrow\; T - F_g = ma_y \;\rightarrow\; T - mg = ma_y$$

We know from personal experience that an object suspended by a rope will not spontaneously move unless the rope breaks. Because of this, it is safe for us to assume that the vertical position of the block will not change and, hence, that the vertical component of the acceleration of the block must be zero. Substituting $a_y = 0$ into the equation above yields

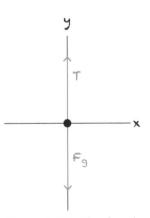

Figure 8.10: The free body diagram for the block in Figure 8.9.

$$a_y = 0 \;\rightarrow\; T - mg = 0 \;\rightarrow\; T = mg$$

The magnitude of the tension in the rope is, hence, equal to the magnitude of the force of gravity acting on the block.

Example 8-8:

Problem: A block with a mass of 4 kg is pulled across a horizontal surface at constant speed by a horizontally directed rope, as shown in Figure 8.11. The coefficient of kinetic friction between the block and the surface is $\mu_k = 0.2$. What is the tension in the rope?

Figure 8.11: A 4 kg block pulled across a horizontal surface by a rope in Example 8-8.

Solution: Let's define the x-axis for the reference frame for this system to be horizontal and parallel to the surface on which the block is sliding. The positive direction of the x-axis will point in the same direction as the direction of the tension (*i.e.*, the positive direction of the x-axis will be to the right in Figure 8.11). The y-axis of the reference frame will be perpendicular to the x-axis with positive direction pointing up from the horizontal surface. In the free body diagram for the block, we will denote the magnitude of the tension as T, the magnitude of the force of kinetic friction as f_k, the magnitude of the normal force as n, and the magnitude of the force of gravity as F_g. With these definitions, the free body diagram for the block is shown in Figure 8.12.

Applying Newton's 2nd law to each of the coordinate axes in this free body diagram yields the following equations:

$$\left(F_{net}\right)_x = ma_x \quad \rightarrow \quad T - f_k = ma_x \quad \rightarrow \quad T - \mu_k n = ma_x$$

$$\left(F_{net}\right)_y = ma_y \quad \rightarrow \quad n - F_g = ma_y \quad \rightarrow \quad n - mg = ma_y$$

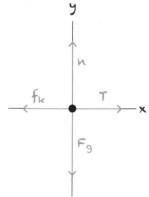

Figure 8.12: The free body diagram for the block in Example 8-8.

Since the vertical position of the block will not change as it is pulled across the horizontal surface, we know that the component of the block's acceleration along the y-axis will be zero. Furthermore, since the speed of the block is constant, we know that the component of the block's acceleration along the x-axis must also be zero. Substitution of $a_x = 0$ and $a_y = 0$ into the equations above yields

$$a_x = 0 \quad \rightarrow \quad T - \mu_k n = 0 \quad \rightarrow \quad T = \mu_k n$$

$$a_y = 0 \quad \rightarrow \quad n - mg = 0 \quad \rightarrow \quad n = mg$$

Combining these two equations gives us

$$T = \mu_k mg \quad \rightarrow \quad T = (0.2)(4\,\text{kg})\left(9.8\,\frac{\text{m}}{\text{s}^2}\right)$$

$$T = 7.84\,N$$

8-9 Weight, Apparent Weight, and Fictitious Forces

An object's weight is a scalar quantity, denoted by the variable w, and is defined to be the magnitude of the force of gravity acting on the object.

$$w = F_g$$

Thus, the weight of a 10 kg object on the surface of the Earth would be 98 N. Since the magnitude of g^2 varies from planet to planet or between planets and moons, so, too, does an object's weight vary. For example, an object weighs less on the Moon than on the Earth since $g_{Earth} < g_{Moon}$. Hence, although an object's mass is invariant, an object's weight may change.

Although few of us have travelled to other planets or moons, we are, nevertheless, accustomed to the sensation of changes in our weight. For example, when riding a roller coaster, we often experience moments when we feel heavier or lighter than normal. To account for these variations in our perception of weight, it is useful to introduce the concept of ***apparent weight***.

Apparent weight: The magnitude of the normal force that a surface exerts to support an object.

We will use the variable w_{app} to denote the apparent weight of an object.

---

2   See Section 3-3.

Example 8-9:

Problem: A 60 kg woman is riding in an elevator that is accelerating upwards at 3.2 m/s². What is the woman's apparent weight?

Solution: The weight of the woman is

$$w = mg \quad \rightarrow \quad w = \left(60 \text{kg}\right)\left(9.8\frac{\text{m}}{\text{s}^2}\right) \quad \rightarrow \quad w = 588\text{N}$$

To calculate her apparent weight, we must determine the magnitude of the normal force that the floor of the elevator exerts on her. We begin this calculation by drawing the free body diagram for the woman. In the reference frame for this free body diagram, we will define the vertical axis along which the woman is moving to be the y-axis and, further, specify that the positive direction for the y-axis points upwards from the surface of the Earth. We will define the x-axis for the reference frame of this free body diagram to be horizontal and parallel to the floor of the elevator. In this free body diagram, we will denote the magnitude of the normal force as n and the magnitude of the force of gravity as F_g. With these definitions, the free body diagram for the woman is shown in Figure 8.13.

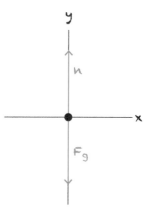

Figure 8.13: The free body diagram for a woman riding in an elevator.

Applying Newton's 2nd law to each of the coordinate axes in this free body diagram yields the following equations:

$$\left(F_{net}\right)_x = ma_x \quad \rightarrow \quad 0 = ma_x \quad \rightarrow \quad a_x = 0$$

$$\left(F_{net}\right)_y = ma_y \quad \rightarrow \quad n - F_g = ma_y \quad \rightarrow \quad n - mg = ma_y$$

Hence, the apparent weight of the woman is

$$w_{app} = n \quad \rightarrow \quad w_{app} = ma_y + mg \quad \rightarrow \quad w_{app} = m\left(a_y + g\right)$$

Since the woman is accelerating upwards, the component of her acceleration along the y-axis is positive. Thus,

$$a_y = 3.2\frac{\text{m}}{\text{s}^2} \quad \rightarrow \quad w_{app} = \left(60\text{kg}\right)\left(3.2\frac{\text{m}}{\text{s}^2} + 9.8\frac{\text{m}}{\text{s}^2}\right)$$

$$w_{app} = 780\text{N}$$

Since $w_{app} > w$, the woman will *feel heavier* as she accelerates upwards.

Example 8-10:

Problem: A 60 kg woman is riding in an elevator that is accelerating downwards at 9.8 m/s². What is the woman's apparent weight?

Solution: We can use the same free body diagram as in Example 8-9 (Figure 8.13). Hence, the apparent weight of the woman is, again,

$$w_{app} = m\left(a_y + g\right)$$

Since the woman is accelerating downwards, the component of her acceleration along the y-axis is negative. Thus,

$$a_y = -9.8\frac{m}{s^2} \quad \rightarrow \quad w_{app} = \left(60\,kg\right)\left(-9.8\frac{m}{s^2} + 9.8\frac{m}{s^2}\right)$$

$$w_{app} = 0\,N$$

Since $w_{app} < w$, the woman will *feel lighter* as the she accelerates downwards. In fact, since her apparent weight is zero, she is *weightless*.

Now, let's imagine that the woman riding in the accelerating elevator in Example 8-9 drops a block above the floor of the elevator and measures the motion of the block as it falls. Since the woman is inside the elevator, she would use a reference frame moving with the elevator for her measurements of the position, velocity, and acceleration of the block. What would she perceive for the acceleration of the block within this reference frame?

The acceleration of the block with respect to the elevator and the Earth can be written in terms of a coordinate transformation (Section 2-6).

$$a_{block,Earth} = a_{block,elevator} + a_{elevator,Earth}$$

The woman is measuring the motion of the block relative to the elevator. In this reference frame, the acceleration of the block is

$$a_{block,elevator} = a_{block,Earth} - a_{elevator,Earth}$$

Now, since the Earth is an inertial reference frame[3], we can use Newton's 2nd law to express $a_{block,Earth}$ in terms of the mass of the block and the magnitude of the net force acting on the block relative to the reference frame of the Earth. This net force is simply the magnitude of the force of gravity of the Earth on the block, which we will denote as F_g.

$$a_{block,elevator} = \frac{F_g}{m_{block}} - a_{elevator,Earth}$$

The equation for the net force acting on the block ($m_{block}a_{block,elevator}$) according to the woman (and her reference frame inside the elevator) is, therefore,

$$m_{block}a_{block,elevator} = F_g - m_{block}a_{elevator,Earth}$$

The second term on the right side of this expression ($m_{block}a_{elevator,Earth}$) is referred to as a **fictitious force**; although it has the units of a force, we cannot attribute any agent to it (Section 7-3).

Fictitious force: An apparent force acting on an object in a non-inertial reference frame.

Fictitious forces arise whenever we apply Newton's 2nd law within non-inertial reference frames, such as the accelerating elevator[4]. The acceleration of the elevator gives rise to an apparent force that both affects the acceleration of the block and makes the woman feel heavier or lighter depending upon the direction of the elevator's acceleration.

Similarly, let's consider what happens to you as you drive your car around a turn. You *feel* yourself being pushed toward the outside of the turn and interpret this sensation as resulting from the action of a force. However, no such force exists since we cannot attribute any agent to it (Section 7-3). Instead, what is happening is that you are continuing to move in a straight line in accordance with Newton's 1st law but as the car turns you "*collide*" with it. There is no force pushing you around inside the car, but rather the apparent force you feel is just a result of the fact that you are trying to apply Newton's laws within a non-inertial reference frame (*i.e.*, a reference frame fixed within the interior of the car, which is accelerating since the direction of its velocity is changing).

Indeed, someone standing by the side of the road watching you drive your car around the turn would perceive your motion differently; she would be describing everything from her point of view with respect to her inertial reference frame[5]. As you drive your car around the turn, she would see you continue to move in a straight line (in agreement with Newton's 1st law) only to hit the car turning "*beneath*" you. She does not need any fictitious force to explain why you end up pressed against the side of your car as you drive through the turn. Rather, she interprets your motion relative to the car as resulting from the fact that the car is accelerating and you are not.

---

3   A reasonable approximation for this situation (see Section 8-2).
4   Indeed, if $a_{elevator,Earth}$ = 0, there is no fictitious force.
5   Again, we will assume that the surface of the Earth can be treated as an inertial reference frame for this situation.

Lastly, let's consider the case of a weightless astronaut in orbit around the Earth. Since the astronaut is under the influence of a gravitational force from the Earth, there must be an additional fictitious force acting on her to make her weightless. Just as in the case of the weightless woman in the elevator (Example 8-10), the fictitious force acting on the astronaut arises because she is accelerating. Indeed, since the astronaut is moving around the Earth rather than in a straight line, we know that the direction of the astronaut's velocity is changing and, thus, that she is accelerating. Furthermore, based upon the solution to Example 8-10, we can conclude that astronauts in orbit around the Earth are weightless because they are accelerating downwards towards the Earth with an acceleration whose magnitude is exactly equal to the magnitude of the gravitational acceleration at their location. It is interesting to note, however, that since the astronauts stay in orbit, this *"downward"* acceleration is not causing a change in their position. We will resolve this conundrum in Chapter 11 when we discuss an additional acceleration that is associated with circular motion and the associated fictitious force.

Summary

- **Reference frame:** A system of coordinate axes used to describe the position, velocity, and acceleration of a system.
- **Inertial reference frame:** A reference frame that is not accelerating. Newton's laws are valid in inertial reference frames only.
- **Non-inertial reference frame:** A reference frame that is accelerating. Fictitious forces appear to act in non-inertial reference frames.
- **Newton's 1st law:** An object that is at rest will remain at rest, or an object that is moving will continue to move in a straight line with constant speed if and only if the net force acting on the object is zero.
- **Newton's 2nd law:** The net force acting on an object is equal to the time rate of change of that object's linear momentum.

$$F_{net} = \frac{dp}{dt}$$

For systems of constant mass, we can express Newton's 2nd law as

$$F_{net} = ma$$

- **Free body diagram:** A pictorial representation of the forces that act on a system.
- **Kinetic Friction:** The force of friction that opposes the continued motion of an object. The magnitude of the force of kinetic friction is determined from the coefficient of kinetic friction and the magnitude of the normal force

$$f_k = \mu_k n$$

The direction of the force of kinetic friction is always opposite the direction of the velocity.
- **Static Friction:** The force of friction that opposes the start of motion. The magnitude of the force of static friction is determined from the coefficient of static friction and the magnitude of the normal force

$$f_s \leq \mu_s n$$

The direction of the force of static friction is as required to prevent the start of motion.

- **Tension**: The force that exists within ropes (and cables, strings, *etc.*) when they are taut.
- **Weight**: The magnitude of the force of gravity acting on an object.
- **Apparent weight**: The magnitude of the normal force that a surface exerts to support an object.
- **Fictitious force**: An apparent force acting on an object in a non-inertial reference frame.

Problems

1. A 27 kg object is accelerating at a rate of 1.7 m/s². What is the magnitude of the net force that acts on the object?

2. A constant 10 N force pushes on a 2 kg block. If the block started at rest, how long would it take the block to move 10 m while being pushed by the force?

3. Draw the free body diagram for a skydiver in free-fall.

4. Draw the free body diagram for a woman waterskiing.

5. A 2 kg block moving along a horizontal surface at 4 m/s is subject to a force of kinetic friction with a coefficient of kinetic friction equal to 0.35. What distance will the block travel before coming to a stop?

6. A block with a mass of 4 kg is pulled across a horizontal surface at constant speed by a massless rope, as shown in the figure at right. The coefficient of kinetic friction between the block and the surface is $\mu_k = 0.2$. What is the tension in the rope?

7. A block with a mass of 4 kg is attached to a massless rope and is, initially, at rest on a horizontal surface, as shown in the figure at right. The coefficient of static friction between the block and the surface is 0.4. What is the maximum tension that can be exerted by the rope without the block starting to move?

8. After landing with an initial speed of 80 m/s, an airplane comes to a stop after moving 500 m down the runway under constant acceleration. What is the magnitude of the average net force that a 75 kg person riding on the airplane would experience as the airplane slows to a stop? You may assume that the runway is a horizontal surface.

9. A 78 kg man is riding in an elevator that is accelerating upwards at 1.8 m/s². What is his apparent weight?

10. A 60 kg woman is riding in an elevator that is accelerating downwards at 3.8 m/s². What is her apparent weight?

CHAPTER NINE
Newtonian Mechanics II

9-1 Introduction

Newton's laws provide the bridge between a description of the forces acting on a system and the associated kinematic description of the motion of the system. To take full advantage of the usefulness of this relationship between force and kinematics, we must include a description of force, position, velocity, and acceleration as vector quantities. The goal of this chapter is to accomplish this task by employing the vector notation presented in Appendix B to perform the vector mathematics inherent in Newton's 2nd law and in the associated kinematic calculations. For this reason, it is advisable to review the material presented in Appendix B and Appendix C before moving ahead with the material in this chapter.

9-2 Newton's 2nd Law

As discussed in Section 8-3, Newton's 2nd law defines the relationship between the net force acting on a system and that system's acceleration. In Equation 9-1, we now express that relationship for systems of constant mass using appropriate vector notation.

$$\vec{F}_{net} = m\vec{a}$$

(9-1)

Example 9-1:

Problem: The position of a 2 kg object is given by the following equation.

$$\vec{r}(t) = \left[\left(1\frac{m}{s^3}\right)t^3\right]\hat{x} + \left[\left(2\frac{m}{s^2}\right)t^2\right]\hat{y}$$

What is the net force that acts on this object?

Solution: We can determine the acceleration of the object using Equation C-1 and Equation C-3.

$$\vec{v} = \frac{d\vec{r}}{dt} \quad \rightarrow \quad \vec{v} = \left[\left(3\frac{m}{s^3}\right)t^2\right]\hat{x} + \left[\left(4\frac{m}{s^2}\right)t\right]\hat{y}$$

$$\vec{a} = \frac{d\vec{v}}{dt} \quad \rightarrow \quad \vec{a} = \left[\left(6\frac{m}{s^3}\right)t\right]\hat{x} + \left[4\frac{m}{s^2}\right]\hat{y}$$

The net force acting on the object is then found using Equation 9-1.

$$\vec{F}_{net} = m\vec{a} \quad \rightarrow \quad \vec{F}_{net} = \left(2\text{kg}\right)\left[\left[\left(6\frac{m}{s^3}\right)t\right]\hat{x} + \left[4\frac{m}{s^2}\right]\hat{y}\right]$$

$$\vec{F}_{net} = \left[\left(12\frac{N}{s}\right)t\right]\hat{x} + \left[8N\right]\hat{y}$$

Example 9-2:

Problem: Two perpendicularly aligned forces are acting on a 5 kg block, as shown in Figure 9.1. What is the magnitude of the resulting acceleration of the block?

Solution: Let's define a reference frame for this system consisting of perpendicular x and y axes that are parallel to 8 N and 6 N forces, respectively. Furthermore, let's define the positive direction for these axes to be the same as the direction of these forces, as shown in Figure 9.2.

Using this reference frame, we can express the net force acting on this block as

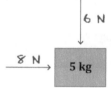

Figure 9.1: Two forces acting on a 5 kg block in Example 9-2.

$$\vec{F}_{net} = \left[8N\right]\hat{x} + \left[6N\right]\hat{y}$$

The acceleration of the block can then be determined using Equation 9-1.

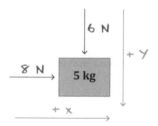

Figure 9.2: Definition of the reference frame for the system in Figure 9.1.

$$\vec{F}_{net} = m\vec{a} \quad \rightarrow \quad \left[8N\right]\hat{x} + \left[6N\right]\hat{y} = \left(5\text{kg}\right)\vec{a}$$

$$\vec{a} = \left[\frac{8}{5}\frac{m}{s^2}\right]\hat{x} + \left[\frac{6}{5}\frac{m}{s^2}\right]\hat{y}$$

The magnitude[1] of the acceleration is, thus,

$$a = \sqrt{\left(\frac{8}{5}\frac{m}{s^2}\right)^2 + \left(\frac{6}{5}\frac{m}{s^2}\right)^2} \rightarrow a = 2\frac{m}{s^2}$$

We also could have determined the magnitude of the acceleration from the magnitude of the net force.

$$F_{net} = \sqrt{(8N)^2 + (6N)^2} \rightarrow F_{net} = 10N$$

$$F_{net} = ma \rightarrow 10N = (5kg)a \rightarrow a = 2\frac{m}{s^2}$$

As discussed in Appendix B, vector arithmetic is greatly simplified by vector decomposition. We will, therefore, always decompose all forces into their components along the coordinate axes of the free body diagram before applying Newton's 2nd law to that free body diagram.

Example 9-3:

Problem: A block is suspended from the ceiling by two ropes, as shown in Figure 9.3. What is the magnitude of the tension in each rope?

Solution: Let's define a reference frame for this system in which the y-axis denotes the vertical axis with a positive direction pointing up from the ground. The x-axis of this reference frame will be perpendicular to the y-axis with a positive direction pointing to the right in Figure 9.3. In the free body diagram for the block, we will denote the magnitude of the tension in rope 1 as T_1, the magnitude of the tension in rope 2 as T_2, and the magnitude of the force of gravity as F_g. With these definitions, the free body diagram for the block is shown in Figure 9.4.

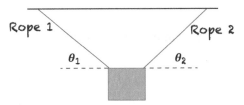

Figure 9.3: A block suspended from the ceiling by two ropes in Example 9-3.

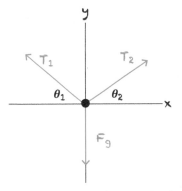

Figure 9.4: The free body diagram for the block in Figure 9.3.

---

1   See Section B-4.

In order to simplify our application of Newton's 2nd law to this free body diagram, we next decompose the two tension vectors into their components along the x and y axes of the reference frame. The free body diagram for the block after this decomposition is shown in Figure 9.5.

Applying Newton's 2nd law to each of the coordinate axes in this free body diagram yields the following equations[2]:

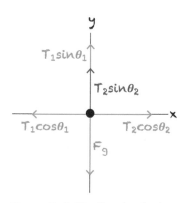

Figure 9.5: The free body diagram for the block in Figure 9.3: It was obtained by decomposing the tension vectors in Figure 9.4.

$$\left(F_{net}\right)_x = ma_x \;\; \rightarrow \;\; T_2\cos\theta_2 - T_1\cos\theta_1 = ma_x$$

$$\left(F_{net}\right)_y = ma_y \;\; \rightarrow \;\; T_1\sin\theta_1 + T_2\sin\theta_2 - F_g = ma_y$$

$$T_1\sin\theta_1 + T_2\sin\theta_2 - mg = ma_y$$

We can safely assume that the block will remain at rest and, thus, that the components of its acceleration along the x and y axes will both be zero. Substitution of $a_x = 0$ and $a_y = 0$ into the equations above yields

$$a_x = 0 \;\; \rightarrow \;\; T_2\cos\theta_2 = T_1\cos\theta_1$$

$$a_y = 0 \;\; \rightarrow \;\; T_1\sin\theta_1 + T_2\sin\theta_2 = mg$$

We can now algebraically solve for T_1 and T_2.

$$T_2 = T_1\frac{\cos\theta_1}{\cos\theta_2} \;\; \rightarrow \;\; T_1\sin\theta_1 + \left(T_1\frac{\cos\theta_1}{\cos\theta_2}\right)\sin\theta_2 = mg$$

$$T_1\left(\sin\theta_1 + \cos\theta_1\tan\theta_2\right) = mg \;\; \rightarrow \;\; T_1 = \frac{mg}{\sin\theta_1 + \cos\theta_1\tan\theta_2}$$

Similarly,

$$T_2 = \frac{mg}{\sin\theta_2 + \cos\theta_2\tan\theta_1}$$

---

2 Recall that we will denote the x-axis component of the net force as $(F_{net})_x$ and the y-axis component of the net force as $(F_{net})_y$.

9-3 Redrawing Free Body Diagrams

Although vector decomposition is an important step in the application of Newton's 2nd law to free body diagrams, it will be of limited effectiveness if the reference frames of these free body diagrams are not appropriate for the solution of the associated problems. The most useful reference frames for free body diagrams are those which have a coordinate axis aligned with the direction of motion of the system.

Whenever possible, free body diagrams should be constructed such that at least one of their axes corresponds to an axis along which the system is moving.

Let's consider a system that consists of a block being pulled across a horizontal and frictionless surface by a rope, as shown in Figure 9.6.

The direction of the block's displacement is parallel to the horizontal surface. Because of this, we should choose one of the coordinate axes in the reference frame for the block to be aligned with this direction. Let's define this to be the *x*-axis and, further, specify that the positive direction for the *x*-axis points to the right in Figure 9.6. We can then define the *y*-axis to be perpendicular to the *x*-axis with a positive direction pointing up from the horizontal surface. In the free body diagram for the block, we will denote the magnitude of the tension in the rope as T, the magnitude of the normal force as n, and the magnitude of the force of gravity as F_g. With these definitions, the free body diagram for the block is shown in Figure 9.7.

The next step in our solution is to simplify this free body diagram by decomposing the vector for the tension. The free body diagram for the block after this decomposition is shown in Figure 9.8.

Applying Newton's 2nd law to each of the coordinate axes in this free body diagram yields the following equations:

$$\left(F_{net}\right)_x = ma_x \quad \rightarrow \quad T\cos\theta = ma_x$$

$$\left(F_{net}\right)_y = ma_y \quad \rightarrow \quad n + T\sin\theta - F_g = ma_y \quad \rightarrow \quad n + T\sin\theta - mg = ma_y$$

Now, let's assume that as we pull the block along the horizontal surface, the tension in the rope is not sufficient to lift the block up off of the surface. In other words, let's assume that there is no displacement of the block along the *y*-axis in Figure 9.8 and,

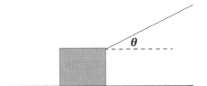

Figure 9.6: A block being pulled across a horizontal surface by a rope.

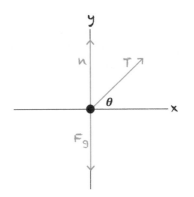

Figure 9.7: The free body diagram for the block in Figure 9.6.

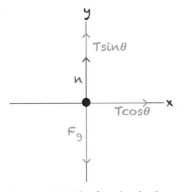

Figure 9.8: The free body diagram for the block in Figure 9.7.

therefore, that the component of the block's acceleration along the y-axis is zero. Substitution of $a_y = 0$ into the equation above yields

$$a_y = 0 \;\rightarrow\; n + T\sin\theta = mg \;\rightarrow\; n = mg - T\sin\theta$$

Since the magnitude of the normal force cannot be less than zero[3], there is a limit for the magnitude of the tension in the rope such that $a_y = 0$. In other words, there is an upper limit with how strongly we can pull on the rope without lifting the block off the surface.

$$n \geq 0 \;\rightarrow\; mg - T\sin\theta \geq 0 \;\rightarrow\; mg \geq T\sin\theta \;\rightarrow\; T \leq \frac{mg}{\sin\theta}$$

Let's examine the predictions of this equation under two extreme values of the angle θ[4]. First, let's consider the situation in which the rope is oriented parallel to the horizontal surface (*i.e.*, $\theta = 0°$).

$$\theta = 0° \;\rightarrow\; T \leq \frac{mg}{\sin\left(0°\right)} \;\rightarrow\; T \leq \infty$$

In other words, it is impossible to lift the block off of the horizontal surface in Figure 9.6 if the rope is aligned parallel to that surface. No matter how strongly we pull on the rope (up to infinite force), the block will never move in the vertical direction. This is consistent with our physical intuition. Next, let's consider the situation in which the rope is oriented perpendicular to the horizontal surface (*i.e.*, $\theta = 90°$).

$$\theta = 90° \;\rightarrow\; T \leq \frac{mg}{\sin\left(90°\right)} \;\rightarrow\; T \leq mg$$

We now see that there is an upper limit to the magnitude of the tension. This indicates that the block will not lift off the surface unless the magnitude of the tension force is greater than the magnitude of the force of gravity acting on the block. Again, this is consistent with our physical intuition.

It is possible, however, that our initial choice of reference frame may not be ideal for the final solution of the problem. In these situations, we must choose a new reference frame and redraw our free body diagram. Let's consider the system shown in Figure 9.9 that consists of a block sliding down a frictionless ramp.

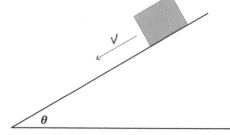

Figure 9.9: A block sliding down a ramp.

---

3   The magnitude of a vector cannot be less than zero (see Section B-4).
4   As mentioned earlier, whenever possible, always check your solution in a few limiting cases.

There are two forces acting on the block: the force of gravity and the normal force. In the reference frame for this system, let's denote the vertical axis as the *y*-axis with a positive direction for the *y*-axis pointing up from the surface of the Earth. The *x*-axis for the reference frame will be perpendicular to the *y*-axis with a positive direction for the *x*-axis pointing to the right in Figure 9.9. In the free body diagram for the block, we will denote the magnitude of the normal force as *n* and the magnitude of the force of gravity as F_g. With these definitions, the free body diagram for the block is shown in Figure 9.10.

As the block slides down the ramp, it will be moving along both the *x*-axis and *y*-axis of this reference frame. As shown in the solution to Example 4-3, this motion can be described most easily with respect to a coordinate axis that is parallel to the surface of the ramp rather than with respect to the reference frame in Figure 9.10. Thus, it would

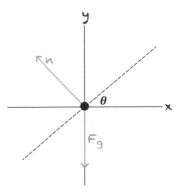

Figure 9.10: The free body diagram for the block in Figure 9.9. The surface of the ramp is indicated by the dashed line.

be best if one of the axes of the reference frame and associated free body diagram for the block were directed parallel to the surface of the ramp. To accomplish this, we can redraw our free body diagram with a new *x*-axis defined to be parallel to the surface of the ramp with a positive direction pointing up the surface of the ramp[5] and a new *y*-axis defined to be perpendicular to the surface of the ramp (*i.e.*, perpendicular to the new *x*-axis) with a positive direction pointing up

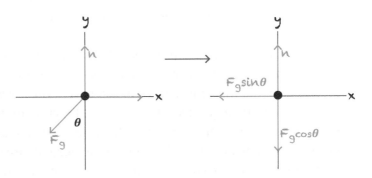

Figure 9.11: Free body diagram for the object in Figure 9.10. The force of gravity is, subsequently, decomposed into its *x*-axis and *y*-axis components.

from the surface of the ramp. This is the equivalent of rotating our original reference frame and associated free body diagram (Figure 9.10) clockwise through the angle θ (*i.e.*, the angle of the ramp). The redrawn free body diagram is shown in Figure 9.11.

In Figure 9.11, the force of gravity is further decomposed into its components along the *x* and *y* axes of the reference frame. Applying Newton's 2nd law to each of the coordinate axes in this free body diagram yields the following equations:

$$\left(F_{net}\right)_x = ma_x \;\rightarrow\; -F_g\sin\theta = ma_x \;\rightarrow\; -mg\sin\theta = ma_x$$

$$a_x = -g\sin\theta$$

$$\left(F_{net}\right)_y = ma_y \;\rightarrow\; n-F_g\cos\theta = ma_y \;\rightarrow\; n-mg\cos\theta = ma_y$$

---

5   This is the orientation of the *s*-axis in Example 4-3.

Since the object doesn't spontaneously lift off the ramp as it is sliding down, the component of the block's acceleration along the y-axis will be zero. Substitution of $a_y = 0$ into our equation above yields

$$a_y = 0 \quad \rightarrow \quad n - mg\cos\theta = 0 \quad \rightarrow \quad n = mg\cos\theta$$

It is worth noting that the magnitude of the component of the acceleration along the x-axis is identical to that which we determined in Example 4-3 using an energy-based approach to this problem.

Example 9-4:

Problem: A 4 kg block is sliding down a ramp, as shown in Figure 9.9. The angle of the ramp is $\theta = 30°$, and the coefficient of kinetic friction between the block and the surface is $\mu_k = 0.2$. What is the magnitude of the acceleration of the block?

Solution: In the reference frame for this system, let's denote the vertical direction as the y-axis with a positive direction for the y-axis pointing up from the surface of the Earth. The x-axis will be perpendicular to the y-axis with a positive direction for the x-axis pointing to the right in Figure 9.9. In the free body diagram for the block, we will denote the magnitude of the normal force as n, the magnitude of the force of kinetic friction as f_k, and the magnitude of the force of gravity as F_g. With these definitions, the free body diagram for the block is shown in Figure 9.12.

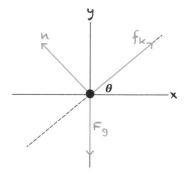

Figure 9.12: The free body diagram for the block in Example 9-4. The surface of the ramp is indicated by the dashed line.

However, as discussed earlier, since the block is sliding down the ramp, it would be best to use a reference frame in which one of the coordinate axes was directed parallel to the direction of the block's velocity (*i.e.*, parallel to the surface of the ramp). As before, we can obtain such a reference frame and corresponding free body diagram by rotating the free body diagram in Figure 9.12 clockwise through an angle θ. This new free body diagram is shown in Figure 9.13.

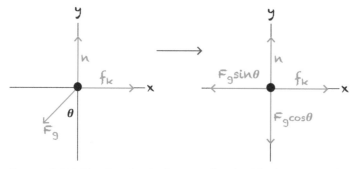

Figure 9.13: The free body diagram for the block in Example 9-4. The force of gravity is, subsequently, decomposed into its x-axis and y-axis components.

Applying Newton's 2nd law to each of the coordinate axes in this free body diagram yields the following equations:

$$\left(F_{net}\right)_x = ma_x \quad \rightarrow \quad -F_g\sin\theta + f_k = ma_x \quad \rightarrow \quad -mg\sin\theta + \mu_k n = ma_x$$

$$\left(F_{net}\right)_y = ma_y \quad \rightarrow \quad n - F_g\cos\theta = ma_y \quad \rightarrow \quad n - mg\cos\theta = ma_y$$

Since there is no displacement of block along the y-axis as it slides down the ramp, the component of the block's acceleration along the y-axis will be zero. Substitution of $a_y = 0$ into the equation above yields

$$a_y = 0 \quad \rightarrow \quad n = mg\cos\theta$$

We can then substitute this value for the magnitude of the normal force into the equation obtained from the net force acting along the x-axis.

$$-mg\sin\theta + \mu_k\left(mg\cos\theta\right) = ma_x \quad \rightarrow \quad a_x = \left(-\sin\theta + \mu_k\cos\theta\right)g$$

Substitution of the values of these variables for this system then yields

$$a_x = \left(-\sin\left(30°\right) + \left(0.2\right)\cos\left(30°\right)\right)\left(9.8\frac{m}{s^2}\right) \quad \rightarrow \quad a_x = -3.2\frac{m}{s^2}$$

The magnitude of the acceleration of the block has decreased since kinetic friction is dissipating energy from this system as the block slides down the ramp.

Example 9-5:

Problem: A 4 kg block is at rest on a flat board. The board is then slowly rotated upwards around one end until the block slips, as shown in Figure 9.14.

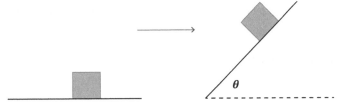

Figure 9.14: The system in Example 9-5.

At what angle θ will the block start to move if the coefficient of static friction between the block and the board is $\mu_s = 0.6$?

Solution: Based upon our solution to Example 9-4, let's define the x-axis of the reference frame for this system to be parallel to the board with a positive direction pointing up from the bottom of the board when the board is tilted. The y-axis of this reference frame will be perpendicular to the x-axis with a positive direction pointing up from the surface of the board. In the free body diagram for the block, we will denote the magnitude of the normal force as n, the magnitude of the force of static friction as f_s, and the magnitude of the force of gravity as F_g. With these definitions, the free body diagram for the block is shown in Figure 9.15.

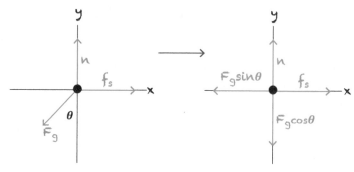

Figure 9.15: The free body diagram of the block in Example 9-5. The force of gravity is, subsequently, decomposed into its x-axis and y-axis components.

Applying Newton's 2nd law to each of the coordinate axes in this free body diagram yields the following equations:

$$\left(F_{net}\right)_x = ma_x \quad \rightarrow \quad -F_g \sin\theta + f_s = ma_x \quad \rightarrow \quad -mg\sin\theta + f_s = ma_x$$

$$\left(F_{net}\right)_y = ma_y \quad \rightarrow \quad n - F_g \cos\theta = ma_y \quad \rightarrow \quad n - mg\cos\theta = ma_y$$

As we are interested in the situation in which the block does not start to move, we can substitute $a_x = 0$ and $a_y = 0$ into the equations above.

$$a_x = 0 \quad \rightarrow \quad f_s = mg\sin\theta$$

$$a_y = 0 \quad \rightarrow \quad n = mg\cos\theta$$

Hence,

$$f_s \le \mu_s n \quad \rightarrow \quad mg\sin\theta \le \mu_s n \quad \rightarrow \quad mg\sin\theta \le \mu_s mg\cos\theta$$

Simplifying this equation gives us

$$\sin\theta \le \mu_s \cos\theta \quad \rightarrow \quad \tan\theta \le \mu_s$$

This is the condition such that the block does not slip (*i.e.*, this is the condition such that $a_x = 0$ and $a_y = 0$). When we substitute the value of μ_s for this system, we obtain

$$\tan\theta \leq 0.6 \;\rightarrow\; \theta \leq 31° \;\rightarrow\; \theta_{max} = 31°$$

Therefore, the block will start to slip once the angle θ in Figure 9.14 is larger than 31°. It is worth noting that this angle is independent of the mass of the object and the magnitude of the acceleration due to gravity.

Example 9-6:

Problem: A 4 kg block is being pulled across a horizontal surface by a rope, as shown in Figure 9.6. The coefficient of kinetic friction between the block and the horizontal surface is $\mu_k = 0.15$, and the angle between the rope and the horizontal is $\theta = 60°$. What is the magnitude of the tension if the block is moving at constant speed?

Solution: Let's define the x-axis of the reference frame for this system to be parallel to the horizontal surface along which the block moves with a positive direction pointing to the right in Figure 9.6. We can then define the y-axis to be perpendicular to the x-axis with a positive direction pointing up from the horizontal surface. In the free body diagram for the block, we will denote the magnitude of the tension in rope as T, the magnitude of the normal force as n, the magnitude of the force of kinetic friction as f_k, and

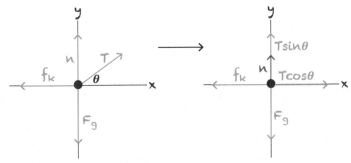

Figure 9.16: The free body diagram for the block in Example 9-6.

the magnitude of the force of gravity as F_g. With these definitions, the free body diagram for the block is shown in Figure 9.16.

Applying Newton's 2nd law to each of the coordinate axes in this free body diagram yields the following equations:

$$\left(F_{net}\right)_x = ma_x \;\rightarrow\; T\cos\theta - f_k = ma_x \;\rightarrow\; T\cos\theta - \mu_k n = ma_x$$

$$\left(F_{net}\right)_y = ma_y \;\rightarrow\; n + T\sin\theta - F_g = ma_y \;\rightarrow\; n + T\sin\theta - mg = ma_y$$

If the block is moving at constant speed, then the acceleration of the block must be zero. Substitution of $a_x = 0$ and $a_y = 0$ into the equations above yields

$$a_x = 0 \quad \rightarrow \quad T\cos\theta = \mu_k n$$

$$a_y = 0 \quad \rightarrow \quad n + T\sin\theta - mg = 0 \quad \rightarrow \quad n = mg - T\sin\theta$$

We can solve for the magnitude of the tension by combining these two equations.

$$T\cos\theta = \mu_k \left(mg - T\sin\theta \right) \quad \rightarrow \quad T\left(\cos\theta + \mu_k \sin\theta \right) = \mu_k mg$$

$$T = \frac{\mu_k mg}{\cos\theta + \mu_k \sin\theta} \quad \rightarrow \quad T = \frac{(0.15)(4\,\text{kg})\left(9.8\,\dfrac{\text{m}}{\text{s}^2} \right)}{\cos(60°) + (0.15)\sin(60°)}$$

$$T = 9.3N$$

It is worth noting that the magnitude of the normal force acting on the block is less than the magnitude of the force of gravity acting on the block since there is a component of the tension in the rope that pulls up on the block.

9-4 Work

In Section 7-5, we defined work in terms of an integral of a force acting over a displacement (Equation 7-6). In order to correctly include the vector nature of both the force and displacement, we need to rewrite Equation 7-6 as Equation 9-2.

$$W = \int \vec{F} \cdot d\vec{r}$$

(9-2)

In this equation, the differential vector $d\vec{r}$ is defined to be

$$d\vec{r} = \left(dx \right)\hat{x} + \left(dy \right)\hat{y}$$

Example 9-7:

Problem: What is the work done by the force $\vec{F} = (8\text{N})\hat{x} + (6\text{N})\hat{y}$ acting on an object moving from $\vec{r_i} = (1\text{m})\hat{x} + (2\text{m})\hat{y}$ to $\vec{r_f} = (3\text{m})\hat{x} + (5\text{m})\hat{y}$?

Solution: The work is found using Equation 9-2.

$$W = \int \left[(8\text{N})\hat{x} + (6\text{N})\hat{y} \right] \bullet \left[(dx)\hat{x} + (dy)\hat{y} \right]$$

$$W = \int (8\text{N})dx + (6\text{N})dy \quad \rightarrow \quad W = \int_{1\text{m}}^{3\text{m}} (8\text{N})dx + \int_{2\text{m}}^{5\text{m}} (6\text{N})dy$$

$$W = (8\text{N})(3\text{m} - 1\text{m}) + (6\text{N})(5\text{m} - 2\text{m}) \quad \rightarrow \quad W = 34\text{J}$$

As discussed previously in Section 7-5 and shown directly in Example 9-7, it is only the component of the force acting on an object that is parallel to a displacement of the object that does work[6]. Hence, we could also express Equation 9-2 in terms of this parallel component of the force.

$$W = \int F_{\parallel} dr$$

(9-3)

Let's revisit Example 9-4 in which a block is sliding down a ramp (Figure 9.9), and use Equation 7-8 to determine the magnitude of the block's acceleration. As shown in the free body diagram for the block (Figure 9.13), the three forces acting on the block are the force of gravity, the normal force, and the force of kinetic friction. Since the displacement of the block is along the x-axis, the net work done on the block consists of the work done by $(F_{net})_x$ during the displacement of the block.

$$W_{net} = \int (F_{net})_x \, dx \quad \rightarrow \quad W_{net} = \int_{x_i}^{x_f} \left[-mg\sin\theta + \mu_k (mg\cos\theta) \right] dx$$

Since $(F_{net})_x$ is constant, this integral becomes

$$W_{net} = \left[-mg\sin\theta + \mu_k (mg\cos\theta) \right] \int_{x_i}^{x_f} dx \quad \rightarrow \quad W_{net} = \left[-mg\sin\theta + \mu_k (mg\cos\theta) \right] \Delta x$$

---

6   This also follows directly from the dot product present in Equation 9-2 (see Section B-6)

Substitution into Equation 7-8 gives us

$$W_{net} = \Delta K \quad \rightarrow \quad \left[-mg\sin\theta + \mu_k \left(mg\cos\theta \right) \right] \Delta x = \frac{1}{2}mv_f^2 - \frac{1}{2}mv_i^2$$

Simplifying this equation then yields

$$v_f^2 = v_i^2 + 2\left[\left(-\sin\theta + \mu_k \cos\theta \right) g \right] \Delta x$$

Upon comparison with the constant acceleration kinematic equations[7] (Section 2-5), we see that the acceleration for the block is

$$a = \left(-\sin\theta + \mu_k \cos\theta \right) g$$

This result is identical to that obtained in Example 9-4. It is worth noting that although the *y*-axis forces in this example do no work on the block, they nevertheless contribute something to the motion of the object as it slides down the ramp. Specifically, they provide a constraint on the motion of the block such that it slides down the ramp rather than straight vertically down toward the ground.

The presence of the dot product in Equation 9-2 is also consistent with our previous statements that the work done by friction is always negative (Section 3-6 and Section 4-6). Regardless of the definition of the positive direction in the free body diagram of an object, the direction of the force of kinetic friction acting on an object will always be opposite the direction of the displacement of the object. Hence,

$$W_{f_k} = \int \vec{f}_k \cdot d\vec{r} \quad \rightarrow \quad W_{f_k} \int f_k \, dr \cos\left(180° \right)$$

$$W_{f_k} = -\int f_k \, dr \quad \rightarrow \quad W_{f_k} \leq 0$$

Finally, we can relate the average force associated with the displacement of an object to the change in the object's kinetic energy using Equation 9-4.

$$\Delta K = \left(\vec{F}_{net} \right)_{avg} \cdot \Delta \vec{r}$$

(9-4)

The derivation of Equation 9-4 follows directly from the derivation of Equation 7-9.

---

7   Since the kinetic energy of the block is linearly dependent upon its position, we know that the acceleration of the block is constant (Section 4-2). We could have also concluded this from the fact that the net force acting on the block is constant.

9-5 Power

The instantaneous power associated with the work done by a force acting on an object moving with an instantaneous velocity $\vec{v}$ is given by Equation 9-5.

$$P = \vec{F} \cdot \vec{v}$$

(9-5)

Example 9-8:

Problem: A 2 kg block is pulled across a horizontal and frictionless surface by a rope, as shown in Figure 9.6. The tension in the rope is 10 N, and the angle between the rope and the horizontal direction is $\theta = 30°$. What is the instantaneous power supplied by the tension force to the block when the block is moving at 2 m/s?

Solution: We can determine the instantaneous power using Equation 9-5.

$$P_T = \vec{T} \cdot \vec{v} \quad \rightarrow \quad P_T = Tv\cos\theta \quad \rightarrow \quad P_T = \left(10\text{N}\right)\left(2\frac{\text{m}}{\text{s}}\right)\cos\left(30°\right)$$

$$P_T = 17.3\text{W}$$

The power is positive since the tension force is supplying energy to the block.

The dot product in Equation 9-5 indicates that power is supplied to an object only by the components of the forces acting on an object that are oriented parallel or anti-parallel to the velocity of the object. This follows directly from the fact that only those components of the forces do work on an object[8] (Equation 9-2). Similarly, if the work done by a force is positive, then the power supplied by that force is also positive, and if the work done by a force is negative, then the power supplied by that force is also negative.

Example 9-9:

Problem: A 3 kg block is sliding across a horizontal surface. The coefficient of kinetic friction between the block and the surface is $\mu_k = 0.2$. What is the instantaneous power supplied by the force of kinetic friction to the block when the speed of the block is 4 m/s?

---

8   An object's displacement and velocity have the same direction.

Solution: Let's define the *x*-axis of the reference frame for this system to be parallel to the horizontal surface along which the block slides. The positive direction of the *x*-axis will be oriented with the direction of the velocity of the block. We will define the *y*-axis to be perpendicular to the *x*-axis with a positive direction pointing up from the horizontal surface. In the free body diagram for the block, we will denote the magnitude of the normal force as *n*, the magnitude of the force of kinetic friction as f_k, and the magnitude of the force of gravity as F_g. With these definitions, the free body diagram for the block is shown in Figure 9.17.

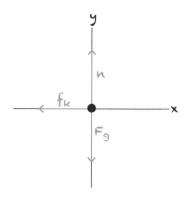

Figure 9.17: The free body diagram for the block in Example 9-9.

Applying Newton's 2nd law to each of the coordinate axes in this free body diagram yields the following equations:

$$\left(F_{net} \right)_x = ma_x \;\; \rightarrow \;\; -f_k = ma_x \;\; \rightarrow \;\; -\mu_k n = ma_x$$

$$\left(F_{net} \right)_y = ma_y \;\; \rightarrow \;\; n - F_g = ma_y \;\; \rightarrow \;\; n - mg = ma_y$$

Since the block is sliding across a horizontal surface, we know that the vertical position of the block will not change as the block slides. Because of this, the vertical component of the acceleration of the block must be zero. Substitution of $a_y = 0$ into the equation above yields

$$a_y = 0 \;\; \rightarrow \;\; n = mg$$

Therefore, the instantaneous power supplied by the force of kinetic friction acting on the block would be

$$P_{f_k} = \vec{f}_k \bullet \vec{v} \;\; \rightarrow \;\; P_{f_k} = f_k v \cos\left(180° \right) \;\; \rightarrow \;\; P_{f_k} = -f_k v$$

$$P_{f_k} = -\mu_k n v \;\; \rightarrow \;\; P_{f_k} = -\mu_k mg v$$

Substitution of the values for our system gives us

$$P_{f_k} = -\left(0.2 \right)\left(3\text{kg} \right)\left(9.8 \frac{\text{m}}{\text{s}^2} \right)\left(4 \frac{\text{m}}{\text{s}} \right)$$

$$P_{f_k} = -23.52\text{W}$$

We see from the solution to Example 9-9 that the power supplied by the force of kinetic friction is negative since this force dissipates energy from the system. The general relationship between power and work can be determined from the definition of the velocity (Equation C-1)

$$\vec{v} = \frac{d\vec{r}}{dt} \quad \rightarrow \quad P = \vec{F} \cdot \frac{d\vec{r}}{dt} \quad \rightarrow \quad Pdt = \vec{F} \cdot d\vec{r} \quad \rightarrow \quad \int Pdt = \int \vec{F} \cdot d\vec{r}$$

$$\int Pdt = W$$

(9-6)

Example 9-10:

Problem: A 4 kg block is pushed across a frictionless horizontal surface by a horizontally oriented force whose magnitude varies in time. The instantaneous power supplied by the pushing force to the block is

$$P_{push}(t) = \left(5\frac{W}{s} \right) t$$

If the block starts from rest at $t = 0$ s, what is the speed of the block at $t = 5$ s?

Solution: The three forces acting on the block are the normal force, the force of gravity, and the external pushing force. Since the displacement of the block is along the horizontal surface, there will be no work done on the block by the normal force or the force of gravity. Thus, the net work done on the block is the work done by the external pushing force. Combining Equation 7-8 and Equation 9-6 gives us

$$W_{net} = W_{push} \quad \rightarrow \quad \Delta K = W_{push} \quad \rightarrow \quad \Delta K = \int P_{push}\, dt$$

Substitution of the values for our system gives us

$$\frac{1}{2}mv_{5s}^2 - \frac{1}{2}mv_{0s}^2 = \int_{0s}^{5s} P_{push}(t)dt \quad \rightarrow \quad \frac{1}{2}(4\,kg)v_{5s}^2 - \frac{1}{2}(4\,kg)\left(0\frac{m}{s}\right)^2 = \left(5\frac{W}{s}\right)\int_{0s}^{5s} tdt$$

$$(2\,kg)v_{5s}^2 = \left(5\frac{W}{s}\right)\frac{t^2}{2}\Big|_{0s}^{5s} \quad \rightarrow \quad (2\,kg)v_{5s}^2 = \left(5\frac{W}{s}\right)\left(\frac{(5s)^2}{2} - \frac{(0s)^2}{2}\right)$$

$$(2\,kg)v_{5s}^2 = 62.5\,Ws \quad \rightarrow \quad v_{5s}^2 = 31.25\frac{m^2}{s^2} \quad \rightarrow \quad v_{5s} = 5.6\frac{m}{s}$$

Equation 9-6 is, of course, just another way of writing Equation 4-2. We can, therefore, also write Equation 4-1 as Equation 9-7.

$$P_{avg} \Delta t = W$$

(9-7)

9-6 General Problem-Solving Strategy

Based upon the solutions to the problems presented in this chapter, and those in the preceding two chapters, we have developed the following general strategy for using Newton's 2nd law to solve kinematics problems.

Step 1: **Specify the reference frame for the system.**

Step 2: **Identify the forces that act on the system.**

Step 3: **Draw the free body diagram for the system.** All of the identified forces in Step 2 should be included with their correct orientation within the reference frame of the system.

Step 4: **If necessary, redraw the free body diagram.** Whenever possible, free body diagrams should be constructed such that at least one of their coordinate axes corresponds to an axis along which the system is moving. If the original reference frame does not satisfy this goal, a new reference frame that does satisfy this goal should be defined. The free body diagram for the system can then be redrawn using the new reference frame.

Step 5: **Decompose all vectors into their components along the coordinate axes of the free body diagram.**

Step 6: **Apply Newton's 2nd law to each of the coordinate axes of the free body diagram.** This will generate a single algebraic equation for each coordinate axis. A ($\pm$) sign can be used to denote the direction of the forces with respect to the coordinate axes.

Step 7: **Use algebra to relate the magnitudes of the forces to each other or to the acceleration of the object.**

Summary

- **Newton's 2nd law:** The net force acting on an object with constant mass is equal to the product of the object's mass and acceleration.

$$\vec{F}_{net} = m\vec{a}$$

- **Whenever possible, free body diagrams should be constructed such that at least one of their axes corresponds to an axis along which the system is moving.**

- **The work done by a force acting on an object is the integral of the dot product of the force with the object's displacement.**

$$W = \int \vec{F} \cdot d\vec{r}$$

The differential displacement in this equation is

$$d\vec{r} = \left(dx\right)\hat{x} + \left(dy\right)\hat{y}$$

- **The instantaneous power supplied by a force acting on an object is equal to the dot product of the force and the velocity of the object.**

$$P = \vec{F} \cdot \vec{v}$$

- **The work done by a force acting on an object is also equal to the integral of the instantaneous power supplied by the force with respect to time.**

$$\int P\,dt = W$$

This equation can also be written in terms of the average power supplied by the force.

$$P_{avg}\,\Delta t = W$$

Problems

1. The position of a 6 kg object is given by the following equation:

$$\vec{r}\left(t\right) = \left[\left(2\frac{m}{s^3}\right)t^3\right]\hat{x} + \left[\left(4\frac{m}{s^2}\right)t^2\right]\hat{y}$$

What is the magnitude of the net force acting on this object at $t = 2$ s?

2. The following net force acts on a 5 kg object:

$$\vec{F}\left(t\right) = \left[\left(3\frac{N}{s}\right)t\right]\hat{x} + \left[\left(2\frac{N}{s^2}\right)t^2\right]\hat{y}$$

What is the magnitude of the acceleration of the object at $t = 2$ s?

3. A 500 g object moving along the x-axis experiences a force given by the following equation:

$$\vec{F} = \left[10N - \left(2\frac{N}{m} \right) x \right] \hat{x}$$ where x is the position of the object along the x-axis and is measured

in meters. The object's velocity at x = 0 m is 24 m/s. What is the object's velocity at x = 5 m?

4. A 2 kg object is subject to the following force: $\vec{F} = \left[\left(6\frac{N}{m} \right) x \right] \hat{x}$ where x is the position of the object

along the x-axis and is measured in meters. The object moves from the origin to $\vec{r} = (2m)\hat{x} + (3m)\hat{y}$.

The object's velocity at the origin is $\vec{v} = \left(4\frac{m}{s} \right)\hat{x} + \left(3\frac{m}{s} \right)\hat{y}$. What is the magnitude of object's

velocity at $\vec{r} = (2m)\hat{x} + (3m)\hat{y}$?

5. A 4 kg block is pushed across a horizontal surface by an external force, as shown in the figure at right. What is the acceleration of the block if the coefficient of kinetic friction between the surface and the block is μ_k = 0.2, the magnitude of the force is 20N, and θ = 30°? What coefficient of kinetic friction would be required for the block to move at constant speed if the magnitude of the force is 20N and θ = 30°?

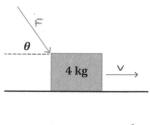

6. A 10 kg block is pulled across a horizontal surface by a rope, as shown in the figure at right. What is the work done by the tension in the rope if θ = 60°, and the block is dragged 10 m at constant velocity? The coefficient of kinetic friction between the block and the surface is 0.2, and you may assume that the magnitude of the tension is constant as the block is pulled.

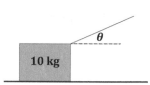

7. A 10 kg block is pulled across a horizontal surface by a rope, as shown in the figure at right. The tension in the rope is constant and equal to 40 N. What is the instantaneous power supplied by the tension in the rope to the block when the block is 5 m away from its starting point? The coefficient of kinetic friction between the block and the surface is 0.2, and you may assume that the block started at rest.

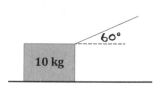

8. A 6 kg block is suspended with two ropes, as shown in the figure at right. What is the tension in each rope if θ = 30°? What is the tension in each rope if θ = 45°?

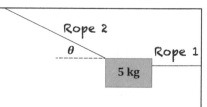

9. A 4 kg block is sliding down a vertical wall while being pushed by an external force, as shown in the figure at right. What is the acceleration of the block if the coefficient of kinetic friction between the wall and the block is $\mu_k = 0.2$, and the magnitude of the force is 20 N? What coefficient of kinetic friction would be required for the block to move down the wall at constant speed if the magnitude of the external force is 100 N? What magnitude of the external force would be required for the block to move down the wall at constant speed if the coefficient of kinetic friction between the wall and the block is $\mu_k = 0.2$?

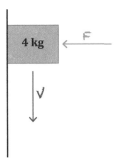

10. A 4 kg block is sliding down a vertical wall while being pushed by an external force, as shown in the figure at right. What is the acceleration of the block if the coefficient of kinetic friction between the wall and the block is $\mu_k = 0.2$, and the magnitude of the force is 20 N? What coefficient of kinetic friction would be required for the block to move down the wall at constant speed if the magnitude of the external force is 30 N? What magnitude of the external force would be required for the block to move down the wall at constant speed if the coefficient of kinetic friction between the wall and the block is $\mu_k = 0.2$?

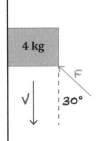

11. An 8 kg block is sliding down a 30° ramp while being pushed by an external force, as shown in the figure at right. The coefficient of kinetic friction between the block and the ramp is $\mu_k = 0.3$. What is the magnitude of the acceleration of the block if the magnitude of the pushing force is 15 N and $\theta = 50°$?

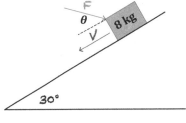

12. An 8 kg block is sliding down a 30° ramp while being pushed by an external force, as shown in the figure at right. The coefficient of kinetic friction between the block and the ramp is $\mu_k = 0.3$, and the block is moving at constant speed. What is the power supplied by the external force if $\theta = 40°$ and the block is moving at a constant speed of 0.3 m/s?

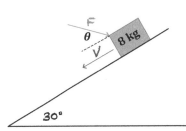

13. A 6 kg block is pushed across a frictionless horizontal surface by a horizontally oriented force whose magnitude varies in time. The instantaneous power supplied by the pushing force to the block is

$$P_{push}(t) = \left(5\frac{W}{s^2}\right)t^2$$

If the block starts from rest at $t = 0$ s, what is the speed of the block at $t = 6$ s? What is magnitude of the average acceleration of the block over this time interval?

CHAPTER TEN
Torque and Rotational Motion

I n addition to causing translational motion, the application of forces can also make objects rotate or twist. In this chapter, we will introduce another form of Newton's 2nd law that describes this relationship between force and rotation. We will first use this new version of Newton's 2nd law to describe the motion of several rotating systems, including those in which both translational motion and rotational motion occur simultaneously. We will then use this form of Newton's 2nd law in Chapter 11 to determine the static equilibrium conditions necessary for a stationary system.

10-2 Center of Mass

Let's consider a system consisting of two small objects, A and B, connected by a rigid but massless rod and separated by a distance L. This system is rotating with constant angular velocity around an axis that is oriented perpendicular to the plane of the system, as shown in Figure 10.1. For which axis of rotation will the rotational kinetic energy be the smallest? We can assume that both objects can be treated as point particles.

The rotational kinetic energy of the system can be determined using Equation 5-6. The first step in applying this equation to this problem is to determine the moment of inertia corresponding to an arbitrary axis location. According to Equation 5-7, the moment of inertia for this collection of point particles is

$$I = m_A r_A^2 + m_B r_B^2$$

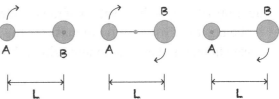

Figure 10.1: A system consisting of two small objects connected by a rigid massless rod. The objects are shown rotating around three possible axes (red circles) that are oriented perpendicular to the longitudinal axis of the system.

The variables r_A and r_B denote the distance between the masses and the axis of rotation and are related by the separation distance L. Hence,

$$I = m_A r_A^2 + m_B \left(L - r_A\right)^2$$

As the axis of rotation is moved, the values of r_A and r_B change, and the moment of inertia changes. According to Equation 5-6, the minimum rotational kinetic energy occurs when the moment of inertia is a minimum. We can determine this minimum through differentiation.

$$\frac{dI}{dr_A} = 0 \quad \rightarrow \quad 2m_A r_A + 2m_B \left(L - r_A\right)\left(-1\right) = 0 \quad \rightarrow \quad m_A r_A = m_B \left(L - r_A\right)$$

$$\left(m_A + m_B\right) r_A = m_B L \quad \rightarrow \quad r_A = \frac{m_B L}{m_A + m_B}$$

This position for the axis of rotation corresponding to the minimum moment of inertia of the system is referred to as the **center of mass** of the system.

Center of mass: The mass-weighted center of a system[1]. The smallest moment of inertia for rotations of a system occurs for rotations around its center of mass. A freely-rotating object will always rotate around its center of mass.

The center of mass for a system of point particles can be determined using Equation 10-1.

$$\vec{r}_{CM} = \frac{m_1 \vec{r}_1 + m_2 \vec{r}_2 + \ldots m_n \vec{r}_n}{m_1 + m_2 + \ldots m_n} = \frac{\sum_{i=1}^{n} m_i \vec{r}_i}{\sum_{i=1}^{n} m_i} \tag{10-1}$$

In Equation 10-1, $\vec{r}_i$ is the position of the ith point particle, m_i is the mass of the ith point particle, and $\vec{r}_{CM}$ is the position of the center of mass for the system. The vector $\vec{r}_{CM}$ in Equation 10-1 can also be expressed in terms of its components along the axes of an associated reference frame. For example,

$$x_{CM} = \frac{m_1 x_1 + m_2 x_2 + \ldots m_n x_n}{m_1 + m_2 + \ldots m_n} = \frac{\sum_{i=1}^{n} m_i x_i}{\sum_{i=1}^{n} m_i} \qquad y_{CM} = \frac{m_1 y_1 + m_2 y_2 + \ldots m_n y_n}{m_1 + m_2 + \ldots m_n} = \frac{\sum_{i=1}^{n} m_i y_i}{\sum_{i=1}^{n} m_i}$$

---

1   See Appendix D for a discussion of the statistical analogies for center of mass and moment of inertia.

In this equation, x_i and y_i are the x-axis and y-axis components, respectively, of the position of the ith particle in the system. For a system consisting of a continuous distribution of mass, the center of mass is found using Equation 10-2.

$$\vec{r}_{CM} = \frac{\int \vec{r}\, dm}{\int dm} \qquad (10\text{-}2)$$

When determining the center of mass for a system consisting of a continuous distribution of mass, we can also frequently apply arguments based on the symmetry of the system to simplify our calculations.

The center of mass of any symmetrical system of uniform mass density is at the physical (i.e., geometric) center of the system.

Example 10-1:

Problem: Where is the center of mass of the system of three objects shown in Figure 10.2? The objects are small enough to be treated as point particles.

Solution: Let's define the origin of the reference frame for this system to be located at the 2 kg object. Furthermore, let's define an x-axis for this reference frame to be parallel to the line connecting all three objects with a positive direction pointing from the 2 kg object toward the 6 kg object. Using Equation 10-1, the center of mass of our system is

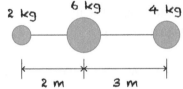

Figure 10.2: The system of three objects in Example 10-1.

$$x_{CM} = \frac{(2\,\text{kg})(0\,\text{m}) + (6\,\text{kg})(2\,\text{m}) + (4\,\text{kg})(2\,\text{m}+3\,\text{m})}{2\,\text{kg} + 6\,\text{kg} + 4\,\text{kg}}$$

$$x_{CM} = 2.67\,\text{m}$$

The center of mass of the system is 2.67 m away from the 2 kg object in the direction of the 6 kg object. We would determine the same location had we chosen a different origin for our reference frame. For example, let's define the origin of the x-axis to be located at the 6 kg object with the positive direction pointing toward the 4 kg object. According to this reference frame, the position of the center of mass is

$$x_{CM} = \frac{(2\,\text{kg})(-2\,\text{m}) + (6\,\text{kg})(0\,\text{m}) + (4\,\text{kg})(3\,\text{m})}{2\,\text{kg} + 6\,\text{kg} + 4\,\text{kg}}$$

Note that the position of the 2 kg object is in the negative direction of this reference frame. Solving this equation for the center of mass yields

$$X_{CM} = 0.67\,\text{m}$$

The center of mass of the system is 0.67 m away from the 6 kg object in the direction of the 4 kg object. Since 6 kg and 2 kg objects are separated by a distance of 2 m, this location of the center of mass is identical to that determined previously using a reference frame with an origin at the 2 kg object (Figure 10.3).

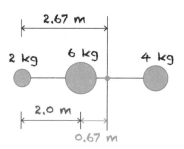

Figure 10.3: The location of the center of mass of the system in Figure 10.2.

The solution of Example 10-1 identifies another important aspect of the center of the mass of a system.

The center of mass of a system is invariant with respect to the origin of the reference frame for the system and with respect to the location of any potential axis of rotation for the system.

This invariance to the location of the axis of rotation distinguishes the center of mass of a system from the moment of inertia of a system that depends upon the location of the axis of rotation (Section 5-5).

Example 10-2:

Problem: Where is the center of mass of the system of three objects shown in Figure 10.4? The objects are small enough to be treated as point particles.

Solution: Let's define a reference frame for this system with an origin at the 2 kg object, an *x*-axis with a positive direction pointing from the 2 kg object to the 6 kg object, and a *y*-axis with a positive direction pointing from the 4 kg object to the 2 kg object, as shown in Figure 10.5.

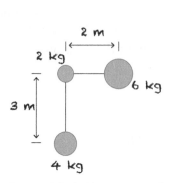

Figure 10.4: The system of objects in Example 10-2.

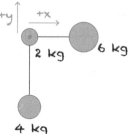

Figure 10.5: The reference frame for determining the center of mass of the system in Example 10-2. The origin is denoted by the red circle.

Applying Equation 10-1 to this system with this reference frame yields

$$x_{CM} = \frac{(2\,kg)(0\,m)+(6\,kg)(2\,m)+(4\,kg)(0\,m)}{2\,kg+6\,kg+4\,kg} = 1\,m$$

$$y_{CM} = \frac{(2\,kg)(0\,m)+(6\,kg)(0\,m)+(4\,kg)(-3\,m)}{2\,kg+6\,kg+4\,kg} = -1\,m$$

As shown in Figure 10.6, the location of center of mass of a system need not correspond to the position of any of the objects in the system.

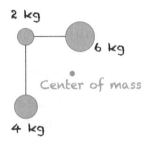

Figure 10.6: The location of the center of mass of the system in Example 10-2.

10-3 Torque

We define the quantity **torque** to be the measure of the effectiveness of an applied force to cause a system to rotate around a specified axis.

Torque: A measure of the ability of a force to cause the rotation of a system around an axis, fulcrum, or pivot. Torque is also frequently called moment of force.

We can think of torque as being a twist applied to a system in the same way we think of forces as being pushes or pulls applied to a system. The torque associated with a force acting on an object is defined in Equation 10-3.

$$\vec{\tau} = \vec{r} \times \vec{F} \qquad \qquad \text{(10-3)}$$

In Equation 10-3, $\vec{F}$ is the force and $\vec{r}$ is the position of that force relative to the axis of rotation (or pivot, fulcrum, *etc.*), as shown in Figure 10.7.

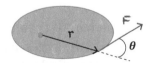

Figure 10.7: The torque caused by an applied force depends upon the distance between the force and the axis of rotation (red circle) and the orientation of the force relative to a line connecting the axis of rotation and the point where the force contacts the object.

Example 10-3:

Problem: What is the torque generated by the force $\vec{F} = (8\text{N})\hat{x} + (6\text{N})\hat{y}$ applied at $\vec{r} = (1\text{m})\hat{x} + (2\text{m})\hat{y}$?

Solution: From Section B-7. we know that we can express Equation 10-3 as

$$\vec{r} \times \vec{F} = \begin{vmatrix} \hat{x} & \hat{y} & \hat{z} \\ r_x & r_y & r_z \\ F_x & F_y & F_z \end{vmatrix} \rightarrow \vec{\tau} = \begin{vmatrix} \hat{x} & \hat{y} & \hat{z} \\ 1\text{m} & 2\text{m} & 0 \\ 8\text{N} & 6\text{N} & 0 \end{vmatrix}$$

$$\vec{\tau} = (0-0)\hat{x} + (0-0)\hat{y} + (6\text{Nm} - 16\text{Nm})\hat{z}$$

$$\vec{\tau} = (-10\text{Nm})\hat{z}$$

The torque is oriented in the negative direction of the z-axis and has a magnitude of 10 Nm. Please note that although the unit Nm is the equivalent of the unit J, the magnitude of the torque is never expressed using the unit J.

The magnitude of the torque vector can be determined using Equation 10-4 (see Section B-7).

$$\tau = \|\vec{\tau}\| = rF\sin\theta \qquad \textbf{(10-4)}$$

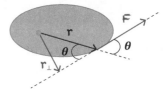

In Equation 10-4, the angle θ is the angle between the position $\vec{r}$ and the force $\vec{F}$, as shown in Figure 10.7. Equation 10-4 is also the basis of two common interpretations of torque. First, the *moment arm of the force*, $r_\perp$, is defined to be the shortest distance between the axis of rotation and the *line of action of the force*, which is parallel to the force (Figure 10.8).

Figure 10.8: The moment arm of the force $r_\perp$ is the shortest distance between the axis of rotation and the line of action of the force (dashed line) and is, therefore, perpendicular to the line of action of the force.

In Equation 10-5, the magnitude of the torque is expressed in terms of the moment arm of the force.

$$\tau = (r\sin\theta)F = r_\perp F \qquad \textbf{(10-5)}$$

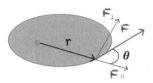

It is clear from Equation 10-5 and Figure 10.8 that the largest moment arm, and, hence, the largest magnitude of torque is achieved when $\vec{F}$ is directed perpendicular to $\vec{r}$ (*i.e.*, when $\theta = 90°$).

Second, it is clear from the definition of the cross product in Equation 10-3 that the only components of $\vec{F}$ that will generate torque are those components perpendicular to $\vec{r}$ (Figure 10.9).

Figure 10.9: It is only the components of the force that are perpendicular to the position vector that generate torque.

In Equation 10-6, the magnitude of the torque is expressed in terms of the magnitude of the component of $\vec{F}$ perpendicular to $\vec{r}$, denoted as $F_\perp$.

$$\tau = r\left(F\sin\theta\right) = rF_\perp \tag{10-6}$$

Another interpretation of Equation 10-6 and Figure 10.9 is that it is only the component of the force perpendicular to the position vector that can cause rotation around the axis.

10-4 Vector Description of Torque and Rotational Motion

Since torque is a measure of the effectiveness of a force to cause rotation, it is often convenient to use the $(\pm)$ sign convention for circular and rotational motion (Section 5-2) to denote the direction of the torque. Thus, *a positive torque causes counterclockwise rotation*, and *a negative torque causes clockwise rotation*. As shown in Table 10-1, this notation for the direction of torque conveniently follows directly from the $\sin\theta$ term in Equation 10-4. Thus, by employing the appropriate definition of θ (Section B-7), we can use Equation 10-4 to determine both the magnitude and the direction of a torque.

Table 10-1. Sign convention for describing the direction of torque and the associated rotational motion.

Orientation of Force		
Angle between $\vec{r}$ and $\vec{F}$	$\theta < 180°$	$\theta > 180°$
$\sin\theta$	Positive	Negative
Direction of torque	Positive	Negative
Direction of resulting rotation	Positive (Counterclockwise)	Negative (Clockwise)

Example 10-4:

Problem: Six forces are acting on a rod that can rotate around an axis passing through its center and oriented perpendicular to the plane of the rod, as shown in Figure 10.10. For each force, identify if the resulting torque is positive or negative.

Solution: According to the (±) sign convention in Table 10-1, positive torques cause counterclockwise rotation, and negative torques cause clockwise rotation. The simplest way to determine the direction of the rotation caused by each torque is to determine the direction of the component of the applied force that causes the torque. As shown in Figure 10.9, it is only the component of the force perpendicular to the position vector that causes torque. In this case, it is only the components of the applied forces perpendicular to the horizontal (or longitudinal axis) of the rod that cause torque.

As shown in Figure 10.11, F_1, F_3, F_4, and F_6 will all cause the rod to rotate counterclockwise around the axis of rotation, and, thus, the torques associated with these forces will be positive. In contrast, F_2 and F_5 will cause the rod to rotate clockwise around the axis of rotation, and, thus, the torques associated with these forces will be negative.

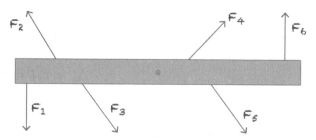

Figure 10.10: A rod that is free to rotate around an axis through its center (red circle) is subject to 6 applied forces.

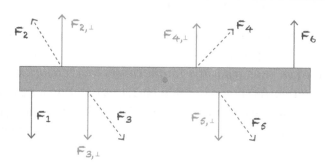

Figure 10.11: A rod that is free to rotate around its center of mass (red circle) is subject to 6 applied forces. The perpendicular components of these forces cause torque.

10-5 Newton's 2nd Law for Rotational Motion

We know from Equation 8.2 that for systems with constant mass, the net force acting on the system is directly proportional to the acceleration of the system. Similarly, we can relate the angular acceleration of an object with constant mass to the net torque acting on the object using Equation 10-7.

$$\tau_{net} = I\alpha \qquad \qquad \text{(10-7)}$$

As expected, the proportionality between the net torque and the angular acceleration depends upon the moment of inertia of the system[2].

---

2   Recall from Section 5-5 and Section 5-8 that the moment of inertia can be interpreted as the rotational motion equivalent of mass.

Example 10-5:

Problem: A uniformly dense rod with a length of 3 m and a mass of 4 kg is free to rotate around its center. What is the angular acceleration of the rod if a net torque of 6 Nm is applied to the rod?

Solution: The moment of inertia of the rod can be found in Table D-2.

$$I = \frac{1}{12}ML^2 \quad \rightarrow \quad I = \frac{1}{12}(4\,\text{kg})(3\,\text{m})^2 \quad \rightarrow \quad I = 3\,\text{kgm}^2$$

The angular acceleration of the rod can then be determined using Equation 10-7.

$$\alpha = \frac{\tau_{net}}{I} \quad \rightarrow \quad \alpha = \frac{6\,\text{Nm}}{3\,\text{kgm}^2} \quad \rightarrow \quad \alpha = 2\frac{\text{rad}}{\text{s}^2}$$

The radian unit can be added since it is dimensionless (Section 5-2).

Example 10-6:

Problem: Two ropes with tensions $T_1 = 5$ N and $T_2 = 2.5$ N, respectively, pull on a pulley, as shown in Figure 10.12.

The pulley is a uniformly dense solid cylinder with a radius of 5 cm and a mass of 4 kg. The pulley rotates around a frictionless axle that passes through its center. What is the angular acceleration of the pulley resulting from the tensions in the ropes?

Solution: The tension in each rope will cause a torque that acts on the pulley. The magnitudes and directions of these torques can be determined using Equation 10-4.

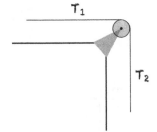

Figure 10.12: A pulley pulled by two ropes in Example 10-6.

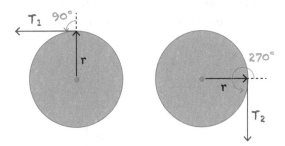

Figure 10.13: Orientation of $\vec{r}$, $\vec{T}_1$ and $\vec{T}_2$.

As shown in Figure 10.13, the angle between $\vec{r}$ and $\vec{T}_1$ is 90° and the angle between $\vec{r}$ and $\vec{T}_2$ is 270°. Hence,

$$\tau_{net} = \tau_{T_1} + \tau_{T_2} \quad \rightarrow \quad \tau_{net} = RT_1\sin 90° + RT_2\sin 270° \quad \rightarrow \quad \tau_{net} = RT_1 - RT_2$$

$$\tau_{net} = R(T_1 - T_2) \quad \rightarrow \quad \tau_{net} = (0.05\,\text{m})(5\,\text{N} - 2.5\,\text{N}) \quad \rightarrow \quad \tau_{net} = 0.125\,\text{Nm}$$

The moment of inertia of the pulley can be found in Table D-2.

$$I = \frac{1}{2}MR^2 \quad \rightarrow \quad I = \frac{1}{2}(4\,\text{kg})(0.05\,\text{m})^2 \quad \rightarrow \quad I = 0.005\,\text{kgm}^2$$

The angular acceleration of the rod can then be determined using Equation 10-7.

$$\alpha = \frac{\tau_{net}}{I} \quad \rightarrow \quad \alpha = \frac{0.125\,\text{Nm}}{0.0025\,\text{kgm}^2} \quad \rightarrow \quad \alpha = 25\,\frac{\text{rad}}{\text{s}^2}$$

The positive sign in our solution indicates that the direction of the angular acceleration is counterclockwise. This makes sense intuitively since $T_1 > T_2$.

A common torque acting on a system results from the force of gravity acting on that system. Let's consider the system shown in Figure 10.14 that consists of a solid disk that can freely rotate around an axle that is oriented perpendicular to the plane of the disk. We can model this solid disk as a composite of infinitesimally small "*bits*" of mass[3]. In Figure 10.14, we denote two of these small bits of mass as m_1 and m_2, which are at distances r_1 and r_2, respectively, from the axis of rotation.

The force of gravity acting on each bit of mass will result in an associated torque with respect to the axis of rotation. We can use Equation 10-5 to describe the magnitudes of these torques in terms of their corresponding moment arms (Figure 10.15).

The magnitude of net torque from the force of gravity acting on the entire disk is, then, the sum of the magnitudes of the torques acting on each constitutive bit of mass in the disk.

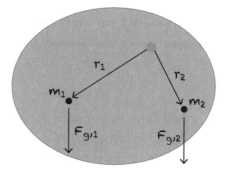

Figure 10.14: A solid disk that can freely rotate around an axle (red circle). The forces of gravity acting on two constitutive bits of the disk are shown.

$$\tau_g = \sum_i \tau_i \quad \rightarrow \quad \tau_g = \sum_i r_{\perp,i} F_{g,i} \quad \rightarrow \quad \tau_g = \sum_i r_{\perp,i} m_i g$$

$$\tau_g = \left(\sum_i r_{\perp,i} m_i \right) g$$

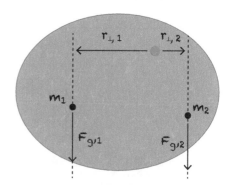

Figure 10.15: A solid disk that is free to rotate around an axle (red circle). The moment arms of the torques associated with the force of gravity acting on two constitutive bits of mass are shown.

---

3   We followed a similar approach in Section 5-5 for the derivation of the moment of inertia for a solid object.

This equation for the net gravitational torque acting on the disk can be simplified using the definition of the center of mass of a system (Equation 10-1).

$$\vec{r}_{CM} = \frac{\sum_{i=1}^{n} m_i \vec{r}_i}{\sum_{i=1}^{n} m_i} \quad \rightarrow \quad \sum_{i=1}^{n} m_i \vec{r}_i = \vec{r}_{CM} \sum_{i=1}^{n} m_i \quad \rightarrow \quad \sum_{i=1}^{n} m_i \vec{r}_i = \vec{r}_{CM} M$$

In this equation, $M = \sum_{i=1}^{n} m_i$ is the total mass of the system. Hence,

$$\sum_i r_{\perp,i} m_i = r_{\perp,CM} M \tag{10-8}$$

In Equation 10-8, $r_{\perp,CM}$ is the mass-averaged moment arm for the force of gravity acting on the disk, as shown in Figure 10.16.

Thus,

$$\tau_g = \left(M r_{\perp,CM} \right) g \quad \rightarrow \quad \tau_g = r_{\perp,CM} \left(Mg \right) \quad \rightarrow \quad \tau_g = r_{\perp,CM} F_g \tag{10-9}$$

Equation 10-9 has the simple interpretation that the gravitational torque acting on a system can be determined by treating the system as if all of its mass was concentrated at its center of mass. For this reason, the center of mass of a system is often also referred to as the center of gravity of a system (*i.e.*, it is the point at which the force of gravity acts). Equation 10-9 also leads to yet another definition of the center of mass of a system.

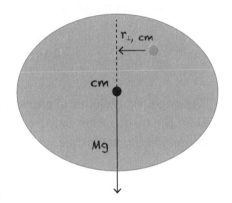

An object can balance on a pivot only if the center of mass of the object is directly above the pivot. In other words, the net gravitational torque will be zero only when $r_{\perp,CM}$ is zero.

Figure 10.16: A solid disk that is free to rotate around an axle (red circle). The position of center of mass relative to the axis of rotation is denoted as $r_{\perp,CM}$.

Example 10-7:

Problem: A uniformly dense solid rod with a length of 3 m and a mass of 4 kg can freely rotate around a frictionless axle located at one end of the rod. The rod is initially orientated horizontally (*i.e.*, parallel to the ground), as shown in Figure 10.17. What is the magnitude of the angular acceleration of the rod resulting from the gravitational torque acting on the rod?

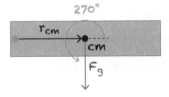

Figure 10.17: A uniformly dense rod that can freely rotate around an axle (red circle) located at one end of the rod. Since the rod is uniformly dense, the center of mass (black circle) is located in the center of the rod.

Solution: The orientation of the force of gravity and the axis of rotation are shown in Figure 10.17.

We can treat the rod as though all of its mass was concentrated at its geometric center since the rod is uniformly dense; the center of mass of a uniformly dense object is located at the geometric center of the object[4]. From Equation 10-5 and Equation 10-9, the gravitational torque acting on the rod is

$$\tau_g = r_{\perp,CM} F_g \quad \rightarrow \quad \tau_g = r_{CM}\left(mg\right)\sin\theta$$

In this equation, θ is the angle between the vector $\vec{r}_{CM}$, which points from the axis of rotation to the location of the center of mass, and $\vec{F}_g$. For the system shown in Figure 10.17, this angle is 270°. Hence,

$$\tau_g = \left(1.5\,\text{m}\right)\left(4\,\text{kg}\right)\left(9.8\frac{\text{m}}{\text{s}^2}\right)\sin 270° \quad \rightarrow \quad \tau_g = -58.8\,\text{Nm}$$

The moment of inertia of the rod can be found in Table D-2.

$$I = \frac{1}{3}ML^2 \quad \rightarrow \quad I = \frac{1}{3}\left(4\,\text{kg}\right)\left(3\,\text{m}\right)^2 \quad \rightarrow \quad I = 12\,\text{kgm}^2$$

The angular acceleration corresponding to this torque can then be found using Equation 10-7; the torque from the force of gravity is the only torque acting on the system and, thus, is equal to the net torque.

$$\alpha = \frac{\tau_g}{I} \quad \rightarrow \quad \alpha = \frac{-58.8\,\text{Nm}}{12\,\text{kgm}^2} \quad \rightarrow \quad \alpha = -4.9\frac{\text{rad}}{\text{s}^2}$$

The negative sign in our solution indicates that this torque will result in a clockwise rotation of the rod. This agrees with the relative positions of the force of gravity and the axle in Figure 10.17. If we had located the axle on the other end of the rod, the angular acceleration would have had the same magnitude but a different sign. It would have been positive, indicating that the rod would move counterclockwise.

10-6 Physical Pendula

In Section 6-5, we defined a simple pendulum to be a small bob suspended from a horizontal surface by a massless rope. Pendula can also be made from any solid object that swings back and forth on a pivot under the influence of gravity. Such systems are referred to as *physical pendula*.

---

4   Section D-4.

Let's consider the physical pendulum shown in Figure 10.18 that consists of an object of mass m, which rotates around a pivot that is a distance d from its center of mass.

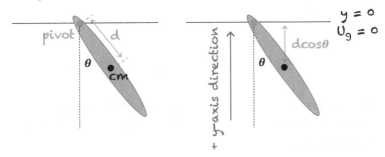

Figure 10.18: A physical pendulum for which the center of mass (black circle) is a distance d from the pivot (red circle).

Just as the gravitational torque acting on a system can be determined by treating the system as if all of its mass were concentrated at its center of mass, so, too, can we determine the gravitational potential energy of a system from the location of the center of mass. The gravitational potential energy of an object near the surface of the Earth can be expressed in terms of the mass of the object (m) and the vertical position of the center of mass (y_{CM})

$$U_g = mgy_{CM} \qquad \text{(10-10)}$$

For the pendulum in Figure 10.18, let's define the zero point of the gravitational potential energy (and the associated y-axis) to be the horizontal surface to which the pendulum is attached (Figure 10.18). Then, the energy of the system would be

$$E = \frac{1}{2}I\omega^2 + mgy_{CM} \quad \rightarrow \quad E = \frac{1}{2}I\omega^2 - mgd\cos\theta$$

If the system is isolated, its energy will be constant.

$$\frac{dE}{d\theta} = 0 \quad \rightarrow \quad I\alpha + mgd\sin\theta = 0 \quad \rightarrow \quad \alpha = -\frac{mgd}{I}\sin\theta$$

This equation for the angular acceleration can be converted into the equation for simple harmonic oscillation by applying the small angle approximation (Section 6-5).

$$\alpha = \frac{d^2\theta}{dt^2} = -\left(\frac{mgd}{I}\right)\theta \quad \rightarrow \quad \omega^2 = \frac{mgd}{I} \quad \rightarrow \quad \omega = \sqrt{\frac{mgd}{I}}$$

The period of oscillation of the pendulum is, therefore,

$$T = \frac{2\pi}{\omega} \quad \rightarrow \quad T = 2\pi\sqrt{\frac{I}{mgd}}$$

As expected, this solution agrees with that obtained in Section 6-5 for a simple pendulum in the appropriate limit. Specifically, for a simple pendulum, the oscillating object can be treated as a point particle with $I = mL^2$ and $d = L$.

$$I = mL^2, d = L \quad \rightarrow \quad \omega = \sqrt{\frac{mgL}{mL^2}} \quad \rightarrow \quad \omega = \sqrt{\frac{g}{L}}$$

It also follows from our solution to this problem that, analogous to Equation 7-1, we can relate the torque generated by a conservative force to the differentiation of the associated potential energy with respect to an angular displacement.

$$\tau_i = -\frac{dU_i}{d\theta} \qquad \qquad \textbf{(10-11)}$$

Using Equation 10-11, we can determine the torque associated with the force of gravity acting on the physical pendulum to be

$$\tau_g = -\frac{dU_g}{d\theta} \quad \rightarrow \quad \tau_g = -\frac{d}{d\theta}\left(-mgd\cos\theta\right) \quad \rightarrow \quad \tau_g = -mgd\sin\theta$$

Since $\tau_g = \tau_{net}$ for the physical pendulum, it follows from Equation 10-7 that

$$-mgd\sin\theta = I\alpha \quad \rightarrow \quad \alpha = -\frac{mgd}{I}\sin\theta$$

This is the same equation we had derived previously for this system. Similarly, we could have also determined the gravitational torque acting on the physical pendulum using Equation 10-4.

According to the orientation of the vectors in Figure 10.19, the gravitational torque is

$$\tau_g = d\left(mg\right)\sin\left(360° - \theta\right) \quad \rightarrow \quad \tau_g = -mgd\sin\theta$$

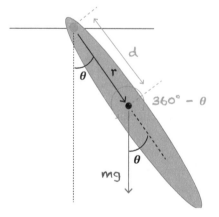

Figure 10.19: Calculating the gravitational torque acting on a physical pendulum.

Example 10-8:

Problem: A uniformly dense rigid rod is pivoted around a friction-less hinge to form a physical pendulum, as shown in Figure 10.20. The length of the rod, denoted by L in Figure 10.20, is 2 m, and the mass of the rod is 4 kg. The distance between the hinge and the center of mass of the rod is $L/4$. What is the period of small amplitude oscillations of this pendulum?

Solution: Let's define the zero point of the gravitational potential energy (and the associated y-axis) to be located at the hinge. Then, the energy of the system would be

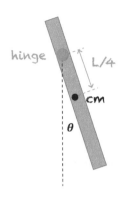

Figure 10.20: A uniformly dense rigid rod of length L pivoted around a frictionless hinge (red circle) a distance $L/4$ from the center of mass (black circle).

$$E = \frac{1}{2}I\omega^2 + mgy_{CM} \quad \rightarrow \quad E = \frac{1}{2}I\omega^2 - mg\left(\frac{L}{4}\right)\cos\theta$$

If the system is isolated, its energy will be constant.

$$\frac{dE}{d\theta} = 0 \quad \rightarrow \quad I\alpha + mg\left(\frac{L}{4}\right)\sin\theta = 0 \quad \rightarrow \quad \alpha = -\frac{mgL}{4I}\sin\theta$$

The moment of inertia of the rod can be found using the values in Table D-2 and the parallel axis theorem (Section D-6).

$$I = I_{CM} + md^2 \quad \rightarrow \quad I = \frac{1}{12}mL^2 + m\left(\frac{L}{4}\right)^2 \quad \rightarrow \quad I = \frac{7}{48}mL^2$$

Substitution then gives us

$$\alpha = -\frac{mgL}{4\left(\dfrac{7}{48}mL^2\right)}\sin\theta \quad \rightarrow \quad \alpha = -\left(\frac{12g}{7L}\right)\sin\theta$$

For small amplitude oscillations, we can apply the small angle approximation (Section 6-5) to this equation.

$$\alpha = \frac{d^2\theta}{dt^2} = -\left(\frac{12g}{7L}\right)\theta \quad \rightarrow \quad \omega^2 = \frac{12g}{7L} \quad \rightarrow \quad \omega = \sqrt{\frac{12g}{7L}}$$

The period of the oscillations can then be determined from the angular frequency using Equation 6.5.

$$T = \frac{2\pi}{\omega} \quad \rightarrow \quad T = 2\pi\sqrt{\frac{7L}{12g}} \quad \rightarrow \quad T = 2\pi\sqrt{\frac{7(2m)}{12\left(9.8\dfrac{m}{s^2}\right)}}$$

$$T = 2.2s$$

Example 10-9:

Problem: A 1.5 m long uniformly dense rigid rod with a mass of 3 kg is suspended from a horizontal surface by a hinge at one end and connected to a vertical surface by a spring with spring constant 10 N/m attached at the other end, as shown in Figure 10.21. When the rod hangs straight down, the spring is at its normal length. What is the period of small oscillations of the rod about its equilibrium position? The system may be considered to be isolated.

Solution: Let's define a reference frame for this system with its origin at the hinge, as shown in Figure 10.22. The y-axis of this reference frame denotes the vertical axis with the positive direction for the y-axis pointing up from the ground. The x-axis of this reference frame will be perpendicular to the y-axis with a positive direction pointing to the right in Figure 10.22.

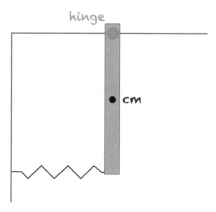

Figure 10.21: A physical pendulum constructed from a vertically suspended rod attached to a nearby vertical surface by a spring.

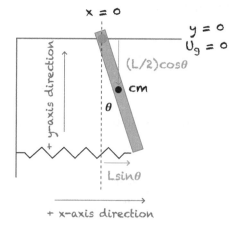

Figure 10.22: The definitions of the parameters in the equation for the energy of the physical pendulum in Example 10-9. The equilibrium position of the rod is indicated by the dashed line and the variable L denotes the length of the rod.

The equation for the energy for this system is

$$E = \frac{1}{2}I\omega^2 + mgy_{CM} + \frac{1}{2}k(\Delta l)^2$$

The variable L in this equation denotes the length of the rod. As before, the position of center of mass of the rod can be related to the angle θ between the rod and the equilibrium position of the rod.

$$y_{CM} = -\frac{L}{2}\cos\theta$$

Similarly, we can relate the displacement of the spring to the angle θ.

$$\Delta l = L\sin\theta$$

Hence,

$$E = \frac{1}{2}I\omega^2 + mg\left(-\frac{L}{2}\cos\theta\right) + \frac{1}{2}k(L\sin\theta)^2$$

$$E = \frac{1}{2}I\omega^2 - \frac{mgL}{2}\cos\theta + \frac{1}{2}kL^2\sin^2\theta$$

Since the system is isolated, the energy must be constant, therefore, we have

$$\frac{dE}{d\theta} = 0 \quad \rightarrow \quad I\alpha + \frac{mgL}{2}\sin\theta + kL^2\sin\theta\cos\theta = 0$$

If we limit ourselves to only small amplitude oscillations, we can use the small angle approximation (Section 6-5) to simplify this expression.

$$I\alpha + \frac{mgL}{2}\theta + kL^2\theta = 0 \quad \rightarrow \quad I\alpha = -\left(\frac{mgL}{2} + kL^2\right)\theta$$

The moment of inertia of the rod can be found in Table D-2.

$$I = \frac{1}{3}mL^2 \quad \rightarrow \quad \frac{1}{3}mL^2\alpha = -\left(\frac{mgL}{2} + kL^2\right)\theta$$

$$\alpha = \frac{d^2\theta}{dt^2} = -\left(\frac{3g}{2L} + \frac{3k}{m}\right)\theta \quad \rightarrow \quad \omega^2 = \frac{3g}{2L} + \frac{3k}{m}$$

Substitution of the values of the parameters for this system gives us

$$\omega^2 = \frac{3\left(9.8\frac{m}{s^2}\right)}{2(1.5m)} + \frac{3\left(10\frac{N}{m}\right)}{(3kg)} \quad\rightarrow\quad \omega^2 = 19.8\frac{rad^2}{s^2} \quad\rightarrow\quad \omega = 4.4\frac{rad}{s}$$

$$T = \frac{2\pi}{\omega} \quad\rightarrow\quad T = \frac{2\pi}{4.4\frac{rad}{s}}$$

$$T = 1.4\,s$$

It is worth noting that the angular frequency of the system in Example 10-9 can also be understood in terms of the contributions of each of the oscillatory elements in the system (Section 6-6).

$$\omega^2 = \frac{3g}{2L} + \frac{k}{\frac{1}{3}m} \quad\rightarrow\quad \omega^2 = \frac{mgd}{I} + \frac{k}{m_{effective}} \quad\rightarrow\quad \omega^2 = \omega^2_{pendulum} + \omega^2_{spring}$$

The effective mass of this system is $\frac{1}{3}m$ owing to the fact that the spring is causing the rod to rotate rather than to move translationally[5].

10-7 Rolling Down a Ramp

Let's now return to the example of an object rolling without slipping down a ramp, as discussed in Section 5-7. As shown in Figure 10.23, the three forces acting on this object are the force of gravity, a frictional force, and the normal force.

We have assumed, for the sake of simplicity, that the object is both symmetric and uniformly dense. Because of this, the axis of rotation for the object will be located at its geometric center (*i.e.*, because of these assumptions the center of mass of the object is at its geometric center). The force of gravity will cause no torque since it acts at the axis of rotation, and, therefore, the moment arm for this force is zero.

As shown in Figure 10.24, there is also no torque from the normal force acting on the rolling object because the angle between $\vec{r}$ and $\vec{n}$ is 180° (Equation 10-4). The angle between $\vec{r}$ and $\vec{F}_f$ is 270°, and, thus, the torque from this friction force, which is also the net torque acting on the object, is

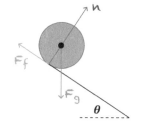

Figure 10.23: The force of gravity (red), the normal force (blue), and the force of friction (orange) acting on an object rolling down a ramp. The center of mass of the object is indicated by the black circle.

$$\tau_{net} = \tau_{F_f} \quad\rightarrow\quad \tau_{net} = RF_f \sin 270° \quad\rightarrow\quad \tau_{net} = -RF_f$$

---

5   See Section 5-8.

In this equation, the variable R denotes the radius of the rolling object, and the negative sign indicates that this torque will cause a clockwise rotation of the rolling object. This is consistent with the orientation of the object and the ramp in Figure 10.23.

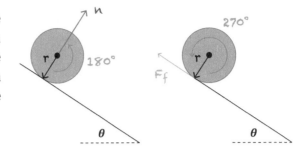

We can also use Newton's 2nd law to determine the translational acceleration of the object from the net force acting on it. The free body diagram for this object, based on Figure 10.23 and Figure 9.13, is shown in Figure 10.25.

Figure 10.24: Calculating the torque from the normal force and the force of friction acting on the rolling object in Figure 10.23.

Applying Newton's 2nd law to each of the coordinate axes in this free body diagram yields the following equations:

$$\left(F_{net}\right)_x = ma_x \;\rightarrow\; F_f - mg\sin\theta = ma_x$$

$$\left(F_{net}\right)_y = ma_y \;\rightarrow\; n - mg\cos\theta = ma_y$$

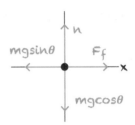

Figure 10.25: The free body diagram for the rolling object in Figure 10.23.

Since there is no displacement of object along the y-axis as it rolls down the ramp, the component of the block's acceleration along the y-axis will be zero. Substitution of $a_y = 0$ into the equation above yields

$$a_y = 0 \;\rightarrow\; n - mg\cos\theta = 0 \;\rightarrow\; n = mg\cos\theta$$

Applying Newton's 2nd law (Equation 10-7) to the net torque acting on this system gives us an equation for the angular acceleration of the rolling object.

$$-RF_f = I\alpha$$

Now, because the object is rolling without slipping, we know that the angular velocity and translational velocity of the objects must be related to each other (Equation 5.10). Similarly, the angular and translational accelerations are related by Equation 10-12.

$$a = \pm\alpha R \qquad\qquad \textbf{(10-12)}$$

In order to combine our equation relating the net force and translational acceleration with our equation relating the net torque and angular acceleration, we must carefully consider the ($\pm$) sign conventions that we have employed for each of these equations. As the object rolls down the ramp, the direction of its angular acceleration will be negative since it will be rotating clockwise (Figure 10.23). Furthermore, as the object rolls down the ramp, the direction of its translational acceleration will also be negative (Figure 10.25). Therefore, for this system,

$$a_x = \alpha R$$

Substitution of this relationship gives us

$$\alpha = \frac{a_x}{R} \quad \rightarrow \quad -RF_f = I\frac{a_x}{R} \quad \rightarrow \quad F_f = -I\frac{a_x}{R^2}$$

$$a_x = \frac{-mg\sin\theta + F_f}{m} \quad \rightarrow \quad ma_x = -mg\sin\theta + \left(-I\frac{a_x}{R^2}\right) \quad \rightarrow \quad mR^2 a_x = -mR^2 g\sin\theta - Ia_x$$

$$\left(mR^2 + I\right)a_x = -mR^2 g\sin\theta \quad \rightarrow \quad a_x = -\left(\frac{mR^2}{mR^2 + I}\right)g\sin\theta$$

This result is identical to that derived in Section 5-7 using an energy-based approach to the problem. However, by using this approach, we have also derived an equation for the magnitude of the force of friction acting on the rolling object.

$$F_f = -I\frac{a_x}{R^2} \quad \rightarrow \quad F_f = -I\frac{\left(-\left(\frac{mR^2}{mR^2 + I}\right)g\sin\theta\right)}{R^2} \quad \rightarrow \quad F_f = \left(\frac{mI}{mR^2 + I}\right)g\sin\theta$$

The force of friction is, thus, constant and has a magnitude that depends upon the physical characteristics of the rolling object (mass, radius, and moment of inertia) and the angle of the ramp.

10-8 Work Done by Torque

We recall that the work done by a force acting on a system is equal to the integral of that force with respect to the translational displacement of the system (Equation 9.2). Similarly, the work done by a torque acting on a system is equal to the integral of the torque with respect to the angular displacement of the system (Equation 10-13).

$$W = \int \vec{\tau} \cdot d\vec{\theta} \tag{10-13}$$

The work done by a torque is the integral of the torque with respect to an angular displacement.

The work done by the net torque acting on a system is equal to the change in the rotational kinetic energy of the system (Equation 10-14).

$$\Delta K_{rot} = \int \vec{\tau}_{net} \cdot d\vec{\theta} \tag{10-14}$$

The direction of the torque and the differential angular displacement vectors in Equation 10-13 and Equation 10-14 can be represented using the same ($\pm$) sign convention that we have used previously (Section 10-4). The work will be positive if the direction of the torque is the same as the direction of the angular displacement. Similarly, the work will be negative if the direction of the torque is opposite the direction of the angular displacement.

Example 10-10:

Problem: A uniformly dense solid disk with a radius of 20 cm and a mass of 4 kg can freely rotate around a frictionless axle that passes through the center of mass of the disk and is oriented perpendicular to the plane of the disk. A constant 20 N force applied tangentially to the outer rim of the disk causes the disk to rotate counterclockwise. If the disk starts from rest, what is its angular velocity after moving through an angular displacement of 3 rad?

Solution: The torque caused by the force, which is also the net torque acting on the disk, can be determined using Equation 10-4. Since the force is applied tangentially to the outer rim of a counterclockwise rotating disk, we have

$$\tau_{net} = (0.2\,\text{m})(20\,\text{N})\sin(90°) \;\rightarrow\; \tau_{net} = 0.4\,\text{Nm}$$

The change in the kinetic energy of the disk can then be determined using Equation 10-14; since the disk is rotating counterclockwise, $d\vec{\theta}$ is in the same direction as $\vec{\tau}_{net}$.

$$\Delta K_{rot} = \int (0.4\,\text{Nm})\,d\theta \;\rightarrow\; \Delta K_{rot} = (0.4\,\text{Nm})\int d\theta \;\rightarrow\; \Delta K_{rot} = (0.4\,\text{Nm})\Delta\theta$$

$$\Delta K_{rot} = (0.4\,\text{Nm})(3\,\text{rad}) \;\rightarrow\; \Delta K_{rot} = 1.2\,\text{Nmrad} \;\rightarrow\; \Delta K_{rot} = 1.2\,\text{J}$$

$$\frac{1}{2}I\omega_f^2 - \frac{1}{2}I\omega_i^2 = 1.2\,\text{J}$$

Substitution of $\omega_i = 0$ into this equation gives us

$$\frac{1}{2}I\omega_f^2 - \frac{1}{2}I(0)^2 = 1.2\,\text{J} \;\rightarrow\; \frac{1}{2}I\omega_f^2 = 1.2\,\text{J}$$

The moment of inertia of a solid disk can be found in Table D-2.

$$I = \frac{1}{2}mR^2 \;\rightarrow\; \frac{1}{2}\left(\frac{1}{2}(4\,\text{kg})(0.2\,\text{m})^2\right)\omega_f^2 = 1.2\,\text{J} \;\rightarrow\; (0.04\,\text{Nm})\omega_f^2 = 1.2\,\text{J}$$

$$\omega_f^2 = \frac{1.2\,\text{J}}{0.04\,\text{Nm}} \;\rightarrow\; \omega_f^2 = 30\frac{\text{rad}^2}{\text{s}^2} \;\rightarrow\; \omega_f = 5.5\frac{\text{rad}}{\text{s}}$$

By analogy to Equation 9-5 we can describe the instantaneous power supplied by a torque acting on a system as the dot product of that torque and the instantaneous angular velocity of the object (Equation 10-15).

$$P = \vec{\tau} \cdot \vec{\omega} \qquad \qquad \textbf{(10-15)}$$

As shown in Section 10-7, it is often the case that we need to consider how both forces and torques acting together on a system affect the motion of the system. These effects can be modeled either in terms of the work done by the forces and torques or by the accelerations caused by them.

Example 10-11:

Problem: A uniformly dense solid cylinder is wrapped by a massless rope that is also attached to the ceiling (Figure 10.26). The mass and radius of the cylinder are 2 kg and 15 cm, respectively. The cylinder is released from rest, and, as it falls to the floor, the rope unwinds from the cylinder causing the cylinder to rotate. You can assume that the cylinder rotates without slipping as the rope unwinds. What is the work done by the torque caused by the tension while the cylinder completes the first two revolutions of its rotation?

Solution: The torque associated with the forces acting on the cylinder can be determined from the orientation of these forces (Figure 10.26) using Equation 10-4.

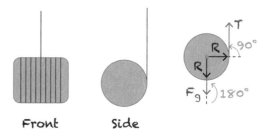

Front   Side

$$\tau_{F_g} = RF_g \sin 180° \quad \rightarrow \quad \tau_{F_g} = 0$$

$$\tau_T = RT \sin 90° \quad \rightarrow \quad \tau_T = RT$$

Figure 10.26: The system in Example 10-11.

As expected, the torque associated with the tension is positive since the tension will cause the cylinder to rotate counterclockwise. The work done by this torque can be found using Equation 10-13. However, in order to perform the integral in Equation 10-13, we must first determine the magnitude of the tension. This can be found by applying Newton's 2nd law to the forces acting on the cylinder.

In the reference frame for this system, let's use the force, gravity, to denote the y-axis with a positive direction pointing up from the surface of the Earth. The x-axis will be perpendicular to the y-axis with a positive direction pointing to the right in the first panel of

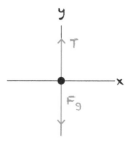

Figure 10.27: The free body diagram for the cylinder in Example 10-11.

Figure 10.26 (*i.e.,* when looking at the cylinder from the front, the positive direction for the x-axis is to the right). In the free body diagram for the cylinder, we will denote the magnitude of the tension as T and the magnitude of the force of gravity as F_g. With these definitions, the free body diagram for the cylinder is shown in Figure 10.27.

Applying Newton's 2nd law to each of the coordinate axes in this free body diagram yields the following equations:

$$\left(F_{net}\right)_x = ma_x \rightarrow 0 = ma_x \rightarrow a_x = 0$$

$$\left(F_{net}\right)_y = ma_y \rightarrow T - F_g = ma_y \rightarrow T - mg = ma_y$$

Similarly, the net torque acting on the cylinder causes an angular acceleration

$$\tau_{net} = \tau_{F_g} + \tau_T \rightarrow \tau_{net} = TR \rightarrow TR = I\alpha$$

Since the cylinder is rolling without slipping with respect to the rope, we know that the angular and translational accelerations of the cylinder must be related (Equation 10-12). The direction of the angular acceleration will be positive because the cylinder rotates counterclockwise. In contrast, the acceleration of the cylinder is in the negative direction for the reference frame used for the free body diagram in Figure 10.27. Hence,

$$\alpha R = -a_y$$

Using this relationship, we can determine the magnitude of the tension.

$$\alpha = -\frac{a_y}{R} \rightarrow TR = I\left(-\frac{a_y}{R}\right) \rightarrow a_y = -\frac{TR^2}{I}$$

Substitution of this value for a_y into our equation for $\left(F_{net}\right)_y$ yields

$$T - mg = m\left(-\frac{TR^2}{I}\right) \rightarrow TI - mIg = -mTR^2 \rightarrow TI + mTR^2 = mIg$$

$$T = \left(\frac{I}{I + mR^2}\right)mg$$

Thus,

$$\tau_T = R\left(\frac{I}{I + mR^2}\right)mg$$

Now, since the cylinder is rotating counterclockwise, $d\vec{\theta}$ is in the same direction as $\vec{\tau}_T$. Furthermore, since the magnitude of the torque is constant, we have

$$W_{\tau_T} = \int \tau_T \, d\theta \rightarrow W_{\tau_T} = \tau_T \int d\theta \rightarrow W_{\tau_T} = \tau_T \Delta\theta \rightarrow W_{\tau_T} = \left(\frac{IRmg}{I + mR^2}\right)\Delta\theta$$

The angular displacement corresponding to 2 revolutions is

$$\Delta\theta = 2\left(2\pi \, \text{rad}\right) \quad \rightarrow \quad \Delta\theta = 4\pi \, \text{rad}$$

The moment of inertia of a solid cylinder can be found in Table D-2.

$$I = \frac{1}{2}mR^2 \quad \rightarrow \quad W_{\tau_T} = \left(\frac{\left(\frac{1}{2}mR^2\right)Rmg}{\frac{1}{2}mR^2 + mR^2}\right)\left(4\pi \, \text{rad}\right) \quad \rightarrow \quad W_{\tau_T} = \left(\frac{\frac{1}{2}Rmg}{\frac{1}{2}+1}\right)\left(4\pi \, \text{rad}\right)$$

$$W_{\tau_T} = \left(\frac{Rmg}{3}\right)\left(4\pi \, \text{rad}\right)$$

Substitution then yields

$$W_{\tau_T} = \left(\frac{\left(0.15\,\text{m}\right)\left(2\,\text{kg}\right)\left(9.8\frac{\text{m}}{\text{s}^2}\right)}{3}\right)\left(4\pi \, \text{rad}\right)$$

$$W = 12.3\,\text{J}$$

Finally, let's now return to the object rolling down a ramp in Figure 10.23. We can use Equation 9.2 and Equation 10-13 to relate the work done on the object to the change in the translational and rotational kinetic energies of the object. Since the only net force acting on the object is acting along the x-axis, we have

$$\Delta K = \int \left(F_{net}\right)_x dx \quad \rightarrow \quad \Delta K = \int \left(-mg\sin\theta + F_f\right)dx$$

These forces are constant as the object rolls down the ramp. Hence,

$$\Delta K = \left(-mg\sin\theta + F_f\right)\int dx \quad \rightarrow \quad \Delta K = \left(-mg\sin\theta + F_f\right)\Delta x$$

$$\Delta K = \left(-mg\sin\theta\right)\Delta x + F_f\Delta x$$

Similarly, since there is only one torque acting on the object, we have

$$\Delta K_{rot} = -\int F_f R\,d\theta$$

And, because this torque is constant as the object rolls down the ramp, this equation can also be readily simplified.

$$\Delta K_{rot} = -F_f R \int d\theta \quad \rightarrow \quad \Delta K_{rot} = -F_f R \Delta\theta$$

The translational and angular displacements of the objects are correlated since the object rolls without slipping. Hence,

$$\Delta x = R\Delta\theta \quad \rightarrow \quad \Delta K_{rot} = -F_f \Delta x$$

Combining the equations for ΔK and ΔK_{rot} then gives us

$$\Delta K = -\left(mg\sin\theta\right)\Delta x - \Delta K_{rot} \quad \rightarrow \quad \Delta K + \Delta K_{rot} = -\left(mg\sin\theta\right)\Delta x$$

We recognize the expression on the right hand side of this equation as the work done by the force of gravity on the object as it rolls down the ramp. Indeed, from Equation 7.6 we have

$$-\left(mg\sin\theta\right)\Delta x = W_g \quad \rightarrow \quad \left(mg\sin\theta\right)\Delta x = \Delta U_g$$

Therefore,

$$\Delta K + \Delta K_{rot} = -\Delta U_g \quad \rightarrow \quad \Delta K + \Delta K_{rot} + \Delta U_g = 0$$

This result demonstrates that the object rolling down the ramp can be modeled as an isolated system, just as we did in Section 5-7. However, it would seem from Figure 10.23 that this system is not isolated since a non-conservative friction force is acting on it. In order for this system to be isolated in the presence of this friction force, the work done by this friction force must be zero. There are two possible explanations for why this work would be zero. Either the magnitude of the force is zero, or the displacement of the object is zero. We know that the former explanation cannot be true since this friction force must be present in order to generate the torque required for the object to rotate, so we must conclude that the displacement over which the force acts must be zero. How can this be true if the object is rolling down the ramp?

The answer is that the *relative* displacement of the object and the ramp at the point of contact between the object and the ramp is zero because the instantaneous velocity of the object at that point is zero. To understand why this is the case, let's remember that rolling without slipping can be modeled as a combination of rotational motion and translational motion (Section 5-6). We can,

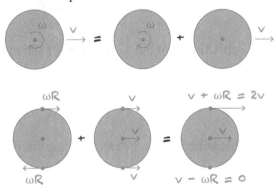

Figure 10.28: Rolling without slipping is a combination of rotational and translational motion. The summation of the velocities associated with each motion results in the rolling object being instantaneously at rest at the point where it contacts the surface along which it is rolling.

therefore, determine the velocity of each constitutive bit of mass in a rolling object by summing its translational and angular velocities (Figure 10.28).

As shown in Figure 10.28, when we sum the velocities associated with the angular and translational movement of the rolling object, we find that $v = 0$ at the point where the object contacts the surface. Therefore, the object is instantaneously at rest at the point where it contacts the surface.

Since there is no displacement between the object and the surface at the point where they contact each other, the work done by the friction force acting at that point (Figure 10.23) must be zero. Indeed, *this friction force is acting to maintain no relative displacement between the rolling object and the surface at this point in order to ensure that the object rolls without slipping*. It follows that since this friction force is acting to prevent motion, it must be static friction.

Example 10-12:

Problem: A solid sphere is rolling without slipping down a ramp. The coefficient of static friction between the sphere and the ramp is $\mu_s = 0.5$. What is the maximum possible angle for the ramp such that the sphere will roll without slipping?

Solution: The magnitude of the force of friction acting on an object that rolls without slipping was determined in Section 10-7. We now recognize this to be the force of static friction.

$$f_s = \left(\frac{I}{mR^2 + I} \right) mg \sin \theta$$

The magnitude of the force of static friction is related to the magnitude of the normal force by Equation 8.4.

$$f_s \leq \mu_s n \quad \rightarrow \quad \left(\frac{I}{mR^2 + I} \right) mg \sin \theta \leq \mu_s n$$

Substitution of the expression for the magnitude of the normal force then gives us

$$n = mg \cos \theta \quad \rightarrow \quad \left(\frac{I}{mR^2 + I} \right) mg \sin \theta \leq \mu_s mg \cos \theta$$

This equation can be readily simplified to

$$\tan \theta \leq \mu_s \left(\frac{mR^2 + I}{I} \right)$$

The moment of inertia of a solid sphere can be found in Table D-2.

$$I = \frac{2}{5}mR^2 \quad \rightarrow \quad \tan\theta \leq \mu_s \left(\frac{mR^2 + \frac{2}{5}mR^2}{\frac{2}{5}mR^2} \right) \quad \rightarrow \quad \tan\theta \leq \mu_s \left(\frac{7}{2} \right)$$

Hence,

$$\tan\theta \leq (0.5)\left(\frac{7}{2} \right) \quad \rightarrow \quad \tan\theta \leq 1.75 \quad \rightarrow \quad \theta \leq 60.3°$$

$$\theta_{max} = 60.3°$$

10-9 General Problem-Solving Strategy

We can now modify the problem-solving strategy presented in Section 9-6 to include the application of the rotational form of Newton's 2nd law.

Step 1: Specify the reference frame for the system.

Step 2: Identify the forces that act on the system.

Step 3: Draw the free body diagram for the system. All of the identified forces in Step 2 should be included with their correct orientation within the reference frame of the system.

Step 4: If necessary, redraw the free body diagram. Whenever possible, free body diagrams should be constructed such that at least one of their coordinate axes corresponds to an axis along which the system is moving. If the original reference frame does not satisfy this goal, it should be redrawn with new coordinate axes that do satisfy this goal.

Step 5: Decompose all vectors into their components along the coordinate axes of the free body diagram.

Step 6: Apply Newton's 2nd law to each of the coordinate axes of the free body diagram. This will generate a single algebraic equation for each coordinate axis. A $(\pm)$ sign can be used to denote the direction of the forces with respect to the coordinate axes.

Step 7: Determine the torque associated with each of the forces acting on the object and then combine these torques to determine the net torque acting on the object.

Step 8: Apply Newton's 2nd law to this net torque to determine the angular acceleration of the object.

Step 9: Determine the relationship between the angular and translational accelerations of the object.

$$a = \pm\alpha R$$

Be careful with the $(\pm)$ sign conventions for the accelerations!

Step 10: Use algebra to relate the magnitudes of the forces to each other or to the acceleration of the object.

- **Center of mass:** The mass weighted center of a system.

$$\vec{r}_{CM} = \frac{\sum\limits_{i=1}^{n} m_i \vec{r}_i}{\sum\limits_{i=1}^{n} m_i}$$

The center of mass has the following important properties:
- The center of mass of any symmetrical object of uniform density is at the physical (*i.e.*, geometric) center of the object.
- The force of gravity acting on a system can be modeled as though it is acting on the center of mass of the system.
- An object can balance on a pivot only if the center of mass of the object is directly above the pivot.
- The center of mass is invariant with respect to the origin of the reference frame for the system and with respect to the location of any potential axis of rotation for the system.
- An object that is freely rotating will always rotate around its center of mass.

- **Torque:** A measure of the ability of a force to cause the rotation of a system around an axis, fulcrum, or pivot. Torque is also frequently called moment of force.

$$\vec{\tau} = \vec{r} \times \vec{F}$$

The magnitude of the torque can also be expressed as

$$\tau = rF\sin\theta \qquad \tau = r_{\perp}F \qquad \tau = rF_{\perp}$$

Positive torques cause counterclockwise rotation, and negative torques cause clockwise rotations.

- **Newton's 2nd law:** The net torque acting on an object with constant moment of inertia is equal to the product of the object's moment of inertia and angular acceleration.

$$\tau_{net} = I\alpha$$

- **The work done by a torque acting on an object is the integral of the dot product of the torque with the object's angular displacement.**

$$W = \int \vec{\tau} \cdot d\vec{\theta}$$

The work done by the net torque acting on a system is equal to the change in the rotational kinetic energy of the system.

$$\Delta K_{rot} = \int \vec{\tau}_{net} \cdot d\vec{\theta}$$

The instantaneous power supplied by a torque acting on an object is equal to the dot product of the torque and the angular velocity of the object.

$$P = \vec{\tau} \cdot \vec{\omega}$$

Problems

1. What is the location of the center of mass of the system of 3 point particles shown in the figure at right?

2. What is the torque generated by the force $\vec{F} = (3N)\hat{x} + (4N)\hat{y}$ applied at $\vec{r} = (6m)\hat{x} + (8m)\hat{y}$?

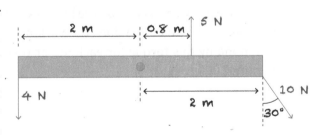

3. A thin uniformly dense rod with a length of 4 m and a mass of 2 kg is free to rotate around a frictionless axle at one end of the rod. What is the angular acceleration of the rod if a net torque of 12 Nm is applied to the rod?

4. A thin uniformly dense rod with a length of 4 m and a mass of 6 kg is free to rotate around a frictionless axle through the center of the rod. Three forces are acting on the rod, as shown in the figure at right. What is the net torque acting on the rod? What is the angular acceleration of the rod resulting from this net torque?

5. A thin uniformly dense rod with a length of 50 cm and a mass of 0.2 kg is standing perfectly vertical on a horizontal surface, as shown in the figure at right. When given a slight (*i.e.*, negligible) push, the rod begins to topple over. Let's assume that static friction is sufficient to allow the rod to fall over without slipping at the base. What is the magnitude of the

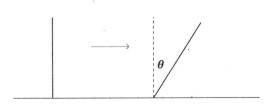

angular acceleration of the rod when it is at $\theta = 30°$ relative to the vertical axis? For what angle θ is the magnitude of the angular acceleration the largest?

6. A thin uniformly dense rod of length 1.5 m is pivoted on a hinge at one end and held horizontally by a spring with spring constant 10 N/m attached at the other end, as shown in the figure at right. What is the frequency of small oscillations of the rod?

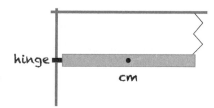

7. A thin uniformly dense rod of length 2.8 m oscillates as a physical pendulum, as shown in the figure at right. What value of the distance x between the rod's center of mass and pivot point corresponds to the smallest period of simple harmonic oscillations of the rod?

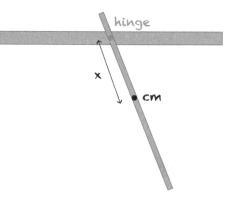

8. A thin uniformly dense rod with a length of 1.5 m long and a mass of 3 kg is suspended from a vertical surface by a spring with spring constant 10 N/m and is free to rotate around a frictionless axle that passes through its center of mass, as shown in the figure at right. What is the frequency of small angle oscillations of the rod?

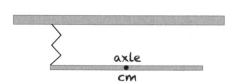

9. A uniformly dense solid sphere with a mass of 4 kg and a radius of 10 cm is rolling down a 30° ramp, as shown in the figure at right. The force of static friction acting on the block does no work, but the torque associated with this force does do work on the sphere. What is the work done by this torque for each meter that the sphere rolls down the ramp?

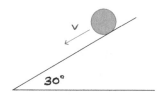

CHAPTER ELEVEN

Further Applications of Newtonian Mechanics

11-1 Introduction

I n the preceding four chapters, we developed a framework for solving mechanics problems using forces. We further showed that, often, the solution obtained by this force-based approach was identical to the solution previously obtained using an energy-based approach. In this chapter, we turn our attention to specific classes of problems for which an energy-based approach does not work at all or at least not nearly as well as a force-based approach. In each of these cases, the system is either not moving (and thus the energy of the system is not changing) or the motion of the system does not cause a change in the energy of the system. In either case, it is simplest to describe the mechanics of the system using forces.

11-2 Static Equilibrium

A system is said to be in static equilibrium if no net force and no net torque act upon it.

A system is in static equilibrium if $\vec{F}_{net} = 0$ *and* $\vec{\tau}_{net} = 0$ *for the system.*

This condition is commonly referred to as a balance of forces ($\vec{F}_{net} = 0$) and a balance of torques ($\vec{\tau}_{net} = 0$).

Consider the system shown in Figure 11.1 that consists of a rigid and uniformly dense beam with a mass of 10 kg and a length of 3 m that rests on two supports.

Let's define a reference frame for this system in which the *y*-axis denotes the vertical axis with a positive direction pointing up from the ground. The *x*-axis of this reference frame will be perpendicular to the *y*-axis with

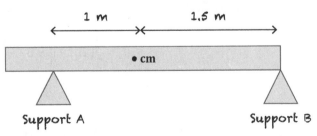

Figure 11.1: A beam resting on two supports.

a positive direction pointing to the right in Figure 11.1. In the free body diagram for the beam, we will denote the magnitude of the force exerted by support A on the beam as n_A, the magnitude of the force exerted by support B on the beam as n_B, and the magnitude of the force of gravity as F_g. With these definitions, the free body diagram for the beam is shown in Figure 11.2.

Applying the $\vec{F}_{net} = 0$ condition for static equilibrium to the free body diagram in Figure 11.2 yields

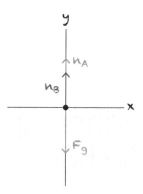

$$\left(F_{net}\right)_y = 0 \ \rightarrow \ n_A + n_B - F_g = 0 \ \rightarrow \ n_A + n_B - mg = 0 \ \rightarrow \ n_A + n_B = mg$$

Figure 11.2: The free body diagram for the beam in Figure 11.1.

To apply the $\vec{\tau}_{net} = 0$ condition for static equilibrium, we need to specify the axis with respect to which the torques will be determined (Equation 10-3). It doesn't matter where we choose to locate this axis, however, since static equilibrium requires that $\vec{\tau}_{net} = 0$ for all potential axes of rotation[1]. For example, we could place the axis of rotation at the point where support A contacts the beam (Figure 11-3).

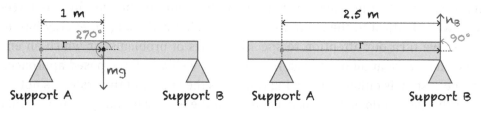

Figure 11.3: The rigid beam from Figure 11.1 with an axis of rotation located at the point where support A contacts the beam (red circle).

Applying the $\vec{\tau}_{net} = 0$ condition for static equilibrium with respect to this axis of rotation yields[2]

$$\vec{\tau}_{net} = 0 \ \rightarrow \ n_A\left(0\text{m}\right) + \left(1.0\text{m}\right)mg\sin\left(270°\right) + \left(2.5\text{m}\right)n_B\sin\left(90°\right) = 0$$

$$-\left(1.0\text{m}\right)mg + \left(2.5\text{m}\right)n_B = 0 \ \rightarrow \ \left(1.0\text{m}\right)mg = \left(2.5\text{m}\right)n_B \rightarrow \ n_B = \frac{2}{5}mg$$

Notice that the force n_A produces no torque since it has no moment arm for rotations about this axis (Equation 10-5). Substitution of the values of our problem then gives us

$$n_B = \frac{2}{5}\left(10\text{kg}\right)\left(9.8\frac{\text{m}}{\text{s}^2}\right) \ \rightarrow \ n_B = 39.2\text{N}$$

---

1   If a net torque existed for an axis of rotation, the object would experience angular acceleration around that axis. Thus, to ensure that the object has no angular acceleration, the net torque must be zero for all possible axes of rotation.
2   Recall from Section 10-5 that we can model the force of gravity to act at the center of mass of an object.

We can then combine this result with the equation derived from the $\vec{F}_{net} = 0$ condition for static equilibrium to determine the value for n_A.

$$n_A + \frac{2}{5}mg = mg \;\;\rightarrow\;\; n_A = \frac{3}{5}mg \;\;\rightarrow\;\; n_A = \frac{3}{5}(10\text{kg})\left(9.8\frac{\text{m}}{\text{s}^2}\right)$$

$$n_A = 58.8\text{N}$$

Alternatively, we could have solved this problem with the axis of rotation located at the center of mass of the beam (Figure 11.4).

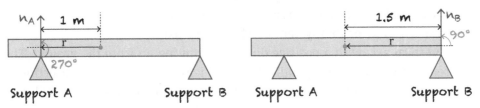

Figure 11.4: The rigid beam from Figure 11.1 with an axis of rotation located at the center of mass of the beam (red circle).

Applying the $\vec{\tau}_{net} = 0$ condition for static equilibrium with respect to this axis of rotation yields

$$\vec{\tau}_{net} = 0 \;\;\rightarrow\;\; (0\text{m})mg + (1.0\text{m})n_A \sin(270°) + (1.5\text{m})n_B \sin(90°) = 0$$

$$-(1.0\text{m})n_A + (1.5\text{m})n_B = 0 \;\;\rightarrow\;\; (1.0\text{m})n_A = (1.5\text{m})n_B \;\;\rightarrow\;\; n_B = \frac{2}{3}n_A$$

For this axis of rotation, there is no torque generated by the force of gravity since there is no moment arm for this force for rotations around this axis (Equation 10-5). Substitution of this result into the equation derived from the $\vec{F}_{net} = 0$ condition for static equilibrium gives us

$$n_A + \frac{2}{3}n_A = mg \;\;\rightarrow\;\; n_A = \frac{3}{5}mg \;\;\rightarrow\;\; n_A = \frac{3}{5}(10\text{kg})\left(9.8\frac{\text{m}}{\text{s}^2}\right)$$

$$n_A = 58.8\text{N}$$

$$n_B = \frac{2}{3}(58.8\text{N}) \;\;\rightarrow\;\; n_B = 39.2\text{N}$$

As anticipated, the results are identical to those obtained with the other axis of rotation.

Since the application of the $\vec{\tau}_{net} = 0$ condition for static equilibrium is independent of the location of the axis of rotation, we should always place the axis of rotation where one or more forces act on the system. Placing the axis of rotation there will simplify our equation for $\vec{\tau}_{net} = 0$ since there will be no torques from the forces acting there.

Example 11-1:

Problem: A rigid and uniformly dense beam of length L and mass m is supported by a hinge at one end and by a massless rope on the other end, as shown in Figure 11.5. What is the tension in the rope? What is the force exerted by the hinge on the beam?

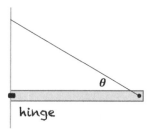

hinge

Figure 11.5: A rigid beam supported by a hinge and a massless rope.

Solution: Since the beam is in static equilibrium, we can apply the conditions of $\vec{F}_{net} = 0$ and $\vec{\tau}_{net} = 0$ to the beam to determine the magnitudes of these forces. Let's begin by defining a reference frame for this system in which the y-axis denotes the vertical axis with a positive direction pointing up from the ground. The x-axis of this reference frame will be perpendicular to the y-axis with a positive direction pointing to the right, as in Figure 11.5. In the free body diagram for the beam, we will denote the magnitude of the tension as T, the magnitude of the horizontal component of force exerted by the hinge on the beam as n_x, the magnitude of the vertical component of force exerted by the hinge on the beam as n_y[3], and the magnitude of the force of gravity as F_g. With these definitions, the free body diagram for the beam is shown in Figure 11.6.

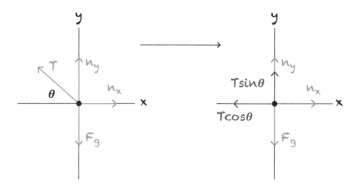

Figure 11.6: The free body diagram for the beam in Figure 11.5.

Applying the $\vec{F}_{net} = 0$ condition for static equilibrium to the free body diagram in Figure 11-6 yields

$$\left(F_{net}\right)_x = 0 \quad \rightarrow \quad n_x - T\cos\theta = 0 \quad \rightarrow \quad n_x = T\cos\theta$$

$$\left(F_{net}\right)_y = 0 \quad \rightarrow \quad n_y + T\sin\theta - F_g = 0 \quad \rightarrow \quad n_y + T\sin\theta - mg = 0$$

---

3   It is worth noting that we do not know *a priori* that both n_x and n_y exist, but it is safe for us to include them in our free body diagram. We can determine from the solution of our subsequent calculations if these components are present. For example, if we determine that $n_y = 0$, we will know that this component does not exist.

$$n_y + T\sin\theta = mg$$

The next step in our solution is to choose an axis of rotation for the $\vec{\tau}_{net} = 0$ condition for static equilibrium. The best location for this axis is at the hinge since two of the forces in our free body diagram (n_x and n_y) act on the beam there; hence, there will be no torque from these forces for this axis of rotation. Furthermore, if the axis of rotation is located at the hinge, then only the y-axis components of the forces in the free body diagram of the beam are capable of causing rotation (Figure 11-7).

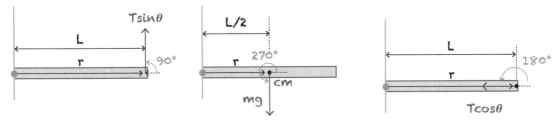

Figure 11.7: Only the components of forces oriented along the y-axis in the free body diagram in Figure 11.6 are capable of causing torque around the axis of rotation (red circle).

As shown in Figure 11.7, the net torque acting on the beam about this axis of rotation is

$$\vec{\tau}_{net} = 0 \;\rightarrow\; (0)n_y + (L)(T\sin\theta)\sin(90°) + \left(\frac{L}{2}\right)mg\sin(270°) = 0$$

The n_y force does not generate any torque about this axis of rotation since its moment arm is zero. Simplifying this equation gives us

$$T\sin\theta(L) - mg\left(\frac{L}{2}\right) = 0 \;\rightarrow\; T\sin\theta(L) = mg\left(\frac{L}{2}\right)$$

$$T\sin\theta = \frac{mg}{2} \;\rightarrow\; T = \frac{mg}{2\sin\theta}$$

We can then substitute this result into our equations for $\vec{F}_{net} = 0$ to determine n_x and n_y.

$$n_x = \left(\frac{mg}{2\sin\theta}\right)\cos\theta \;\rightarrow\; n_x = \left(\frac{mg}{2}\right)\cot\theta$$

$$n_y = mg - T\sin\theta \;\rightarrow\; n_y = mg - \frac{mg}{2} \;\rightarrow\; n_y = \frac{mg}{2}$$

The force exerted by the hinge on the beam has components along both the horizontal and vertical directions in Figure 11.5 (the x-axis and y-axis, respectively, in Figure 11.6). Interestingly, the magnitudes of n_x, n_y, and T are all independent of the length of the beam.

11-3 Levers

The conditions for static equilibrium also provide the basis for understanding the function of another simple machine: the lever. Recall from Section 7-7 that simple machines are devices that allow for the reduction in the magnitude of the force necessary to do a specific amount of work by increasing the displacement over which the force acts. Levers are simple machines that consist of a beam or rigid rod that is pivoted around a fixed hinge or fulcrum. The position of an object (referred to as the load) on the beam can be changed by applying an external force (referred to as the effort) to the beam. As shown in Figure 11.8, levers are divided into three classes based upon the relative position of the fulcrum, the effort, and the load.

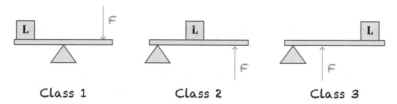

Figure 11.8: The three classes of levers. The load is denoted by the square with the label L and the effort as an the externally applied force F.

Common examples of the different classes of levers are:

Class 1 levers: scissors, pliers, and crowbar.
Class 2 levers: wheelbarrow, nutcracker, and bottle opener.
Class 3 levers: human arm, tweezers, and human jaw.

The mechanical advantage of a lever depends upon the positions of the load and effort relative to the fulcrum, which defines the axis of rotation for the system. When the lever is in static equilibrium, the torque generated by the effort is equal in magnitude but opposite in direction to the torque generated by the load[4]. Let's consider the situation shown in Figure 11.9 when the beam is horizontally oriented and in static equilibrium.

---

4   There is no torque generated by the force of the fulcrum pushing up on the beam since there is no moment arm for this force.

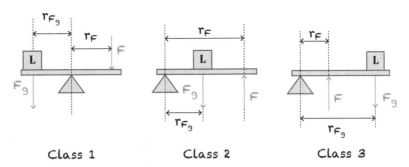

Class 1   Class 2   Class 3

Figure 11.9: The three classes of levers in static equilibrium with the beam parallel to the ground.

Applying the $\vec{\tau}_{net} = 0$ condition for static equilibrium with respect to an axis of rotation located at the fulcrum for each of the levers in Figure 11.9 yields

$$\vec{\tau}_{net} = 0 \quad \rightarrow \quad n r_{F_g} F_g = r_F F \quad \rightarrow \quad \left(\frac{r_F}{r_{F_g}}\right) F = F_g$$

Hence, the mechanical advantage of the lever is the ratio $\frac{r_F}{r_{F_g}}$ as this is the amount by which the applied force (*i.e.*, the effort) is amplified. For class 1 levers, this ratio can be greater than 1 or less than 1. All class 2 levers will have a mechanical advantage greater than 1, and all class 3 levers will have a mechanical advantage less than 1.

11-4 Centripetal Acceleration

Let's now reconsider the system first presented in Section 5-2 that consists of a block moving in a uniform circle of constant radius R, as shown in Figure 11.10.

The position of the block can be expressed in terms of its components along the x and y axes in Figure 11.10 as

$$\vec{r} = (R\cos\theta)\hat{x} + (R\sin\theta)\hat{y} \quad \rightarrow \quad \vec{r} = R\hat{r}$$

In this equation, we have defined the new unit vector $\hat{r}$ (the radial unit vector) to point from the origin of the circle to the location of the moving block.

$$\hat{r} = (\cos\theta)\hat{x} + (\sin\theta)\hat{y}$$

Naturally, as the block moves around the circle, the orientation of $\hat{r}$ relative to the x and y axes in Figure 11.10 will change, but it will, nevertheless, always point from the origin

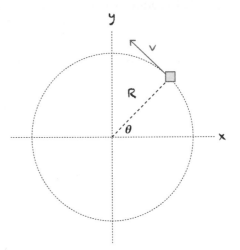

Figure 11.10: A block moving in a circle of radius R. The direction of the velocity of the block is indicated by the arrow.

of the circle to the location of the block. The velocity of the block is found through differentiation (Equation C-1).

$$\vec{v} = \frac{d\vec{r}}{dt} \quad \rightarrow \quad \vec{v} = R\frac{d\hat{r}}{dt} \quad \rightarrow \quad \vec{v} = R\left[\left(\frac{d}{dt}\cos\theta\right)\hat{x} + \left(\frac{d}{dt}\sin\theta\right)\hat{y}\right]$$

$$\vec{v} = R\left[\left(-\sin\theta\frac{d\theta}{dt}\right)\hat{x} + \left(\cos\theta\frac{d\theta}{dt}\right)\hat{y}\right] \quad \rightarrow \quad \vec{v} = R\left[\left(-\sin\theta\omega\right)\hat{x} + \left(\cos\theta\omega\right)\hat{y}\right]$$

$$\vec{v} = R\omega\left[\left(-\sin\theta\right)\hat{x} + \left(\cos\theta\right)\hat{y}\right]$$

$$\vec{v} = \left(R\omega\right)\hat{t}$$

(11-1)

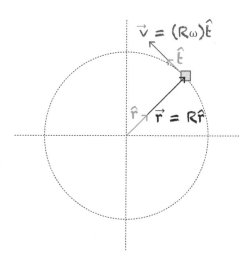

Figure 11.11: The direction for the radial and tangential unit vectors for an object moving in a circle.

We recognize that the velocity in Equation 11-1 is identical to the tangential velocity defined in Equation 5.4. Furthermore, in Equation 11-1, we have defined the new unit vector $\hat{t}$ (the tangential unit vector) to point tangential to the circle around which the block is moving[5].

$$\hat{t} = \left(-\sin\theta\right)\hat{x} + \left(\cos\theta\right)\hat{y}$$

The direction for $\hat{r}$ and $\hat{t}$ are shown in Figure 11.11; $\hat{t}$ always points in the counterclockwise direction. It is clear from this definition of the direction of $\hat{t}$ and the definition of the tangential velocity (Equation 11-1) that a positive angular velocity (or a positive tangential velocity) corresponds to counterclockwise motion, and a negative angular velocity (or negative tangential velocity) corresponds to clockwise motion[6].

The acceleration of the block is then found from this velocity through differentiation (Equation C-3).

$$\vec{a} = \frac{d\vec{v}}{dt} \quad \rightarrow \quad \vec{a} = \left(R\frac{d\omega}{dt}\right)\hat{t} + \left(R\omega\right)\frac{d\hat{t}}{dt}$$

$$\vec{a} = \left(R\frac{d\omega}{dt}\right)\hat{t} + \left(R\omega\right)\left[\left(\frac{d}{dt}\left(-\sin\theta\right)\right)\hat{x} + \left(\frac{d}{dt}\cos\theta\right)\hat{y}\right]$$

$$\vec{a} = \left(R\alpha\right)\hat{t} + \left(R\omega\right)\left[\left(-\cos\theta\frac{d\theta}{dt}\right)\hat{x} + \left(-\sin\theta\frac{d\theta}{dt}\right)\hat{y}\right]$$

---

5   You should confirm that $\hat{r}$ is perpendicular to $\hat{t}$ by showing that $\hat{r}\bullet\hat{t} = 0$.
6   This is consistent with our definition that counterclockwise motion is positive (Section 5-2).

$$\vec{a} = \left(R\alpha \right)\hat{t} + \left(-R\omega^2 \right)\left[\left(\cos\theta \right)\hat{x} + \left(\sin\theta \right)\hat{y} \right]$$

$$\vec{a} = \left(R\alpha \right)\hat{t} + \left(-R\omega^2 \right)\hat{r} \tag{11-2}$$

The first term in Equation 11-2 is the angular acceleration (Equation 5.5). The second term in Equation 11-2 is the centripetal acceleration and is directed radially toward the center of the circle (*i.e.*, it is directed in the $-\hat{r}$ direction). We will denote the magnitude of the centripetal acceleration as a_c, which can be expressed either in terms of the angular velocity or the tangential velocity.

$$a_c = R\omega^2 = \frac{v_t^2}{R} \tag{11-3}$$

Centripetal acceleration is required for the change in the direction of the velocity of the object as it moves around the circle and will always be present even if the speed of the object is constant.

Example 11-2:

Problem: A model train moves along a horizontal circular track with a radius of 0.5 m. Starting from rest, the train accelerates at 0.2 m/s². Through what total angle has the train travelled, when the magnitude of its centripetal acceleration is 0.32 m/s²?

Solution: The angular displacement of the train can be found using the constant angular acceleration kinematic equations (Section 5-4).

$$\omega_f^2 = \omega_i^2 + 2\alpha\Delta\theta \quad \rightarrow \quad \Delta\theta = \frac{\omega_f^2}{2\alpha}$$

Substitution of Equation 11-3 into this expression yields

$$\omega^2 = \frac{a_c}{R} \quad \rightarrow \quad \Delta\theta = \frac{\dfrac{a_c}{R}}{2\alpha} \quad \rightarrow \quad \Delta\theta = \frac{a_c}{2\alpha R}$$

The angular acceleration is related to the tangential acceleration by Equation 5.5.

$$\alpha = \frac{a_t}{R} \quad \rightarrow \quad \Delta\theta = \frac{a_c}{2\left(\dfrac{a_t}{R}\right)R} \quad \rightarrow \quad \Delta\theta = \frac{a_c}{2a_t}$$

Substitution of the values for our system gives us

$$\Delta\theta = \frac{0.32\frac{m}{s^2}}{2\left(0.2\frac{m}{s^2}\right)} \quad \rightarrow \quad \Delta\theta = 0.8\,rad$$

Since an object must experience centripetal acceleration to move in a circle, we know from Newton's 2nd law that a net force must act on an object moving in a circle. Furthermore, some component of this net force must be in the same direction as the centripetal acceleration, namely, toward the center of the circle around which the object is moving.

Example 11-3:

Problem: A 2 kg block is released from rest at the top of the frictionless track shown in Figure 11.12. After initially passing through a shallow valley, it then slides over a small hill, the top of which can be approximated as the arc of a circle with a radius of 1.2 m. If the speed of the block at the top of this hill is 3 m/s, what is the apparent weight of the block at the top of this hill?

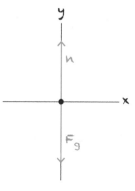

Figure 11.12: A block sliding along a frictionless track.

Solution: Let's begin by defining a reference frame for this system when the block is at the top of the small hill. In this reference frame, the y-axis denotes the vertical axis with a positive direction pointing up from the ground. The x-axis of this reference frame will be perpendicular to the y-axis with a positive direction pointing in the same direction as the block's velocity (*i.e.*, to the right in Figure 11.12). In the free body diagram for the block, we will denote the magnitude of the normal force as n and the magnitude of the force of gravity as F_g. With these definitions, the free body diagram for the block at the top of the small hill in Figure 11.12 is shown in Figure 11.13.

Applying Newton's 2nd law to the x-axis in this free body diagram yields the following trivial result:

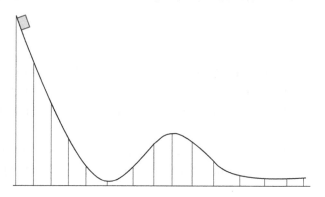

Figure 11.13: The free body diagram for the block in Example 11-3 when the block is at the top of the small hill in Figure 11.12.

$$\left(F_{net}\right)_x = ma_x \quad \rightarrow \quad 0 = ma_x \quad \rightarrow \quad a_x = 0$$

Something more interesting is happening along the y-axis, however. Specifically, since the block is moving around part of a circle, centripetal acceleration must be acting on the block to change the direction of its velocity. The direction of this acceleration must be toward the center of the circle, which is the negative y-axis direction for the free body diagram in 11-13. Hence, from Equation 11-3, we have

$$\left(F_{net}\right)_y = ma_y \quad \rightarrow \quad n - F_g = -m\frac{v_t^2}{R} \quad \rightarrow \quad n - mg = -m\frac{v_t^2}{R} \quad \rightarrow \quad n = m\left(g - \frac{v_t^2}{R}\right)$$

The apparent weight of the block is, thus,

$$w_{app} = n \quad \rightarrow \quad n = \left(2\,kg\right)\left(9.8\frac{m}{s^2} - \frac{\left(3\frac{m}{s}\right)^2}{1.2\,m}\right) \quad \rightarrow \quad w_{app} = 4.6\,N$$

The apparent weight of the block has decreased due to the block's acceleration.

Example 11-4:

Problem: A small 3 kg bob is attached to a 0.5 m long massless string and swings as a simple pendulum, as shown in Figure 11.14. The pendulum is released from rest with an angle $\theta = 30°$ relative to the vertical. What is the tension in the string when $\theta = 0°$? You can consider the system to be isolated and can model the bob as a point particle.

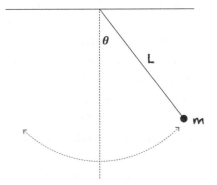

Figure 11.14: The pendulum in Example 11.4. The variables L and m denote the length of the string and the mass of the bob, respectively.

Solution: The tension in the string must give rise to the net force that is necessary for the centripetal acceleration of the bob. Since the magnitude of this acceleration depends upon the speed of the bob (Equation 11-3), we can begin our solution to this problem by using energy conservation to determine the speed of the bob when $\theta = 0°$. From the discussion in Section 6-6, we can write the equation for the energy of this system as

$$E = \frac{1}{2}I\omega^2 - mgL\cos\theta$$

In this equation, the variables L and m denote the length of the string and the mass of the bob, respectively. Since the system is isolated, we have

$$\Delta E = 0 \quad \rightarrow \quad \left(\frac{1}{2}I\omega_f^2 - \frac{1}{2}I\omega_i^2\right) + \left(mgL\cos\theta_i - mgL\cos\theta_f\right) = 0$$

When the pendulum is at its maximum angle ($\theta = 30°$), the speed of the bob is zero. The speed of the bob at $\theta = 0°$ is, thus,

$$\left(\frac{1}{2}I\omega_{\theta=0}^2 - 0\right) + \left(mgL\cos\left(30°\right) - mgL\cos\left(0°\right)\right) = 0 \quad \rightarrow \quad \frac{1}{2}I\omega_{\theta=0}^2 + mgL\left(\frac{\sqrt{3}}{2}-1\right) = 0$$

$$I\omega_{\theta=0}^2 + mgL\left(\sqrt{3}-2\right) = 0 \quad \rightarrow \quad \omega_{\theta=0}^2 = \frac{mgL}{I}\left(2-\sqrt{3}\right)$$

Substitution of the moment of inertia for a point particle then gives us

$$I = mL^2 \quad \rightarrow \quad \omega_{\theta=0}^2 = \frac{mgL}{mL^2}\left(2-\sqrt{3}\right) \rightarrow \quad \omega_{\theta=0}^2 = \frac{g}{L}\left(2-\sqrt{3}\right)$$

The next step in our solution is to draw the free body diagram for the bob when $\theta = 0°$. Let's define a reference frame for this system when $\theta = 0°$ with a y-axis denoting the vertical axis with a positive direction pointing up from the ground. The x-axis of this reference frame will be perpendicular to the y-axis with a positive direction pointing to the right in Figure 11.14. In the free body diagram for the bob, we will denote the magnitude of the tension in the rope as T and the magnitude of the force of gravity as F_g. With these definitions, the free body diagram for the bob is shown in Figure 11.15.

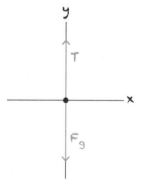

Figure 11.15: The free body diagram for the pendulum in Example 11-4 when $\theta = 0°$.

Applying Newton's 2nd law to each of the coordinate axes in this free body diagram yields the following equations:

$$\left(F_{net}\right)_x = ma_x \quad \rightarrow \quad 0 = ma_x \quad \rightarrow \quad a_x = 0$$

$$\left(F_{net}\right)_y = ma_y \quad \rightarrow \quad T - F_g = ma_y \quad \rightarrow \quad T - mg = ma_y$$

Since the bob is swinging through a circle, centripetal acceleration must be acting on the bob to change the direction of its velocity. The direction of this acceleration must be toward the center of the circle, which is the positive y-axis direction for the free body diagram in 11-15. Thus, from Equation 11-3, we have

$$a_y = \omega_{\theta=0}^2 R \;\; \rightarrow \;\; T - mg = m\omega_{\theta=0}^2 R \;\; \rightarrow \;\; T = mg + m\omega_{\theta=0}^2 R \;\; \rightarrow \;\; T = m\left(g + \omega_{\theta=0}^2 R\right)$$

The radius of the circle is equal to the length of the string.

$$R = L \;\; \rightarrow \;\; T = m\left(g + \omega_{\theta=0}^2 L\right)$$

Hence,

$$T = m\left(g + \frac{g}{L}\left(2 - \sqrt{3}\right)L\right) \;\; \rightarrow \;\; T = mg\left(1 + 2 - \sqrt{3}\right)$$

Substitution of the values for our system gives us

$$T = \left(3\,\text{kg}\right)\left(9.8\,\frac{\text{m}}{\text{s}^2}\right)\left(1 + 2 - \sqrt{3}\right) \;\; \rightarrow \;\; T = 37.3\,\text{N}$$

Although a radially oriented component of net force is required for circular motion, this component of the net force will do no work as long as the radius of the circle is constant (*i.e.*, if there is no radial displacement of the object). The tension in the string in Example 11-4 will do no work on the bob since the total energy of the bob remains constant as the bob swings back and forth. Although the radially acting component of the net force responsible for the centripetal acceleration of an object does no work on the object[7], it, nevertheless, influences the motion of the object by providing a geometric constraint on the motion. This is similar to how the presence of the ramp in Example 4-3 provided a constraint linking the horizontal and vertical motions of a block sliding down the ramp.

---

7   The torque associated with this force does work on the bob, however, since the bob does experience an angular displacement.

11-5 The Fictitious Centrifugal Force

Imagine that you are swinging a bucket full of water in a vertical circle. Based upon your intuition (or perhaps personal experience), you suspect that if the bucket moves too slowly, the water will fall out when the bucket is inverted, but if you swing the bucket fast enough, the water will always stay in the bucket. What is the minimum angular velocity with which you can swing the bucket without the water falling out?

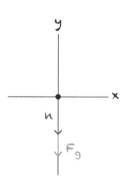

Let's begin our solution to this problem by defining a reference frame for this system in which the y-axis denotes the vertical axis with a positive direction pointing up from the ground. The x-axis for this reference frame will be perpendicular to the y-axis and have a positive direction pointing parallel to the direction of the bucket's velocity at the top of the vertical circle; of course, the velocity of the water is the same as the velocity of the bucket. In the free body diagram for the water, we will denote the magnitude of the normal force exerted by the bucket on the water as n and the magnitude of

Figure 11.16: The free body diagram for the water when the bucket is at the top of the vertical circle.

the force of gravity as F_g. With these definitions, the free body diagram for the water when it is at the top of the vertical circle is shown in Figure 11.16.

Applying Newton's 2nd law to each of the coordinate axes in this free body diagram yields the following equations:

$$\left(F_{net}\right)_x = ma_x \quad \rightarrow \quad 0 = ma_x \quad \rightarrow \quad a_x = 0$$

$$\left(F_{net}\right)_y = ma_y \quad \rightarrow \quad -F_g - n = ma_y \quad \rightarrow \quad -mg - n = ma_y$$

Since the water is moving in a circle, centripetal acceleration must be acting on the water to change the direction of its velocity. The direction of this acceleration must be toward the center of the circle, which is the negative y-axis direction for the free body diagram in 11-16. Hence, from Equation 11-3, we have

$$a_y = -\omega^2 R \quad \rightarrow \quad -mg - n = m\left(-\omega^2 R\right) \quad \rightarrow \quad n = m\omega^2 R - mg$$

$$n = m\left(\omega^2 R - g\right)$$

In this equation, R denotes the radius of the vertical circle around which you are swinging the bucket.

Not surprisingly, the magnitude of the normal force exerted by the bucket on the water is a function of the angular velocity of the water. Indeed, it is this force that is required to change the direction of the tangential velocity of the water and, thereby, keep the water moving in a circle[8]. An increase in the tangential velocity of the water (which, according to Equation 5.4, is equivalent to an increase in the angular velocity of the water) will, naturally, result in an increase in the magnitude of the centripetal acceleration required to change the direction of the water's velocity. This, in turn, requires an increase in the magnitude of the net force acting radially and, hence, an increase in the magnitude of the normal force exerted by the bucket on the water when the bucket is at the top of its vertical circle.

As long as the normal force exists (*i.e.,* as long as $n \geq 0$), the water is in contact with the bucket and will not fall out. Therefore, the minimum angular velocity for keeping the water in the bucket occurs when the magnitude of the normal force is zero.

$$ n = 0 \quad \rightarrow \quad \omega = \pm \sqrt{\frac{g}{R}} $$

The ($\pm$) sign in this equation indicates that the result is valid for either direction of the angular velocity[9]. Since the magnitude of the normal force acting on the water is also equal to the apparent weight[10] of the water, we see that this minimum angular velocity corresponds to the condition where the water is weightless.

It is interesting to note that if the angular velocity is small enough such that $\omega^2 R < g$, then the magnitude of the normal force exerted by the bucket on the water is less than zero. Since the magnitude of a vector cannot be negative[11], we interpret this result as indicating the water has lost contact with the bucket. In other words, if we spin the bucket too slowly, the water will fall out of the bucket.

At the top of the vertical circle the force of gravity pulls the water straight down toward the center of the circle. Therefore, if the bucket was not moving, the water would fall straight down to the ground. If the bucket is spinning around in the circle, the force of gravity acting on the water will contribute the net force required for the water to move with the bucket (*i.e.,* for the water's centripetal acceleration). However, since the magnitude of the force of gravity is constant regardless of the angular velocity of the bucket, there is a lower limit to the magnitude of the net force that can act on the water; this occurs when the magnitude of the normal force is zero. If the magnitude of this minimum net force (*i.e.,* the magnitude of the force of gravity acting on the water) is larger than what is required for the centripetal acceleration of the water, the total radial acceleration of the water will be larger than the centripetal acceleration of the water alone. The remaining radial acceleration (the difference between the total radial acceleration and the centripetal acceleration) will cause the water to have a displacement toward the center of the circle and fall out of the bucket. You can also think of this as both the water and the bucket undergoing circular motion but around circles of different radii. This difference in radii results in a displacement of the water relative to the bucket.

As discussed in Section 8-9, fictitious forces appear to act inside non-inertial (*i.e.,* accelerating) reference frames. A common example of an accelerating reference frame is one that moves with a rotating object or an object moving in a circle. For example, a person moving with the block as it passes over the hill (Example 11-3), who is using a reference frame that is fixed with the block, would

---

8   Recall from Newton's 1st law (Section 8-3) that the water will continue to move in a straight line unless a net force acts upon it.

9   See Section 5-2.

10   See Section 8-9.

11   See Section B-4.

perceive the normal force and the force of gravity acting on the block but not the acceleration[12]. Hence, this person would need to add a fictitious force pointing up (in the positive y-axis direction in Figure 11.13) to obtain a "*net*" force of zero and, thus, no acceleration for the block. This fictitious force, associated with the centripetal acceleration of the system, is referred to as the fictitious centrifugal force since it is directed away from the center of the circle.

$$\vec{F}_{centrifugal} = \left(m\omega^2 R\right)\hat{r}$$

(11-4)

This fictitious centrifugal force can also be considered to give rise to the change in the apparent weight of the water, as shown in the vertically spinning bucket or the tension in the string of the pendulum in Example 11-4.

An object on the surface of the Earth will experience a fictitious centrifugal force pushing it out from the surface of the Earth due to the Earth's rotation. As shown in Figure 11.17, we can describe the radius of the circular motion of the object associated with the Earth's rotation (*i.e.*, the value of R in Equation 11-4) in terms of the radius of the Earth and the polar angle φ describing the position of the object.

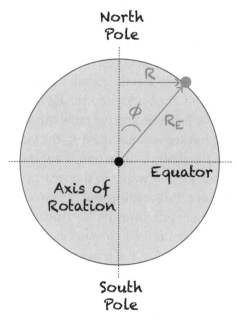

Figure 11.17: An object on the surface of the Earth will experience circular motion due to the rotation of the Earth. The radius of this circular motion depends upon the latitude of the object and the radius of the Earth, denoted by R_E.

The magnitude of the fictitious centrifugal force acting on an object on the surface of the Earth is, thus,

---

12   Since the reference frame is moving with the block, there is no movement of the block relative to the reference frame. Hence, in that reference frame, the block has no acceleration.

$$F_{centrifugal,Earth} = m\omega_E^2 R_E \sin\phi$$

(11-5)

Hence, the magnitude of this fictitious centrifugal force depends upon the latitude of the object and is largest at the equator.

Example 11-5:

Problem: A 10 kg object is at rest on the surface of the Earth at the equator. What is the magnitude of the fictitious centrifugal force acting on the object?

Solution: We first must solve for the angular velocity of the Earth.

$$\omega_E = 2\pi \frac{\text{rad}}{\text{day}}\left(\frac{1\,\text{day}}{24\,\text{hr}}\right)\left(\frac{1\,\text{hr}}{60\,\text{min}}\right)\left(\frac{1\,\text{min}}{60\,\text{s}}\right) \rightarrow \omega_E = 7.3\times10^{-5}\frac{\text{rad}}{\text{s}}$$

Since the object is at the Equator, the radius of its circular motion is equal to the radius of the Earth. From Equation 11-5, we have

$$F_{centrifugal,Earth} = (10\,\text{kg})\left(7.3\times10^{-5}\frac{\text{rad}}{\text{s}}\right)^2 (6.37\times10^6\,\text{m})\sin(90°)$$

$$F_{centrifugal,Earth} = 0.34\,\text{N}$$

The magnitude of this force is small compared to the magnitude of the force of gravity acting on the object.

$$F_g = mg \rightarrow F_g = (10\,\text{kg})\left(9.8\frac{\text{m}}{\text{s}^2}\right) \rightarrow F_g = 980\,\text{N}$$

Thus, the fictitious centrifugal force can be neglected, and the object can be considered to be in an inertial reference frame[13].

---

13   However, it is, nevertheless, true that your apparent weight would be smallest at the equator.

The fictitious centrifugal force is also apparent when you drive your car around a turn, as discussed in Section 8-9. You feel yourself being pushed to the outside of the turn and interpret this sensation as resulting from a fictitious centrifugal force. Of course, this fictitious force "*appears*" only because you are describing your motion using a non-inertial reference frame; specifically, a reference frame fixed within a car experiencing centripetal acceleration.

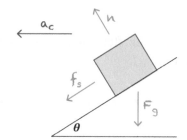

Figure 11.18: The forces acting on a car driving around a banked circle. The normal force is denoted by n, the magnitude of the force of static friction as f_s, and the magnitude of the force of gravity as F_g. The direction of the centripetal acceleration required for the car to drive around the turn is indicated in blue. Components of both n and f_s will give rise to the net force required for the centripetal acceleration.

Naturally, in order for the car to experience the centripetal acceleration necessary to drive safely around a turn, a net force with a component directed toward the center of the circle must act on the car. In general, this component of the net force is the force of static friction acting between the tires and the road. It is a force of static friction since this force is acting to *prevent the motion* of the car relative to the road. In other words, this force is acting to keep the radius of the car's trajectory the same as the radius of the turn. Since there is an upper limit to the magnitude of the static friction force (depending upon the tire material and the condition of the road), turns are often also banked so that a component of the normal force acting on the car also can contribute to the net radially directed force acting on the car, as shown in Figure 11.18.

Something similar happens when a pilot needs to turn an airplane. She will rotate the airplane around its longitudinal axis so that a component of the lift[14] is oriented in the direction she wants to turn the airplane.

Summary

- **A force-based approach is necessary to describe the mechanics of systems in static equilibrium.**
- **The two conditions for a system to be in static equilibrium are $\vec{F}_{net} = 0$ and $\vec{\tau}_{net} = 0$.**
- **The axis of rotation for the $\vec{\tau}_{net} = 0$ condition for static equilibrium should always be located where one or more forces act on the system.**
- **The mechanical advantage of a lever is equal to the ratio of the moment arm of the effort to the moment arm of the load.**
- **Any object moving in a circle, or through part of a circle, must experience centripetal acceleration.** The direction of this acceleration is always toward the center of the circle, and the magnitude of the acceleration is

---

14   Lift is a force that acts perpendicular to the surface of an airplane's wings.

$$a_c = R\omega^2 = \frac{v_t^2}{R}$$

In this equation, R is the radius of the circle.

- **Any object moving in a circle, or through part of a circle, must experience a net force that has a component directed toward the center of the circle.**
- **A fictitious centrifugal force appears to act inside non-inertial reference frames undergoing circular or rotational motion.**

Problems

1. A 3 m long cantilever with a mass of 250 kg is attached to a hinge and also held in place by a steel cable that is attached to the far end of the cantilever at an angle of 30° with respect to the cantilever, as shown in the figure at right. A 5 kg mass also hangs from the far end of the cantilever. What is the magnitude of the force that the hinge exerts on the cantilever? What is the tension in the steel cable?

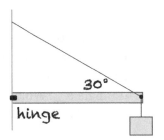

2. A child's mobile consists of four blocks supported by massless rods, as shown in the figure at right. The entire mobile is in static equilibrium. What is the unknown mass of the topmost block?

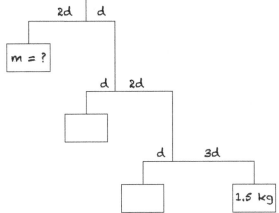

3. A person is riding on a roller coaster that passes through a vertical loop with a radius of 10 m. What is the minimum tangential velocity that the roller coaster must have at the top of the loop for the person to not fall out?

4. A block is released from rest at the top of the frictionless track, as shown in the figure at right. After sliding down the initial hill, the block moves through a vertical loop. From what minimum height must the block be released, in order for the block to not fall off of the track at the top of the vertical loop? Express your answer as a multiple of the radius of the loop.

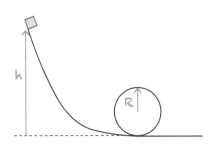

5. A uniformly dense rigid rod with a length of 0.5 m and a mass of 4 kg is held in place by two massless ropes, as shown in the figure at right. What is the tension in each rope if the angle $\theta = 20°$?

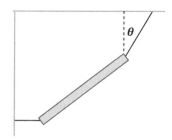

6. A block with a mass of 2 kg is sliding down a frictionless semicircular track with a radius of 0.5 m, as shown in the figure at right. At what angle θ_{max} will the block fly off of the track?

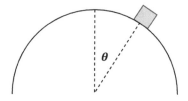

7. A block with a mass of 2 kg is sliding down a semicircular track with a radius of 0.5 m, as shown in the figure below. A uniformly dense solid sphere with a mass of 2 kg and a radius of 0.01 m is rolling without slipping down an identical track. Each object will fly off its track at a characteristic angle θ_{max}. Which object will have a larger value of θ_{max}? You should assume that any potential losses of energy with changes in position due to friction will be identical for both objects.

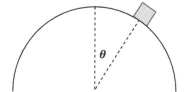 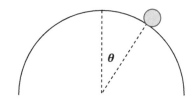

8. In a conical pendulum, a bob attached to a string moves in a horizontal circle, as shown in the figure at right. What is the period of the pendulum if the mass of the bob is 3 kg, the length of the string is 0.75 m, and the angle $\theta = 30°$? In other words, how long does it take the bob to complete one revolution?

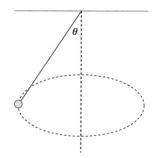

9. A ride often found at amusement parks is a large rotating cylinder. In this ride, people stand with their backs against the curved inside wall of the cylinder. As the cylinder spins very rapidly around an axis through its center, these riders are pressed against the wall by the fictitious

centrifugal force. Eventually the floor is pulled away and the riders are suspended in the air. If the radius of the cylinder is 5 m and the coefficient of static friction between the people and the wall is 0.4, what is the maximum period of rotation of the cylinder for the floor to be removed safely?

10. An airplane is flying in a horizontal circle at a speed of 400 km/hr. If its wings are tilted at a 30° angle relative to the horizontal, what is the radius of the circle in which the plane is flying?

CHAPTER TWELVE

Newtonian Mechanics for Systems of Moving Objects

The third of Newton's three laws of motion describes the relationship between the forces that interacting objects (or systems of objects) exert on each other. The correct application of Newton's 3rd law is essential when using forces to describe the kinematics of a system of interacting moving objects. However, as we shall see in examples in this chapter, the forces acting between objects within the same system frequently do not contribute to the kinematics of the system as a whole. Thus, it is often more efficient to apply Newton's laws to the entire system rather than to each object in the system individually in order to describe the motion of the objects or the system.

12-2 Newton's 3rd Law

Newton's 3rd law can be expressed as

Every force is always accompanied by a separate force of the same magnitude, but oriented in the opposite direction. Thus, the forces that interacting objects (or systems of objects) exert on each other are always equal in magnitude and opposite in direction.

Newton's 3rd law is often colloquially expressed as *"for every action there is an equal and opposite reaction."*

When a child runs across her backyard, her feet push backward on the Earth, and the Earth pushes forward on her. It is the force of the Earth pushing on her, together with the other forces that act on her, that determine her acceleration. She cannot make herself accelerate by exerting a force on the Earth since this is not a force that acts on her (Section 8-4). However, it follows from Newton's 3rd law that she can increase the magnitude of the force that the Earth exerts on her by increasing the magnitude of the force she exerts on the Earth (*i.e.,* by pushing "*harder*" on the Earth).

Similarly, when a person climbs a rope, it is the tension in the rope pulling up on the person that influences his acceleration. However, we recognize from Newton's 3rd law that the tension in the rope (*i.e.,* the force of the rope pulling up on the person) results from the person pulling down on the rope.

While, at first glance, this may seem like nothing more than semantics, Newton's 3rd law does have an immediate practical use in constructing free body diagrams for systems consisting of multiple interacting masses. For example, consider the system shown in Figure 12.1 that consists of two blocks resting on a horizontal surface.

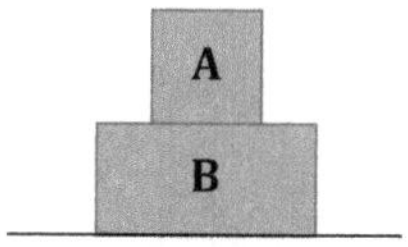

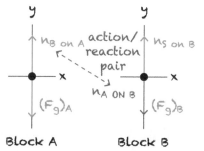

Figure 12.1: A system consisting of two blocks at rest on a horizontal surface.

Let's define a reference frame for this system in which the y-axis denotes the vertical axis with a positive direction pointing up from the ground. The x-axis for this reference frame will be perpendicular to the y-axis and have a positive direction pointing to the right in Figure 12.1. According to this reference frame, the free body diagrams for the blocks are shown in Figure 12-2.

There are two forces acting on block A: the force of gravity and a normal force. The normal force acting on block A, denoted as $n_{B \, on \, A}$ in Figure 12.2, results from the interaction between block A and block B. Specifically, it is the force of block B pushing up on block A. From Newton's 3rd law, we know that if block B pushes up on block A, then block A must push down on block B. For this reason, the force $n_{A \, on \, B}$ appears in the free body diagram

Figure 12.2: Free body diagrams for the two blocks in Figure 12.1. The forces $n_{B \, on \, A}$ and $n_{A \, on \, B}$ form an action/reaction pair.

for block B. From the fact that the free body diagrams were drawn using the same reference frame, it follows that if $n_{B \, on \, A}$ is in the positive y-axis direction, then $n_{A \, on \, B}$ must be in the negative y-axis direction. It is common to use the language of Newton's 3rd law to describe the forces $n_{B \, on \, A}$ and $n_{A \, on \, B}$ as an *action/reaction pair*.

The force of the horizontal surface pushing up on block B appears as $n_{S \, on \, B}$ in the free body diagram for block B. If we were to draw a free body diagram for the horizontal surface, we would need to include a force $n_{B \, on \, S}$ to satisfy Newton's 3rd law. In this case, $n_{S \, on \, B}$ and $n_{B \, on \, S}$ would form an action/reaction pair.

Applying Newton's 2nd law to each of the coordinate axes in the free body diagram for block A yields the following equations:

$$\left(F_{net}\right)_x = ma_x \quad \rightarrow \quad 0 = m_A a_{A,x} \quad \rightarrow \quad a_{A,x} = 0$$

$$\left(F_{net}\right)_y = ma_y \quad \rightarrow \quad n_{B \, on \, A} - \left(F_g\right)_A = m_A a_{A,y} \quad \rightarrow \quad n_{B \, on \, A} - m_A g = m_A a_{A,y}$$

We can safely assume that block A will remain at rest and, thus, that the component of its acceleration along the y-axis will be zero. Substitution of $a_{A,y} = 0$ into the equation above yields

$$a_{A,y} = 0 \quad \rightarrow \quad n_{B \, on \, A} = m_A g$$

Applying Newton's 2nd law to each of the coordinate axes in the free body diagram for block B yields the following equations:

$$\left(F_{net}\right)_x = ma_x \quad \rightarrow \quad 0 = m_B a_{B,x} \quad \rightarrow \quad a_{B,x} = 0$$

$$\left(F_{net}\right)_y = ma_y \quad \rightarrow \quad n_{SonB} - n_{AonB} - \left(F_g\right)_B = m_B a_{B,y} \quad \rightarrow \quad n_{SonB} - n_{AonB} - m_B g = m_B a_{B,y}$$

We can also assume that block B will remain at rest and, thus, that the component of its acceleration along the y-axis will be zero, too. Substitution of $a_{B,y} = 0$ into the equation above yields

$$a_{B,y} = 0 \quad \rightarrow \quad n_{SonB} = n_{AonB} + m_B g$$

From Newton's 3rd law, we know that the magnitude of the force of block A pushing on block B must be equal to the magnitude of the force of block B pushing on block A[1].

$$n_{AonB} = n_{BonA}$$

Hence,

$$n_{SonB} = n_{BonA} + m_B g$$

$$n_{SonB} = m_A g + m_B g \quad \rightarrow \quad n_{SonB} = \left(m_A + m_B\right)g \quad \rightarrow \quad w_{app,B} = \left(m_A + m_B\right)g$$

As expected, the normal force exerted by the horizontal surface on block B is equal in magnitude to the total apparent weight of both blocks. In other words, the surface must exert a force sufficient to support both blocks.

12-3 Newton's Laws Applied to Systems with Multiple Moving Objects

When we used an energy-based approach to describe the kinematics of a system of multiple objects moving together, we employed relationships between the speeds of the moving objects to simplify our calculations (see Section 4-5). When using a force-based approach, we instead use relationships

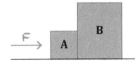

Figure 12.3: A system consisting of two blocks on a horizontal surface.

---

1   We had already taken into account the opposite directions of these two forces when we drew the free body diagrams for the blocks (Figure 12.2).

between the accelerations of the objects. Let's consider the system shown in Figure 12.3 consisting of two blocks on a horizontal and frictionless surface.

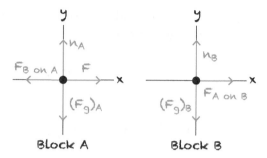

When an external horizontal force is applied to block A, both blocks will move together across the surface. We can determine the acceleration of block B using Newton's laws. Let's define a reference frame for this system in which the y-axis denotes the vertical axis with a positive direction pointing up from the ground. The x-axis for this reference frame will be perpendicular to the y-axis and have a positive direction pointing to the right, as in

Figure 12.4: Free body diagrams for the blocks in Figure 12-3. The forces $F_{B \, on \, A}$ and $F_{A \, on \, B}$ form an action/reaction pair.

Figure 12.3. In the free body diagrams for the blocks, we will denote the magnitude of the normal force as n and the magnitude of the force of gravity as F_g. According to these definitions, the free body diagrams for the blocks are shown in Figure 12.4.

The external force acting on block A will cause block A to move and, consequently, to push against block B (Figure 12.3). We will denote the force of block A pushing on block B as $F_{A \, on \, B}$ in the free body diagram for block B (Figure 12.4). From Newton's 3rd law, we know that if block A pushes on block B, then block B must push on block A. We will denote this force as $F_{B \, on \, A}$ in the free body diagram for block A. From the fact that the free body diagrams were drawn using the same reference frame, it follows that since $F_{A \, on \, B}$ is in the positive x-axis direction, then $F_{B \, on \, A}$ must be in the negative x-axis direction.

Applying Newton's 2nd law to each of the coordinate axes in the free body diagram for block A yields the following equations:

$$\left(F_{net}\right)_x = ma_x \quad \rightarrow \quad F - F_{B \, on \, A} = m_A a_{A,x}$$

$$\left(F_{net}\right)_y = ma_y \quad \rightarrow \quad n_A - \left(F_g\right)_A = m_A a_{A,y} \quad \rightarrow \quad n_A - m_A g = m_A a_{A,y}$$

Since there is no displacement of block A along the y-axis in Figure 12.4, the component of the acceleration of block A along the y-axis is zero. Substitution of $a_{A,y} = 0$ into the equation above yields

$$a_{A,y} = 0 \quad \rightarrow \quad n_A = m_A g$$

Applying Newton's 2nd law to each of the coordinate axes in the free body diagram for block B yields the following equations:

$$\left(F_{net}\right)_x = ma_x \quad \rightarrow \quad F_{A \, on \, B} = m_B a_{B,x}$$

$$\left(F_{net}\right)_y = ma_y \quad \rightarrow \quad n_B - \left(F_g\right)_B = m_B a_{B,y} \quad \rightarrow \quad n_B - m_B g = m_B a_{B,y}$$

Since there is also no displacement of block B along the y-axis in Figure 12.14, the component of the acceleration of block B along the y-axis is zero. Substitution of $a_{B,y} = 0$ into the equation above yields

$$a_{B,y} = 0 \quad \rightarrow \quad n_B = m_B g$$

From Newton's 3rd law, we know that the magnitude of the force of block A pushing on block B must be equal to the magnitude of the force of block B pushing on block A[2].

$$F_{B \text{ on } A} = F_{A \text{ on } B}$$

Substitution of this expression into our equation for the x-axis component of the net force acting on block A gives us

$$F - F_{A \text{ on } B} = m_A a_{A,x}$$

The next step in our solution is to identify the relationships, if any, between the accelerations of the objects in our system. In this case, we know that the accelerations of the blocks must have the same magnitude and the same direction.

$$a_{A,x} = a_{B,x}$$

Substitution of this expression into our equation for the x-axis component of the net force acting on block A gives us

$$F - F_{A \text{ on } B} = m_A a_{B,x}$$

We can then combine this expression with the equation for the x-axis component of the net force acting on block B to determine the magnitude of $a_{b,x}$.

$$F - m_B a_{B,x} = m_A a_{B,x} \quad \rightarrow \quad F = m_B a_{B,x} + m_A a_{B,x} \quad \rightarrow \quad F = \left(m_B + m_A \right) a_{B,x}$$

$$a_{B,x} = \frac{F}{m_B + m_A}$$

---

2   We had already taken into account the opposite directions of these two forces when we drew the free body diagrams for the blocks (Figure 12.4).

It is worth noting that the term in the denominator of this equation is the effective mass of the system.

$$m_{effective} = m_B + m_A$$

This makes sense since the action of the force must result in the acceleration of the entire system (*i.e.*, both blocks).

Example 12-1:

Problem: The coefficient of static friction between block A and block B in Figure 12.5 is 0.3. The masses of block A and block B are 1.5 kg and 3.0 kg, respectively. What is the maximum magnitude of the external force in Figure 12.5 that can be applied to block B without block A slipping off the top of block B?

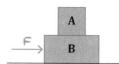

Figure 12.5: A system consisting of two blocks on a horizontal surface.

Solution: What force acting on block A keeps block A from slipping off block B? Since this force acts to *prevent the motion of block A* relative to block B, it must be static friction. We also anticipate from Newton's 2nd law that the acceleration of block B will be in the same direction as the external force acting on block B (*i.e.*, to the right in Figure 12.5). Thus, in order to prevent the motion of block A relative to block B (*i.e.*, to prevent block A from moving to the left relative to block B), the direction of the force of static friction acting on block A must be the same as the direction of the external force acting on block B (*i.e.*, to the right in Figure 12.5).

The next step in the solution of this problem is to draw the free body diagrams for the objects in the system. As before, let's define a common reference frame for these free body diagrams in which the y-axis denotes the vertical axis with a positive direction pointing up from the ground. The x-axis for this reference frame will be perpendicular to the y-axis and have a positive direction pointing to the right in Figure 12.5. Using these definitions the free body diagrams for the blocks are shown in Figure 12.6.

There are two forces that result from the interaction between the two blocks and, therefore, appear on both free body diagrams. The normal force that block B exerts on block A, denoted as n_A, acts in the positive y-axis direction in the free body diagram for block A and in the negative y-axis direction in the free body diagram for block B[3]. Similarly, the force

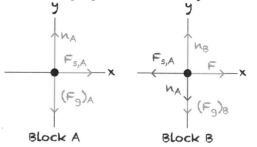

Figure 12.6: Free body diagrams for the blocks in Figure 12.5. The forces n_A and $f_{s,A}$ result from the interaction between the two blocks and, thus, appear on the free body diagram for each block.

---

3   We are going to omit the step of writing the separate forces $n_{B\,on\,A}$ and $n_{A\,on\,B}$. We already know that the magnitude of these two forces will be the same from Newton's 3rd law, so we will write only one of them. We will further simplify our

of static friction between the two blocks, denoted as $f_{s,A}$, acts in the positive x-axis direction in the free body diagram for block A and in the negative x-axis direction in the free body diagram for block B.

Applying Newton's 2nd law to each of the coordinate axes in the free body diagram for block A yields the following equations:

$$\left(F_{net}\right)_x = ma_x \;\; \rightarrow \;\; f_{s,A} = m_A a_{A,x}$$

$$\left(F_{net}\right)_y = ma_y \;\; \rightarrow \;\; n_A - \left(F_g\right)_A = m_A a_{A,y} \;\; \rightarrow \;\; n_A - m_A g = m_A a_{A,y}$$

Since there is no displacement of block A along the y-axis in Figure 12.6, the component of the acceleration of block A along the y-axis is zero. Substitution of $a_{A,y} = 0$ into the equation above yields

$$a_{A,y} = 0 \;\; \rightarrow \;\; n_A = m_A g$$

Applying Newton's 2nd law to each of the coordinate axes in the free body diagram for block B yields the following equations:

$$\left(F_{net}\right)_x = ma_x \;\; \rightarrow \;\; F - f_{s,A} = m_B a_{B,x}$$

$$\left(F_{net}\right)_y = ma_y \;\; \rightarrow \;\; n_B - n_A - \left(F_g\right)_B = m_B a_{B,y} \;\; \rightarrow \;\; n_B - n_A - m_B g = m_B a_{B,y}$$

Since there is also no displacement of block B along the y-axis in Figure 12.6, the component of the acceleration of block B along the y-axis is also zero. Substitution of $a_{B,y} = 0$ into the equation above yields

$$a_{B,y} = 0 \;\; \rightarrow \;\; n_B = n_A + m_B g$$

The next step in our solution is to identify the relationships, if any, between the accelerations of the objects in our system. In order for block A not to slip off of block B, the acceleration of block A must have the same magnitude and direction as the acceleration of block B. In other words, *the two blocks must have the same acceleration so that there is no relative motion between them.* Hence,

$$a_{A,x} = a_{B,x} \;\; \rightarrow \;\; \frac{f_{s,A}}{m_A} = \frac{F - f_{s,A}}{m_B}$$

Solving for $f_{s,A}$ yields

---

nomenclature by denoting this force as n_A since it is the normal force that is supporting (*i.e.,* "pushing up on") block A.

$$m_B f_{s,A} = m_A F - m_A f_{s,A} \;\rightarrow\; \left(m_B + m_A\right)f_{s,A} = m_A F \;\rightarrow\; f_{s,A} = \frac{m_A}{m_B + m_A}F$$

We can then use the definition of the magnitude of the force of static friction (Equation 8.4) to solve for the limits on the external force[4].

$$f_{s,A} \leq \mu_s n_A \;\rightarrow\; \frac{m_A}{m_B + m_A}F \leq \mu_s n_A \;\rightarrow\; F \leq \frac{\mu_s n_A\left(m_B + m_A\right)}{m_A}$$

As expected, the magnitude of the external force has an upper limit. In other words, there is a maximum magnitude for the external force that can be applied to block B such that the two blocks have the same acceleration. Substitution of the previously derived equation for n_A into this inequality for the external force gives us

$$F \leq \frac{\mu_s\left(m_A g\right)\left(m_B + m_A\right)}{m_A} \;\rightarrow\; F \leq \mu_s\left(m_B + m_A\right)g$$

$$F \leq \left(0.3\right)\left(3.0\,\text{kg} + 1.5\,\text{kg}\right)\left(9.8\,\frac{\text{m}}{\text{s}^2}\right) \;\rightarrow\; F \leq 13.2\,\text{N}$$

The maximum value for the external force is, therefore,

$$F_{\text{max}} = 13.2\,\text{N}$$

12-4 Newton's Laws Applied to Systems with Multiple Moving Objects Connected by Ropes and Pulleys

Consider the system shown in Figure 12.7 consisting of two blocks connected by a massless rope. An external force is applied to block A to pull it (together with block B) across a horizontal surface. What is the magnitude of the acceleration of block B?

The first step in this process is to draw the free body diagrams for the objects in the system. Let's define a common reference frame for these free body diagrams in which the y-axis denotes the vertical axis with a positive direction pointing up from the ground. The x-axis for this reference frame will be perpendicular to the y-axis

Figure 12.7: A system consisting of two blocks connected by a massless rope.

---

4   The normal force n_A is the normal force associated with this friction force since, like the friction force, it arises because of an interaction between the two blocks.

and have a positive direction pointing to the right in Figure 12.7. With these definitions, the free body diagrams for the objects in Figure 12.7 are shown in Figure 12.8.

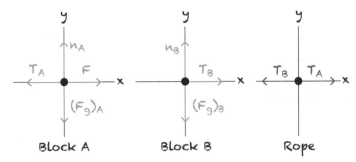

Figure 12.8: The free body diagrams for the system in Figure 12.7. The forces T_A and T_B result from the interaction between the rope and the blocks and, thus, appear on more than one free body diagram.

In these free body diagrams, T_A is the magnitude of the tension acting on block A, and T_B is the magnitude of the tension acting on block B. There is no force of gravity acting on the rope since the rope is massless. The tensions in the rope form action/reaction pairs since the magnitude of the force of the rope pulling on the each block is equal to the magnitude of the force of each block pulling on the rope. Thus, the tension T_A appears in the free body diagrams for block A and the rope, and the tension T_B appears in the free body diagrams for block B and the rope.

Applying Newton's 2nd law to each of the coordinate axes in the free body diagram for block A yields the following equations:

$$\left(F_{net}\right)_x = ma_x \quad \rightarrow \quad F - T_A = m_A a_{A,x}$$

$$\left(F_{net}\right)_y = ma_y \quad \rightarrow \quad n_A - \left(F_g\right)_A = m_A a_{A,y} \quad \rightarrow \quad n_A - m_A g = m_A a_{A,y}$$

Since there is no displacement of block A along the y-axis in Figure 12.8, the component of the acceleration of block A along the y-axis is zero. Substitution of $a_{A,y} = 0$ into the equation above yields

$$a_{A,y} = 0 \quad \rightarrow \quad n_A = m_A g$$

Applying Newton's 2nd law to each of the coordinate axes in the free body diagram for block B yields the following equations:

$$\left(F_{net}\right)_x = ma_x \quad \rightarrow \quad T_B = m_B a_{B,x}$$

$$\left(F_{net}\right)_y = ma_y \quad \rightarrow \quad n_B - \left(F_g\right)_B = m_B a_{B,y} \quad \rightarrow \quad n_B - m_B g = m_B a_{B,y}$$

Since there is also no displacement of block B along the y-axis in Figure 12.8, the component of the acceleration of block B along the y-axis is also zero. Substitution of $a_{B,y} = 0$ into the equation above yields

$$a_{B,y} = 0 \quad \rightarrow \quad n_B = m_B g$$

Lastly, when we apply Newton's 2nd law to each of the coordinate axes in the free body diagram for the rope, we obtain

$$\left(F_{net}\right)_x = ma_x \quad \rightarrow \quad T_A - T_B = m_{rope} a_{rope,x}$$

$$\left(F_{net}\right)_y = ma_y \quad \rightarrow \quad 0 = m_{rope} a_{rope,y} \quad \rightarrow \quad a_{rope,y} = 0$$

However, since the rope is massless, we have

$$m_{rope} = 0 \quad \rightarrow \quad T_A - T_B = 0 \quad \rightarrow \quad T_A = T_B$$

In other words, the tension in the rope is constant throughout the rope.

The next step in our solution is to determine the relationships, if any, between the accelerations of the objects in the system. Since the two blocks are connected by a rope, we know that the magnitudes of their accelerations must be the same. It is also clear from Figure 12.7 that as block B moves to the right block, A will also move to the right. Therefore, the direction of the accelerations of the two blocks must be equal, too.

$$a_{A,x} = a_{B,x}$$

Substitution of this equation, together with the equality of T_A and T_B, into our equations for the x-axis component of the net force acting on the two blocks gives us the following two equations:

$$F - T_B = m_A a_{B,x}$$

$$T_B = m_B a_{B,x}$$

Solving these two equations for $a_{B,x}$ gives us

$$F - m_B a_{B,x} = m_A a_{B,x} \quad \rightarrow \quad F = m_A a_{B,x} + m_B a_{B,x} \quad \rightarrow \quad F = \left(m_A + m_B\right) a_{B,x}$$

$$a_{B,x} = \frac{F}{m_A + m_B}$$

Again, we recognize the denominator of this expression as the effective mass of this system.

Example 12-2:

Problem: A system consists of two blocks connected by a massless rope that moves over a massless and frictionless pulley, as shown in Figure 12.9.

The horizontal surface across which block B moves is frictionless, but kinetic friction does exist between the two blocks. The rope moves over the pulley without slipping. What is the magnitude of the acceleration of block A?

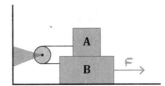

Figure 12.9: A system consisting of two blocks connected by a massless rope that moves over a massless pulley.

Solution: The first step in this process is to draw the free body diagrams block A and block B[5]. Let's define a common reference frame for these free body diagrams in which the y-axis denotes the vertical axis with a positive direction pointing up from the ground. The x-axis for this reference frame will be perpendicular to the y-axis and have a positive direction pointing to the right in Figure 12.9. With these definitions, the free body diagrams for the blocks are shown in Figure 12.10.

In these free body diagrams, T_A is the magnitude of the tension in the rope acting on block A, and T_B is the magnitude of the tension in the rope acting on block B. There are also two forces that result from the interaction between the two blocks and, therefore, appear on both free body diagrams: the normal force acting on block A and the force of kinetic friction acting on block A. The normal force that block B exerts on block A, denoted as n_A, acts in the positive y-axis direction in the free body diagram for block A and in the negative y-axis direction in the free body diagram for block B. The force of kinetic friction acting on block A, denoted as $f_{k,A}$, must oppose the motion of block A. Since block A is being pulled in the negative x-axis direction, the force of kinetic friction acting on block A must be oriented in the positive x-axis direction in the free body diagram for bock A. Hence, in the free body diagram for block B, $f_{k,A}$ acts in the negative x-axis direction.

Applying Newton's 2nd law to each of the coordinate axes in the free body diagram for block A yields the following equations:

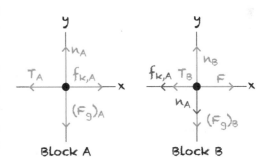

Figure 12.10: The free body diagrams for the blocks in Figure 12.9.

---

5   We now realize that there is no reason to draw the free body diagram for the rope since the rope is massless.

$$\left(F_{net}\right)_x = ma_x \quad \rightarrow \quad f_{k,A} - T_A = m_A a_{A,x}$$

$$\left(F_{net}\right)_y = ma_y \quad \rightarrow \quad n_A - \left(F_g\right)_A = m_A a_{A,y} \quad \rightarrow \quad n_A - m_A g = m_A a_{A,y}$$

Since there is no displacement of block A along the y-axis in Figure 12.10, the component of the acceleration of block A along the y-axis is zero. Substitution of $a_{A,y} = 0$ into the equation above yields

$$a_{A,y} = 0 \quad \rightarrow \quad n_A = m_A g$$

Applying Newton's 2nd law to each of the coordinate axes in the free body diagram for block B yields the following equations:

$$\left(F_{net}\right)_x = ma_x \quad \rightarrow \quad F - f_{k,A} - T_B = m_B a_{B,x}$$

$$\left(F_{net}\right)_y = ma_y \quad \rightarrow \quad n_B - n_A - \left(F_g\right)_B = m_B a_{B,y} \quad \rightarrow \quad n_B - n_A - m_B g = m_B a_{B,y}$$

Since there is also no displacement of block B along the y-axis in Figure 12.10, the component of the acceleration of block B along the y-axis is zero. Substitution of $a_{B,y} = 0$ into the equation above yields

$$a_{B,y} = 0 \quad \rightarrow \quad n_B = n_A + m_B g \quad \rightarrow \quad n_B = m_A g + m_B g \quad \rightarrow \quad n_B = \left(m_A + m_B\right)g$$

The next step in our solution is to determine the relationships, if any, between the accelerations of the objects in the system. Since the two blocks are connected by a rope, we know that the magnitudes of their accelerations must be the same. It is also clear from Figure 12.9 that as block B moves to the right, block A will move to the left. Since we used the same reference frame for both free body diagrams (Figure 12.10), the direction of $a_{A,x}$ must be opposite the direction of $a_{B,x}$.

$$a_{A,x} = -a_{B,x}$$

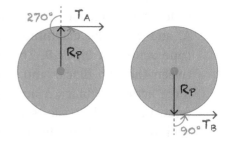

Figure 12.11: The orientation of the tension forces acting on the pulley in Figure 12.9. In each figure, R_p is the radius of the pulley and the red circle is the axis of rotation of the pulley.

Finally, we can apply Newton's 2nd law (Equation 10-7) to the pulley to determine the relationship between the T_A and T_B. The magnitude and direction of the torques resulting from these forces can be determined from the orientation of these forces (Figure 12.11) using Equation 10-4.

$$\tau_{net} = I\alpha \;\;\rightarrow\;\; R_P T_A \sin\left(270°\right) + R_P T_B \sin\left(90°\right) = I\alpha \;\;\rightarrow\;\; -R_P T_A + R_P T_B = I\alpha$$

Since the pulley is massless, the moment of inertia of the pulley is zero.

$$I = 0 \;\;\rightarrow\;\; -R_P T_A + R_P T_B = 0 \;\;\rightarrow\;\; R_P T_A = R_P T_B \;\;\rightarrow\;\; T_A = T_B$$

Hence, the magnitude of the tension in the rope is the same on either side of the pulley. Substitution of this equality together with the equation relating the accelerations of the block gives us the following two equations

$$f_{k,A} - T_A = m_A a_{A,x}$$

$$F - f_{k,A} - T_A = -m_B a_{A,x}$$

Solving these two equations for $a_{A,x}$ gives us

$$T_A = f_{k,A} - m_A a_{A,x} \;\;\rightarrow\;\; F - f_{k,A} - \left(f_{k,A} - m_A a_{A,x}\right) = -m_B a_{A,x}$$

$$F - 2f_{k,A} = -m_B a_{A,x} - m_A a_{A,x} \;\;\rightarrow\;\; F - 2f_{k,A} = -\left(m_B + m_A\right)a_{A,x}$$

The force of kinetic friction results from an interaction between the surfaces of the two blocks. The magnitude of this force of kinetic friction is, therefore, proportional to the normal force acting on block A since this is the normal force corresponding to the interaction between the surfaces of the two blocks.

$$f_{k,A} = \mu_k n_A \;\;\rightarrow\;\; f_{k,A} = \mu_k m_A g \;\;\rightarrow\;\; F - 2\mu_k m_A g = -\left(m_B + m_A\right)a_{A,x}$$

$$a_{A,x} = -\left(\frac{F - 2\mu_k m_A g}{m_B + m_A}\right)$$

The minus sign indicates that the direction of the acceleration is in the negative x-axis direction of the reference frame for the blocks. In this case, it indicates that the block A will accelerate to the left in Figure 12.9. Finally, we notice that the effective mass of the system, yet again, appears in the denominator of an expression for the acceleration of an object in the system.

Now, let's revisit the system from Example 5-10 (Figure 12.12) that consists of two blocks connected to each other by a massless rope that moves over a pulley. The pulley can be modeled as a uniformly dense solid cylinder rotating around an axis through its center. The horizontal surface along which block A slides is frictionless, and the rope moves over the pulley without slipping.

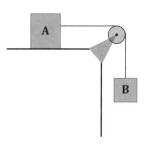

Let's determine the magnitude of the acceleration of block A. We begin by drawing the free body diagrams for the two blocks. We can define a common reference frame for these free body diagrams in which the y-axis denotes the vertical axis with a positive direction pointing up from the ground. The x-axis for this reference frame will be perpendicular to the y-axis and have a positive direction pointing to the right in Figure 12.12. With these definitions the free body diagrams for the blocks are shown in Figure 12.13.

Figure 12.12: A system of two blocks, a rope, and a pulley.

Applying Newton's 2nd law to each of the coordinate axes in the free body diagram for block A yields the following equations:

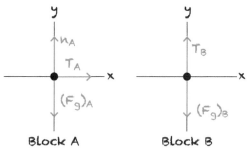

$$\left(F_{net}\right)_x = ma_x \;\rightarrow\; T_A = m_A a_{A,x}$$

Block A

Block B

$$\left(F_{net}\right)_y = ma_y \;\rightarrow\; n_A - \left(F_g\right)_A = m_A a_{A,y} \;\rightarrow\; n_A - m_A g = m_A a_{A,y}$$

Figure 12.13: The free body diagrams for the blocks in Figure 12.12.

Since there is no displacement of block A along the y-axis in Figure 12.13, the component of the acceleration of block A along the y-axis is zero. Substitution of $a_{A,y} = 0$ into the equation above yields

$$a_{A,y} = 0 \;\rightarrow\; n_A = m_A g$$

Applying Newton's 2nd law to each of the coordinate axes in the free body diagram for block B gives us

$$\left(F_{net}\right)_x = ma_x \;\rightarrow\; 0 = m_B a_{B,x} \;\rightarrow\; a_{B,x} = 0$$

$$\left(F_{net}\right)_y = ma_y \;\rightarrow\; T_B - \left(F_g\right)_B = m_B a_{B,y} \;\rightarrow\; T_B - m_B g = m_B a_{B,y}$$

Lastly, we can apply Newton's 2nd law (Equation 10-7) to the pulley to determine the relationship between the T_A and T_B. The magnitude and direction of the torques resulting from these forces can be determined from the orientation of these forces (Figure 12.14) using Equation 10-4.

$$\tau_{net} = I\alpha \;\rightarrow\; R_p T_A \sin\left(90°\right) + R_p T_B \sin\left(270°\right) = I\alpha \;\rightarrow\; R_p T_A - R_p T_B = I\alpha$$

The moment of inertia of a uniformly dense cylinder rotating around an axis through its center can be found in Table D-2.

$$I = \frac{1}{2}m_p R_p^2 \quad \rightarrow \quad R_p T_A - R_p T_B = \frac{1}{2}m_p R_p^2 \alpha \quad \rightarrow \quad T_A - T_B = \frac{1}{2}m_p R_p \alpha$$

In this equation, we have denoted the mass and radius of the pulley as m_p and R_p, respectively. The next step in our solution is to determine the relationships, if any, between the accelerations of the objects in the system. Since the two blocks are connected by a rope, we know that the magnitudes of their accelerations must be the same. It is also clear from Figure 12.9 that as block A moves to the right block B will move down. According to the definitions of the positive directions for the x and y axes in the reference frame for this system, we can express the relationship between the accelerations of the blocks as

$$a_{A,x} = -a_{B,y}$$

Since the rope moves over the pulley without slipping, we can also relate the angular acceleration of the pulley to the translational acceleration of the blocks using Equation 10-12. According to the definition of the reference frame for this system, a positive angular acceleration of the pulley (*i.e.*, counterclockwise acceleration) would correspond to block A accelerating in the negative x-axis direction (*i.e.*, to the left in Figure 12.12) and block B accelerating in the positive y-axis direction (*i.e.*, upwards in Figure 12.12). Hence,

$$a_{A,x} = -a_{B,y} = -\alpha R_p$$

Substitution of this expression gives us the following three equations

$$\alpha R_p = -a_{A,x} \quad \rightarrow \quad T_A - T_B = -\frac{1}{2}m_p a_{A,x}$$

$$a_{B,y} = -a_{A,x} \quad \rightarrow \quad T_B - m_B g = -m_B a_{A,x} \quad \rightarrow \quad T_B = m_B g - m_B a_{A,x}$$

$$T_A = m_A a_{A,x}$$

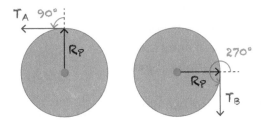

Figure 12.14: The orientation of the tension forces acting on the pulley in Figure 12.12. In each figure, R_p is the radius of the pulley, and the red circle is the axis of rotation of the pulley.

We can now combine these equations to determine $a_{A,x}$:

$$m_A a_{A,x} - \left(m_B g - m_B a_{A,x}\right) = -\frac{1}{2} m_P a_{A,x} \quad \rightarrow \quad m_A a_{A,x} + m_B a_{A,x} + \frac{1}{2} m_P a_{A,x} = m_B g$$

$$\left(m_A + m_B + \frac{1}{2} m_P\right) a_{A,x} = m_B g \quad \rightarrow \quad a_{A,x} = \left(\frac{m_B}{m_A + m_B + \frac{1}{2} m_P}\right) g$$

Not surprisingly, this is the same solution that we obtained in Example 5-10. Furthermore, we recognize the term in the denominator of this expression as the effective mass of the system. More importantly, however, we notice that for this system, T_A is not equal to T_B. Rather

$$T_A - T_B = -\frac{1}{2} m_P \left(\frac{m_B}{m_A + m_B + \frac{1}{2} m_P}\right) g \quad \rightarrow \quad T_B - T_A = \frac{m_P m_B g}{2m_A + 2m_B + m_P}$$

It makes sense that T_B must be greater than T_A, so that the necessary net torque can be generated to cause the pulley to rotate clockwise as the blocks move; however, it is, nevertheless, somewhat surprising that the tension is not constant throughout the rope. We can interpret this difference in the tension in the rope as resulting from the work done by the rope to cause the pulley to rotate. In other words, the energy transferred from the rope to pulley to make the pulley rotate results in a difference in the tension in the rope on either side of the pulley.

Example 12-3:

Problem: A system consists of two blocks connected to each other by a massless rope that moves over a pulley without slipping (Figure 12.12). The pulley can be treated as a uniformly dense cylinder rotating around an axis through its center. Kinetic friction acts on block A as it slides across the horizontal surface. What is the magnitude of the acceleration of block A?

Solution: The free body diagram for the two blocks is shown in Figure 12.15.

Applying Newton's 2nd law to each of the coordinate axes in the free body diagram for block A yields the following equations:

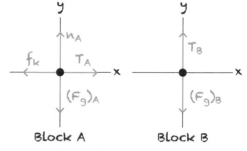

Figure 12.15: The free body diagrams for the system in Example 12-3.

$$\left(F_{net}\right)_x = ma_x \;\; \rightarrow \;\; T_A - f_k = m_A a_{A,x} \;\; \rightarrow \;\; T_A - \mu_k n_A = m_A a_{A,x}$$

$$\left(F_{net}\right)_y = ma_y \;\; \rightarrow \;\; n_A - \left(F_g\right)_A = m_A a_{A,y} \;\; \rightarrow \;\; n_A - m_A g = m_A a_{A,y}$$

Since there is no displacement of block A along the y-axis in Figure 12.15, the component of the acceleration of block A along the y-axis is zero. Substitution of $a_{A,y} = 0$ into the equation above yields

$$a_{A,y} = 0 \;\; \rightarrow \;\; n_A = m_A g$$

Applying Newton's 2nd law to each of the coordinate axes in the free body diagram for block B gives us

$$\left(F_{net}\right)_x = ma_x \;\; \rightarrow \;\; 0 = m_B a_{B,x} \;\; \rightarrow \;\; a_{B,x} = 0$$

$$\left(F_{net}\right)_y = ma_y \;\; \rightarrow \;\; T_B - \left(F_g\right)_B = m_B a_{B,y} \;\; \rightarrow \;\; T_B - m_B g = m_B a_{B,y}$$

Lastly, we can apply Newton's 2nd law (Equation 10-7) to the pulley to determine[6]

$$T_A - T_B = \frac{1}{2} m_P R_P \alpha$$

The next step in our solution is to determine the relationships, if any, between the accelerations of the objects in the system. As explained above, the equation relating the accelerations in this system is

$$a_{A,x} = -a_{B,y} = -\alpha R_P$$

Substitution of this expression gives us three equations for the x-axis components of the net forces acting on the objects in our system.

$$\alpha R_P = -a_{A,x} \;\; \rightarrow \;\; T_A - T_B = -\frac{1}{2} m_P a_{A,x}$$

$$a_{B,y} = -a_{A,x} \;\; \rightarrow \;\; T_B - m_B g = -m_B a_{A,x} \;\; \rightarrow \;\; T_B = m_B g - m_B a_{A,x}$$

$$n_A = m_A g \;\; \rightarrow \;\; T_A - \mu_k n_A = m_A a_{A,x} \;\; \rightarrow \;\; T_A = \mu_k n_A + m_A a_{A,x}$$

We can now combine our equations to determine $a_{A,x}$.

---

6   As before, in this equation, we have denoted the mass and radius of the pulley as m_P and R_P, respectively.

$$\left(\mu_k n_A + m_A a_{A,x}\right) - \left(m_B g - m_B a_{A,x}\right) = -\frac{1}{2} m_P a_{A,x}$$

$$\left(m_A + m_B + \frac{1}{2} m_P\right) a_{A,x} = -\mu_k m_A g + m_B g$$

$$a_{A,x} = \frac{-\mu_k m_A g + m_B g}{m_A + m_B + \frac{1}{2} m_P}$$

As we have seen many times before, the denominator in this expression is the effective mass of the system.

12-5 External and Internal Forces

Let's now return to the system shown in Figure 12.7 that consists of two blocks connected by a massless rope, and use Equation 9.2 to calculate the work done by the tension in the rope as the blocks slide across the horizontal surface. We begin with the work done by the tension on block A. According to the orientation of the tension vector in the free body diagram for block A (Figure 12.8) and the direction of the displacement of the system, we have

$$W = \int \vec{F} \cdot d\vec{r} \quad \rightarrow \quad W_{TonA} = \int \left[\left(T_A\right)\left(-\hat{x}\right)\right] \cdot \left[\left(dx\right)\hat{x}\right] \quad \rightarrow \quad W_{TonA} = \int -T_A \, dx$$

Since the tension is constant, this integral is readily simplified.

$$W_{TonA} = -T_A \int dx \quad \rightarrow \quad W_{TonA} = -T_A \Delta x$$

Similarly, the work done by the tension acting on block B is

$$W_{TonB} = \int \left[\left(T_B\right)\left(\hat{x}\right)\right] \cdot \left[\left(dx\right)\hat{x}\right] \quad \rightarrow \quad W_{TonB} = \int T_B \, dx$$

Again, since the tension is constant, this integral is straightforward.

$$W_{TonB} = T_B \int dx \quad \rightarrow \quad W_{TonB} = T_A \Delta x$$

The total work done by the tension in the rope is simply the sum of the work done by the tension on block A and the work done by the tension on block B.

$$W_T = W_{T\,on\,A} + W_{T\,on\,B} \quad \rightarrow \quad W_T = -T_A \Delta x + T_B \Delta x \quad \rightarrow \quad W_T = \left(-T_A + T_B\right)\Delta x$$

However, since the tension is constant,

$$T_A = T_B \quad \rightarrow \quad W_T = 0$$

the total work done by the tension is zero.

Similarly, let's calculate the total work done by the forces exerted by the two blocks in Figure 12.3 on each other (*i.e.*, the work done by $F_{A\,on\,B}$ and $F_{B\,on\,A}$). According to Equation 9.2 and the free body diagrams in Figure 12.4, we have

$$W_{F_{AonB}} = \int \left[\left(F_{AonB}\right)\left(\hat{x}\right)\right]\bullet\left[\left(dx\right)\hat{x}\right] \quad \rightarrow \quad W_{F_{AonB}} = \int F_{AonB}\,dx$$

$$W_{F_{AonB}} = F_{AonB}\int dx \quad \rightarrow \quad W_{F_{AonB}} = F_{AonB}\Delta x$$

$$W_{F_{BonA}} = \int \left[\left(-F_{BonA}\right)\left(\hat{x}\right)\right]\bullet\left[\left(dx\right)\hat{x}\right] \quad \rightarrow \quad W_{F_{BonA}} = \int -F_{BonA}\,dx$$

$$W_{F_{BonA}} = -F_{BonA}\int dx \quad \rightarrow \quad W_{F_{BonA}} = -F_{BonA}\Delta x$$

The total work done by these two forces is, therefore,

$$W = F_{AonB}\Delta x + \left(-F_{BonA}\Delta x\right) \quad \rightarrow \quad W = \left(F_{AonB} - F_{BonA}\right)\Delta x$$

However, according to Newton's 3rd law, the magnitude of $F_{A\,on\,B}$ is equal to the magnitude of $F_{B\,on\,A}$.

$$F_{AonB} = F_{BonA} \quad \rightarrow \quad W = 0$$

Thus, the total work done by these two forces acting on the blocks is zero.

For both of these systems, we have determined that action/reaction pairs of forces do no net work. This naturally follows from Newton's 3rd law. Specifically, action/reaction pairs of forces have the same magnitude but are oriented in opposite directions. Hence, the work done by the forces will have the same magnitude but opposite sign; therefore, the sum of the work done by these forces must be zero. Let's refer to such action/reaction pairs of forces within systems as ***internal forces***.

Internal force: A force acting between objects within a system. The object and the agent of an internal force are within the system, and, thus, internal forces do no net work on the system.

Similarly, any force whose agent is outside the system is an external force.

External force: A force acting on a system whose agent is outside the system.

Example 12-4:

Problem: A system consists of three blocks connected by massless ropes that are pulled across a horizontal and frictionless surface, as shown in Figure 12.16.

What are the internal forces acting on this system? What are the external forces acting on this system?

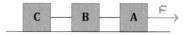

Figure 12.16: A system consisting of three blocks connected by massless ropes that slide across a horizontal and frictionless surface.

Solution: The tensions in the ropes are internal forces. The force of gravity, the normal forces, and the external pulling force are all external forces.

12-6 A System Approach to Newton's 2nd Law

Since there is no net work done by internal forces, there is no change in the energy of the system associated with the actions of internal forces. Thus, internal forces do not affect the motion of the system as a whole[7]. We can, therefore, describe the kinematics of a system in terms of only the external forces acting on the system and express Newton's 2nd law for a system as

$$\left(\vec{F}_{external}\right)_{net} = m_{effective,system}\,\vec{a}_{system}$$

(12-1)

In Equation 12-1, $\left(\vec{F}_{external}\right)_{net}$ is the net external force acting on the system, $m_{effective,system}$ is the total effective mass of the system, and $\vec{a}_{system}$ is the acceleration of the system. Please note that Equation 12-1 also assumes that the effective mass of the system is constant.

Let's consider the system shown in Figure 12.16 that consists of three blocks connected by massless ropes on a horizontal and

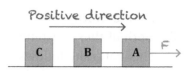

Figure 12.17: The direction of the external force defines the positive direction for the horizontal motion of this system.

---

7   There can be some subtlety in how we describe the motion of the system, as discussed in Chapter 11 for uniform circular motion.

frictionless surface. What is the acceleration of block C when an external force is applied to block A? The first step in answering this question is choosing a reference frame to describe the motion of the system. Since the blocks are sliding across a horizontal surface, there will be no vertical motion of the system. We can, therefore, limit our calculations to the horizontal motion of the system only. Let's define the positive direction for horizontal motion to point in the direction of the external force, as shown in Figure 12-17.

According to this definition of the reference frame, the net external force acting on the system is[8]

$$\left(\vec{F}_{external} \right)_{net} = F$$

The effective mass of this system is simply the sum of the masses of the blocks.

$$m_{effective,system} = m_A + m_B + m_C$$

Hence, according to Equation 12-1, the acceleration of this system is

$$\vec{a}_{system} = \frac{\left(\vec{F}_{external} \right)_{net}}{m_{effective,system}} \quad \rightarrow \quad \vec{a}_{system} = \frac{F}{m_A + m_B + m_C}$$

This acceleration is in the positive direction, which, according to the definition of our reference frame in Figure 12.17, is the same direction as the external force, as expected.

The final step in our solution is to determine the relationships between the accelerations of the objects in the system and the acceleration of the system as a whole. Since the three blocks are connected by ropes, we know that the magnitudes of their accelerations must be the same. It is also clear from Figure 12.17 that the directions of the accelerations of the blocks must also be the same. Lastly, since all of the blocks are moving together, the acceleration of each block is also equal to the acceleration of the system.

$$\vec{a}_C = \vec{a}_{system} \quad \rightarrow \quad \vec{a}_C = \frac{F}{m_A + m_B + m_C}$$

The direction of the acceleration of block C is the same as the direction of the external force (*i.e.*, it is in the positive direction), as described in Figure 12.17.

---

8   For each block, the magnitude of the normal force is equal to the magnitude of the force of gravity. Thus, the sum of the external normal forces and external forces of gravity for this system is zero, and none of these external forces contribute to the net external force acting on the system.

Example 12-5:

Problem: A 24 N external force pushes on the system of three blocks shown in Figure 12.18. The surface across which the blocks slide is horizontal, and the coefficient of kinetic friction between each block and the horizontal surface is 0.2. What is the acceleration of the 3 kg block?

Solution: The first step in our solution is to choose a reference frame to describe the motion of the system. Since the blocks are sliding across a horizontal surface, there will be no vertical motion of the system. We can, therefore, limit our calculations to only the horizontal motion of the system. Let's define the positive direction for horizontal motion to point in the direction of the external force, as shown in Figure 12-19.

According to this definition of the reference frame, the external force acts in the positive direction. This is also the direction that the blocks will move when pushed by this force. The forces of kinetic friction will act to oppose this motion and will, therefore, be oriented in the negative direction. The magnitudes of these kinetic friction forces can be determined using Equation 8.3. Since the blocks are sliding across a horizontal surface, the magnitude of the normal force exerted on each block is equal to the magnitude of the force of gravity acting on that block.

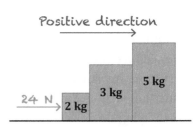

Positive direction

Figure 12.19: The direction of the external force defines the positive direction for the horizontal motion of this system.

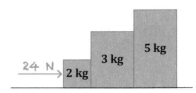

Figure 12.18: A system of three blocks pushed by an external force.

$$f_{k,2kg} = \mu_k n_{2kg} \quad \rightarrow \quad f_{k,2kg} = \mu_k \left(2kg\right)g$$

$$f_{k,3kg} = \mu_k n_{3kg} \quad \rightarrow \quad f_{k,3kg} = \mu_k \left(3kg\right)g$$

$$f_{k,5kg} = \mu_k n_{5kg} \quad \rightarrow \quad f_{k,3kg} = \mu_k \left(5kg\right)g$$

Hence, the net external force acting on the system is[9]

$$\left(\vec{F}_{external}\right)_{net} = F - \mu_k \left(2kg\right)g - \mu_k \left(3kg\right)g - \mu_k \left(5kg\right)g$$

$$\left(\vec{F}_{external}\right)_{net} = F - \mu_k \left(2kg + 3kg + 5kg\right)g \quad \rightarrow \quad \left(\vec{F}_{external}\right)_{net} = F - \mu_k \left(10kg\right)g$$

$$\left(\vec{F}_{external}\right)_{net} = 24N - \left(0.2\right)\left(10kg\right)\left(9.8\frac{m}{s^2}\right) \quad \rightarrow \quad \left(\vec{F}_{external}\right)_{net} = 4.4N$$

The effective mass of this system is

---

9   For each block, the magnitude of the normal force is equal to the magnitude of the force of gravity. Thus, the sum of the external normal forces and external forces of gravity for this system is zero, and none of these external forces contribute to the net external force acting on the system.

$$m_{effective,system} = 2\,\text{kg} + 3\,\text{kg} + 5\,\text{kg} \quad \rightarrow \quad m_{effective,system} = 10\,\text{kg}$$

Hence, according to Equation 12-1, the acceleration of this system is

$$\vec{a}_{system} = \frac{\left(\vec{F}_{external}\right)_{net}}{m_{effective,system}} \quad \rightarrow \quad \vec{a}_{system} = \frac{4.4\,\text{N}}{10\,\text{kg}} \quad \rightarrow \quad \vec{a}_{system} = 0.44\frac{\text{m}}{\text{s}^2}$$

The final step in our solution is to determine the relationship between the acceleration of the system and the acceleration of the 3 kg block. It is clear from Figure 12.19 that the accelerations of the blocks must be the same and equal to the acceleration of the system.

$$\vec{a}_{3\text{kg}} = \vec{a}_{system} \quad \rightarrow \quad \vec{a}_{3\text{kg}} = 0.44\frac{\text{m}}{\text{s}^2}$$

Now, let's consider the system shown in Figure 12.12 consisting of two blocks connected by a massless rope that moves without slipping over a pulley. The pulley has mass, and kinetic friction acts on block A as it slides across the horizontal surface. We can determine the magnitude of the acceleration of block B by applying Equation 12-1 to this system. The first step in this solution is to choose a reference frame to describe the motion of the system. When released from rest, block A will move to the right, block B will move down, and the pulley will rotate clockwise. Let's define this movement of the system to be the positive direction (Figure 12.20).

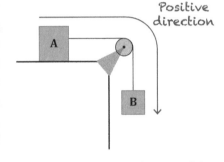

Figure 12.20: The definition of the positive direction for the motion of this system.

There are two external forces acting on this system that affect the movement of the system along this direction of motion: the force of gravity acting on block B and the force of kinetic friction acting on block A[10]. According to the reference frame in Figure 12.20, the force of gravity acting on block B is in the positive direction, and the force of kinetic friction acting on block A is in the negative direction. As before, since block A is sliding across a horizontal surface, the magnitude of the normal force exerted on block A is equal to the magnitude of the force of gravity acting on block A. Hence, the net external force acting on the system is

$$\left(\vec{F}_{external}\right)_{net} = m_B g - \mu_k m_A g$$

---

10   The magnitude of the normal force acting on block A is equal to the magnitude of the force of gravity acting on block A. Thus, the sum of the external normal force and external force of gravity acting on block A is zero, and, therefore, these external forces do not contribute to the net external force acting on the system.

The effective mass for this system is

$$m_{effective,system} = m_A + m_B + \frac{1}{2}m_P$$

In this equation, the mass of the pulley is denoted as m_P. Thus, according to Equation 12-1, the acceleration of this system is

$$\vec{a}_{system} = \frac{\left(\vec{F}_{external}\right)_{net}}{m_{effective,system}} \rightarrow \vec{a}_{system} = \frac{m_B g - \mu_k m_A g}{m_A + m_B + \frac{1}{2}m_P}$$

In this equation, we have denoted the mass of the pulley as m_p. The final step in our solution is to determine the relationship between the acceleration of the system and the acceleration of block B. Since the two blocks are connected by ropes, we know that the magnitudes of their accelerations must be the same and equal to the magnitude of the acceleration of the system. It is also clear from Figure 12.20 that the direction of the acceleration of block B will be in the positive direction of the reference frame for the motion of the system. Thus,

$$\vec{a}_B = \vec{a}_{system} \rightarrow \vec{a}_B = \frac{m_B g - \mu_k m_A g}{m_A + m_B + \frac{1}{2}m_P}$$

Example 12-6:

Problem: A system consists of three blocks connected by two massless ropes that move without slipping over identical pulleys, as shown in Figure 12.21. The pulleys are frictionless but have mass and can be modeled as uniformly dense cylinders rotating around their centers. The horizontal surface across which block B slides is frictionless. What is the magnitude of the tension T_4? You may assume that the mass of block C is larger than the mass of block A.

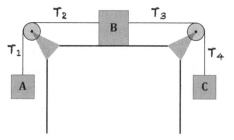

Figure 12.21: The system of three blocks in Example 12-6.

Solution: The first step in this solution is to choose a reference frame to describe the motion of the system. When released from rest, block A will move up, block B will move to the right, block C will move down, and the pulleys will rotate clockwise. Let's define this movement of the system to be the positive direction (Figure 12.22).

There are three external forces acting on this system that affect the movement of the system along this direction of motion: the force of gravity acting on block A, the force of gravity acting on block C, and the force of kinetic friction acting on block B[11]. Since block B is sliding across a horizontal surface, the magnitude of the normal force exerted on block B is equal to the magnitude of the force of gravity acting on block B. Hence, the net external force acting on the system is

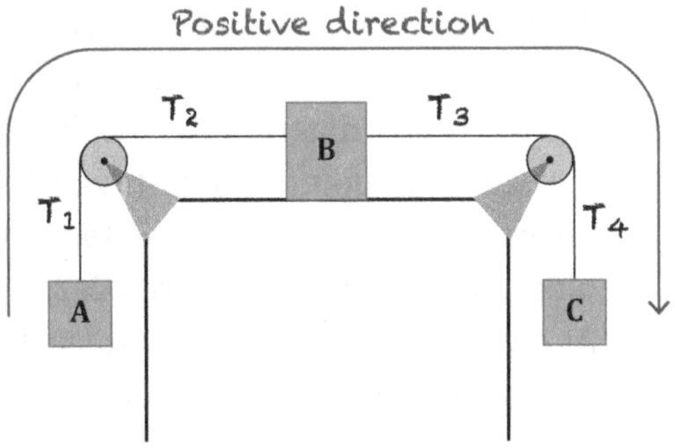

Figure 12.22: The definition of the positive direction for the motion for the system in Figure 12.21 (Example 12-6).

$$\left(\vec{F}_{external}\right)_{net} = m_C g - m_A g - \mu_k m_B g$$

The effective mass of this system is

$$m_{effective,system} = m_A + m_B + m_C + \frac{1}{2}m_P + \frac{1}{2}m_P \quad \rightarrow \quad m_{effective,system} = m_A + m_B + m_C + m_P$$

In this equation, we have denoted the mass of each pulley as m_P. Thus, according to Equation 12-1, the acceleration of this system is

$$\vec{a}_{system} = \frac{\left(\vec{F}_{external}\right)_{net}}{m_{effective,system}} \quad \rightarrow \quad \vec{a}_{system} = \frac{m_C g - m_A g - \mu_k m_B g}{m_A + m_B + m_C + m_P}$$

The next step in our solution is to determine the relationship between the acceleration of the system and the acceleration of block C. Since the three blocks are connected by ropes, we know that the magnitudes of their accelerations must be the same and equal to the magnitude of the acceleration of the system. It is also clear from Figure 12.20 that the direction of the acceleration of block C will be in the positive direction of the reference frame for the motion of the system (Figure 12.22). Thus,

$$\vec{a}_C = \vec{a}_{system} \quad \rightarrow \quad \vec{a}_C = \frac{m_C g - m_A g - \mu_k m_B g}{m_A + m_B + m_C + m_P}$$

Finally, we need to draw the free body diagram for block C so that we can relate the acceleration of block C to the net force acting on block C. To keep things simple, let's use the same ($\pm$) sign convention for the direction of the axes in reference frame of this free body

---

11   The magnitude of the normal force acting on block B is equal to the magnitude of the force of gravity acting on block B. Thus, the sum of the external normal force and external force of gravity acting on block B is zero, and, therefore, these external forces do not contribute to the net external force acting on the system.

diagram as we have used for reference frame for our system in our calculation for the acceleration of the system. Namely, in the free body diagram for block C, the positive direction for the vertical axis points down toward the ground (*i.e.,* in the same direction as the force of gravity acting on block C). This free body diagram is shown in Figure 12-23.

Applying Newton's 2nd law to each of the coordinate axes in the free body diagram for block C yields the following equations:

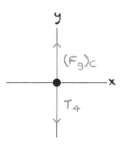

Figure 12.23: The free body diagram for block C in the system shown in Figure 12.21 (Example 12-6). The y-axis of this free body diagram corresponds to the vertical axis with the positive direction pointing down toward the ground.

$$\left(F_{net}\right)_x = ma_x \;\rightarrow\; 0 = m_C a_{C,x} \;\rightarrow\; m_A a_{C,x} = 0$$

$$\left(F_{net}\right)_y = ma_y \;\rightarrow\; \left(F_g\right)_C - T_4 = m_C a_{C,y} \;\rightarrow\; m_C g - T_4 = m_C a_{C,y}$$

$$T_4 = m_C g - m_C a_{C,y} \;\rightarrow\; T_4 = m_C\left(g - a_{C,y}\right)$$

Substitution of the value for $a_{C,y}$ gives us

$$T_4 = m_C\left(g - \frac{m_C g - m_A g - \mu_k m_B g}{m_A + m_B + m_C + m_P}\right) \;\rightarrow\; T_4 = m_C g\left(1 - \frac{m_C - m_A - \mu_k m_B}{m_A + m_B + m_C + m_P}\right)$$

$$T_4 = m_C g\left(\frac{2m_A + \left(\mu_k + 1\right)m_B + m_P}{m_A + m_B + m_C + m_P}\right)$$

Even though this solution is rather involved, it is still simpler than applying Newton's 2nd law to the blocks and pulleys and algebraically solving the resulting equations to determine T_4.

In general, the best approach to describe the kinematics of a system of moving objects is to first determine the acceleration of the system using either an energy-based approach or by applying Newton's 2nd law to the system as a whole. Then, use the acceleration of the system to determine the accelerations and forces acting on each of the objects in the system. This is faster and less error prone than determining these values by solving the equations obtained from applying Newton's 2nd law to each individual object separately.

Summary

- **Newton's 3rd law:** Every force is always accompanied by a separate force of the same magnitude but oriented in the opposite direction.
- **When using Newton's laws to describe the kinematics of a system of many objects moving together, it is simplest to use a common reference frame for the free body diagrams for all of the objects in the system.**
- **When using Newton's laws to describe the kinematics of a system of many objects moving together, we use relationships between the accelerations of the objects in our calculations.**
- **The tension in a massless rope is constant throughout the rope unless the rope moves over a pulley that has mass.** The tension in a rope will be different on either side of a pulley that has mass.
- **An internal force is a force acting between objects within a system.** The object and the agent of an internal force are within the system, and, thus, internal forces do no net work on the system.
- **An external force is a force whose agent is outside the system.**
- **Newton's 2nd law for a system of moving masses:** If the effective mass of a system is constant, then the net external force acting on a system is equal to the product of the effective mass of the system and the acceleration of the system.

$$\left(\vec{F}_{external}\right)_{net} = m_{effective,system}\,\vec{a}_{system}$$

Problems

1. Two blocks, A and B, are connected by a massless rope that moves without slipping over a massless and frictionless pulley, as shown in the figure at right. The coefficient of kinetic friction between block A and the horizontal surface along which it slides is 0.15. What is the magnitude of the acceleration of block B if the mass of block A is 2 kg, and the mass of block B is 3 kg? What is the tension in the rope?

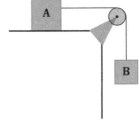

2. Two blocks, A and B, are connected by a massless rope that moves without slipping over a frictionless pulley, as shown in the figure at right. The coefficient of kinetic friction between block A and the horizontal surface along which it slides is 0.15. The pulley can be modeled as a uniformly dense solid cylinder rotating around an axis through its center. What is the magnitude of the acceleration of block A if the mass of block A is 2 kg, the mass of block B is 4 kg, and the mass of the pulley is 3 kg? What is the difference in the tension in the rope on either side of the pulley?

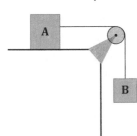

3. Two blocks, A and B, are connected by a massless rope that moves without slipping over a massless and frictionless pulley, as shown in the figure at right. The coefficient of kinetic friction between block A and the ramp along which it slides is 0.15. What is the magnitude of the acceleration of block A if the mass of block A is 2 kg, the mass of block B is 4 kg, and the angle of the ramp is 30°? What is the tension in the rope?

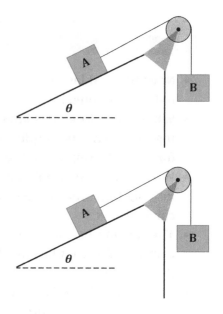

4. Two blocks, A and B, are connected by a massless rope that moves without slipping over a frictionless pulley, as shown in the figure at right. The coefficient of kinetic friction between block A and the ramp along which it slides is 0.15. The pulley can be modeled as a uniformly dense solid cylinder rotating around an axis through its center. What is the magnitude of the acceleration of block A if the mass of block A is 2 kg, the mass of block B is 4 kg, the mass of the pulley is 3 kg, and the angle of the ramp is 20°? What is the difference in the tension in the rope on either side of the pulley?

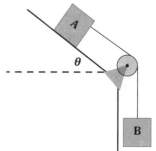

5. Two blocks, A and B, are connected by a massless rope that moves without slipping over a massless and frictionless pulley, as shown in the figure at right. The coefficient of kinetic friction between block A and the ramp along which it slides is 0.15. What is the magnitude of the acceleration of block A if the mass of block A is 2 kg, the mass of block B is 4 kg, and the angle of the ramp is 40°? What is the tension in the rope?

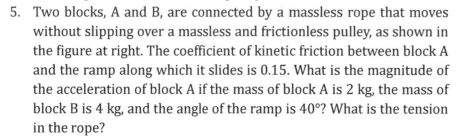

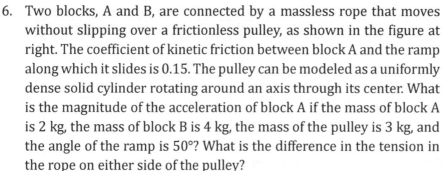

6. Two blocks, A and B, are connected by a massless rope that moves without slipping over a frictionless pulley, as shown in the figure at right. The coefficient of kinetic friction between block A and the ramp along which it slides is 0.15. The pulley can be modeled as a uniformly dense solid cylinder rotating around an axis through its center. What is the magnitude of the acceleration of block A if the mass of block A is 2 kg, the mass of block B is 4 kg, the mass of the pulley is 3 kg, and the angle of the ramp is 50°? What is the difference in the tension in the rope on either side of the pulley?

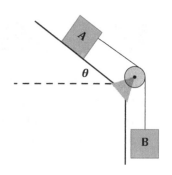

7. Two blocks are attached to one another by a massless rope and are sliding down a ramp, as shown in the figure at right. The coefficient of kinetic friction between block A and the ramp is 0.3, and the coefficient of kinetic friction between block B and the ramp is 0.2. What is the tension in the rope if the mass of block A is 2 kg, the mass of block B is 4 kg, and the angle of the ramp is 30°?

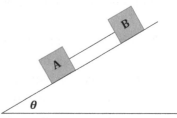

8. Block A in the figure to the right is tied to the wall with a rope and sits on top of block B. Block B is then pulled to the right by an external force.

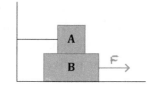

The coefficient of kinetic friction between the blocks is 0.4, and the coefficient of kinetic friction between block B and the floor is 0.3. What is the magnitude of the acceleration of block B if the mass of block A is 2 kg, the mass of block B is 4 kg, and the magnitude of the external force is 20 N?

9. A system consists of three blocks connected by massless ropes that are pulled across a horizontal and frictionless surface, as shown in the figure below.

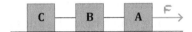

What is the tension in the rope connected block B and block C? What is the tension in the rope connecting block A and block B?

10. A system consists of three blocks connected by massless ropes that are pulled across a horizontal surface, as shown in the figure below.

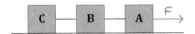

The mass of block A is 2 kg, the mass of block B is 3 kg, and the mass of block C is 4 kg. The coefficient of kinetic friction between block C and the surface is 0.2, the coefficient of kinetic friction between block B and the surface is 0.25, and the coefficient of kinetic friction between block A and the surface is 0.3. What is the tension in the rope connecting block B and block C? What is the tension in the rope connecting block A and block B?

11. A system consists of two blocks on a frictionless and horizontal surface, as shown in the figure at right. When an external horizontal force is applied to block A, both blocks will move together. What is the magnitude of the force block B exerts on block A?

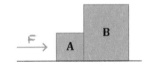

12. A system consists of two blocks on a horizontal surface, as shown in the figure at right. When an external horizontal force is applied to block A, both blocks will move together. The mass of block A is 2 kg, the mass of block B is 4 kg, and the coefficient of static friction between each block and the surface is 0.2. What is the magnitude of the force block A exerts on block B?

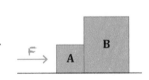

13. Three blocks are hanging from massless ropes that move without slipping over massless and frictionless pulleys, as shown in the figure at right. The mass of block A is 2 kg, the mass of block B is 8 kg, and the mass of block C is 4 kg. What is magnitude of the acceleration of block C when the system is released from rest?

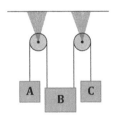

14. Three blocks are hanging from massless ropes that move without slipping over frictionless pulleys, as shown in the figure at right. The mass of block A is 2 kg, the mass of block B is 8 kg, the mass of block C is 4 kg, and the mass of each pulley is 2 kg. The pulleys can be modeled as uniformly dense solid cylinders rotating around an axis through their center. What is magnitude of the acceleration of block C when the system is released from rest?

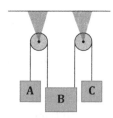

15. The coefficient of static friction between block A and block B in the figure at right is 0.4. The surface along which block B slides is horizontal and frictionless. What is the minimum magnitude for the external force applied to block B such that block A does not slide down block B?

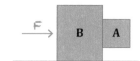

CHAPTER THIRTEEN

Linear Momentum

In the preceding chapters, we developed methods for making predictions about how the position and velocity of a system will change using either the energy of the system or a description of the external forces acting on the system. We further showed that both of these approaches had their origins in Newton's 2nd law. We will now explore another application of Newton's 2nd law that relates the net force or torque acting on a system to a rate of change of that system's momentum. Similar to kinetic energy, momentum is associated with the motion of an object and can be thought of as an intrinsic and extensive property of an object or a system of objects. Furthermore, in the same way those translational and rotational motions are associated with different kinetic energies, so, too, will these motions be associated with different momenta. In this chapter, we will focus on the momentum associated with translational motion, which we call linear momentum, and, in Chapter 14, we will discuss angular momentum, which is the momentum associated with rotational motion.

13-2 Linear Momentum and Newton's 2nd Law

The linear momentum of an object is the product of the mass and velocity of the object.

$$\vec{p} = m\vec{v} \tag{13-1}$$

An object's linear momentum is a vector quantity whose magnitude has units of $\frac{\text{kg m}}{\text{s}}$ and whose direction is equal to the direction of the object's velocity. Since momentum is related to velocity, understanding how momentum varies with time and/or position allows for kinematic calculations. This is similar to the approach presented in Section 4-2 in which the position, velocity, and acceleration of an object could be related through differentiation or integration of an object's kinetic energy. Let's consider two simple cases:

(i) An object with constant mass whose linear momentum is a function of position. Differentiating Equation 13-1 with respect to position gives us

$$\frac{d\vec{p}}{d\vec{r}} = m\frac{d\vec{v}}{d\vec{r}} \quad \rightarrow \quad \frac{d\vec{p}}{d\vec{r}} = m\frac{d\vec{v}}{dt}\frac{dt}{d\vec{r}} \quad \rightarrow \quad \frac{d\vec{p}}{d\vec{r}} = \frac{m\vec{a}}{\vec{v}}$$

If linear momentum is linearly dependent upon position, the acceleration is not constant.

(ii) An object with constant mass whose linear momentum is a function of time. Similarly, if we differentiate Equation 13-1 with respect to time, we obtain

$$\frac{d\vec{p}}{dt} = m\frac{d\vec{v}}{dt} = m\vec{a}$$

If linear momentum is linearly dependent upon time, the acceleration is constant.

Example 13-1:

Problem: A 2 kg object is moving in 1-dimension along the x-axis. The linear momentum of the object increases with the position of the object, according to the following equation[1]:

$$p(x) = 4\frac{\text{kgm}}{\text{s}} + \left(2\frac{\text{kg}}{\text{s}}\right)x$$

At $t = 0$ s, the object is at $x = 2$ m. Where is the object at $t = 2$ s?

Solution: Since the linear momentum is linearly dependent upon the position of the object, we know that the acceleration of the object will not be constant. Thus, we cannot use the constant acceleration kinematics equations to relate the displacement of the object to a time interval. Instead, we begin with the definitions of linear momentum and velocity.

$$p = mv \quad \rightarrow \quad v = \frac{p}{m} \quad \rightarrow \quad \frac{dx}{dt} = \frac{p}{m}$$

Substitution of the equation for the momentum gives us

$$\frac{dx}{dt} = \frac{4\frac{\text{kgm}}{\text{s}} + \left(2\frac{\text{kg}}{\text{s}}\right)x}{2\text{kg}} \quad \rightarrow \quad \frac{dx}{dt} = 2\frac{\text{m}}{\text{s}} + \left(1\frac{1}{\text{s}}\right)x$$

---

1   As before, for 1-dimensional motion we will drop the vector notation (*e.g,.* write momentum as p rather than $\vec{p}$) and use a ($\pm$) sign to denote the direction of the vectors.

Thus,

$$\frac{dx}{2\frac{m}{s}+\left(1\frac{1}{s}\right)x}=dt \quad \rightarrow \quad \int_{2m}^{x}\frac{dx}{2\frac{m}{s}+\left(1\frac{1}{s}\right)x}=\int_{0s}^{2s}dt$$

$$\left(\frac{1}{1\frac{1}{s}}\right)\ln\left(2\frac{m}{s}+\left(1\frac{1}{s}\right)x\right)\Bigg|_{2m}^{x}=t\Big|_{0s}^{2s} \quad \rightarrow \quad (1s)\ln\left(\frac{2\frac{m}{s}+\left(1\frac{1}{s}\right)x}{2\frac{m}{s}+\left(1\frac{1}{s}\right)(2m)}\right)=2s-0s$$

When we now solve for x, we obtain

$$\ln\left(\frac{2\frac{m}{s}+\left(1\frac{1}{s}\right)x}{4\frac{m}{s}}\right)=2 \quad \rightarrow \quad \frac{2\frac{m}{s}+\left(1\frac{1}{s}\right)x}{4\frac{m}{s}}=e^2 \quad \rightarrow \quad \left(1\frac{1}{s}\right)x=\left(4\frac{m}{s}\right)e^2-2\frac{m}{s}$$

$$x=27.6\,m$$

According to Newton's 2nd law (Section 8-4), the first derivative of an object's linear momentum with respect to time is equal to the net force acting on the object.

$$\vec{F}_{net}=\frac{d\vec{p}}{dt} \tag{13-2}$$

As we have seen previously, there are different ways to express Newton's 2nd law (*e.g.*, Equation 7.8, Equation 10-7, and Equation 10-14). Yet another form of Newton's 2nd law can be derived through the integration of Equation 13-2.

$$\vec{F}_{net}=\frac{d\vec{p}}{dt} \quad \rightarrow \quad \vec{F}_{net}dt=d\vec{p} \quad \rightarrow \quad \int\vec{F}_{net}\,dt=\int d\vec{p}$$

$$\int\vec{F}_{net}\,dt=\Delta\vec{p} \tag{13-3}$$

Equation 13-3 is referred to as the impulse-momentum theorem with the vector quantity impulse $\vec{J}$ defined in Equation 13-4.

$$\vec{J}=\int\vec{F}\,dt \tag{13-4}$$

As shown in Figure 13.1, since the impulse associated with a force is the integral of that force with respect to time, it is the same as the area under the curve of force versus time.

As defined in Equation 13-4, impulse is a vector quantity and, thus, we must specify both its magnitude and direction; as always, when dealing with 1-dimensional motion, we will rely upon ($\pm$) signs to denote the direction of a vector.

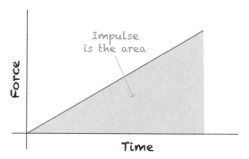

Figure 13.1: Impulse is the integral of force with respect to time.

Example 13-2:

Problem: A 40 g ball is released from rest at a height of 2.5 m above the floor. It collides with the floor and rebounds to a height of 1.6 m. Ignore any effects of air resistance. Figure 13.2 shows the force exerted by the floor on the ball during the collision. We assume that the force acts along the vertical dimension only and will define the positive direction for this axis to point up from the floor. What is the value of F_{max}?

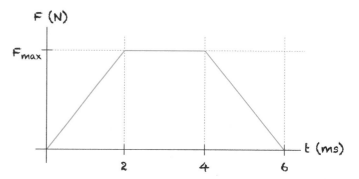

Figure 13.2: The force of the floor on the bouncing ball in Example 13-2.

Solution: We will solve this problem using Equation 13-3. Since both the force and the change in momentum in this equation are vector quantities, the first step in our solution must be to specify the reference frame for defining these vectors. As stated in the problem, we will treat the movement of the ball (and the force exerted by the floor on the ball) as occurring along only 1-dimension, specifically the vertical direction, which we will denote as the y-axis. The positive direction for the y-axis will point up from the floor.

The change in the linear momentum of the ball following its contact with the floor is

$$\Delta p = mv_f - mv_i \quad \rightarrow \quad \Delta p = m\left(v_f - v_i\right)$$

The initial velocity in this equation is the velocity of the ball the instant that it hit the floor. Since we are ignoring air resistance, the ball is in free-fall (Section 4-3), and we can, therefore, determine this velocity using the constant acceleration kinematics equations (Section 2-5).

$$v_{f,y}^2 = v_{i,y}^2 + 2a_y \Delta y \quad \rightarrow \quad v_{f,y}^2 = \left(0\frac{m}{s}\right)^2 + 2\left(-9.8\frac{m}{s^2}\right)(-2.5m)$$

$$v_{f,y}^2 = 49\frac{m^2}{s^2} \quad \rightarrow \quad v_{f,y} = -7\frac{m}{s} \quad \rightarrow \quad v_i = -7\frac{m}{s}$$

The direction of the velocity is negative since the ball is moving downwards (*i.e.*, toward the floor).

The final velocity in our equation for the change in the linear momentum of the ball is the velocity of the ball the instant it leaves the floor on its journey back up into the air. We can also determine this velocity using the same constant acceleration kinematics equation.

$$v_{f,y}^2 = v_{i,y}^2 + 2a_y \Delta y \quad \rightarrow \quad \left(0\frac{m}{s}\right)^2 = v_{i,y}^2 + 2\left(-9.8\frac{m}{s^2}\right)(1.6m)$$

$$v_{i,y}^2 = 31.36\frac{m^2}{s^2} \quad \rightarrow \quad v_{i,y} = 5.6\frac{m}{s} \quad \rightarrow \quad v_f = 5.6\frac{m}{s}$$

The direction of the velocity is positive since the ball is moving upwards (*i.e.*, away from the floor). The change in the linear momentum of the ball is

$$\Delta p = (0.04\,kg)\left(5.6\frac{m}{s} - \left(-7\frac{m}{s}\right)\right) \quad \rightarrow \quad \Delta p = (0.04\,kg)\left(12.6\frac{m}{s}\right)$$

$$\Delta p = 0.504\frac{kg\,m}{s}$$

According to Newton's 2nd law (Equation 13-3), this change in linear momentum results from the impulse associated with the net force acting on the ball. There are two forces acting on the ball when it is in contact with the floor: the force of the floor pushing up on the ball and the force of gravity pulling down on the ball. According to the definition of our reference frame, the net force acting on the ball is, therefore,

$$F_{net} = F_{floor\,on\,ball} - F_g \quad \rightarrow \quad F_{net} = F_{floor\,on\,ball} - mg$$

The net impulse acting on the ball can then be found using Equation 13-4.

$$J_{net} = \int F_{net}\,dt \quad \rightarrow \quad J_{net} = \int \left(F_{floor\,on\,ball} - mg\right)dt$$

$$J_{net} = \int F_{floor\,on\,ball}\,dt + \int \left(-mg\right)dt$$

As expected, the net impulse acting on the ball is simply the sum of the impulses from each of the forces acting on the ball. The impulse from the force of the floor acting on the ball is the area under the curve in Figure 13.2.

$$\int F_{floor\,on\,ball}\,dt = \left(0.004\,\text{s}\right)F_{max}$$

The impulse from the force of gravity is

$$\int\left(-mg\right)dt = -mg\Delta t \quad \rightarrow \quad \int\left(-mg\right)dt = -\left(0.04\,\text{kg}\right)\left(9.8\frac{\text{m}}{\text{s}^2}\right)\left(0.006\,\text{s}\right)$$

$$\int\left(-mg\right)dt = -0.0024\frac{\text{kg m}}{\text{s}}$$

Applying Equation 13-3 gives us

$$J_{net} = \Delta p$$

$$\left(0.004\,\text{s}\right)F_{max} - 0.0024\frac{\text{kg m}}{\text{s}} = 0.504\frac{\text{kg m}}{\text{s}} \quad \rightarrow \quad F_{max} = \frac{0.5064\frac{\text{kg m}}{\text{s}}}{0.004\,\text{s}}$$

$$F_{max} = 126.6\,\text{N}$$

We also see immediately that the contribution of the force of gravity to the net impulse (or the net force) is negligibly small.

$$F_g = mg \quad \rightarrow \quad F_g = \left(0.04\,\text{kg}\right)\left(9.8\frac{\text{m}}{\text{s}^2}\right) \quad \rightarrow \quad F_g = 0.39\,\text{N}$$

In Equation 13-3, Newton's 2nd law is expressed as a relationship between an impulse and a change in linear momentum. Although changes in linear momentum can be readily measured (*i.e.*, both mass and velocity can be easily determined to high levels of accuracy), it is not always straightforward to determine the time dependence of the forces acting to cause that change in linear momentum. However, since we can typically also measure with high precision the time of the inter-action associated with an impulse, we can, nevertheless, estimate the average net force associated with a change in linear momentum[2].

$$\Delta\vec{p} = \int \vec{F}_{net}\,dt \quad \rightarrow \quad \Delta\vec{p} = \left(\vec{F}_{net}\right)_{avg}\int dt$$

---

2   This is analogous to the discussion in Section 7-6 in which we related the change in the kinetic energy of an object to the work done by the average net force acting on an object (Equation 7.9).

$$\Delta \vec{p} = \left(\vec{F}_{net} \right)_{avg} \Delta t \qquad \text{(13-5)}$$

The average net force is clearly not the same as the instantaneous force. Indeed, as shown in Example 13-2, the instantaneous force acting to cause a change in linear momentum may vary during the interval over which the change in linear momentum occurs. Nevertheless, Equation 13-5 does allow us to estimate the magnitude of the net force associated with the change in linear momentum.

Example 13-3:

Problem: A 2 kg block moving along a horizontal frictionless surface bounces off of a wall, as shown in the Figure 13.3. The speed of the block before and after the collision is 7 m/s and 4 m/s, respectively. What is the average force exerted by the wall on the block if the block was in contact with the wall for 1 ms?

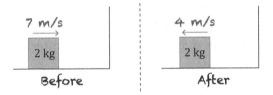

Figure 13.3: The system in Example 13-3.

Solution: We will solve this problem using Equation 13-5. Since both the average net force and the change in linear momentum in this equation are vector quantities, the first step in our solution must be to specify the reference frame for defining these vectors. Let's define the horizontal direction to be the x-axis in the reference frame for this system. The positive direction for the x-axis will point in the same direction as the initial velocity of the block (i.e., to the right in Figure 13.3).

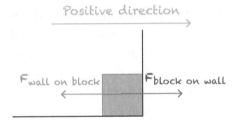

Figure 13.4: The direction of the average net force of the wall on the block in Example 13-3.

The change in the linear momentum of the block resulting from its contact with the wall is

$$\Delta p = mv_f - mv_i \quad \rightarrow \quad \Delta p = m\left(v_f - v_i \right)$$

$$\Delta p = \left(2\,\text{kg} \right)\left(\left(-4\,\frac{\text{m}}{\text{s}} \right) - \left(7\,\frac{\text{m}}{\text{s}} \right) \right) \quad \rightarrow \quad \Delta p = -22\,\frac{\text{kg m}}{\text{s}}$$

Substitution of this change in linear momentum into Equation 13-5 gives us

$$\left(F_{net} \right)_{avg} = \frac{\Delta p}{\Delta t} \quad \rightarrow \quad \left(F_{net} \right)_{avg} = \frac{-22\,\dfrac{\text{kg m}}{\text{s}}}{0.001\,\text{s}}$$

$$\left(F_{net} \right)_{avg} = -22{,}000\,\text{N}$$

The negative sign in our solution indicates that the direction of the average force is opposite the direction of the initial velocity of the block. In other words, as shown in Figure 13.4, the wall pushes the block to the left, as expected.

The relationship between average net force, interaction time, and change in linear momentum expressed in Equation 13-5 is also the motivation for crumple zones in cars. When a car experiences a collision, nothing can be done about the associated change in the linear momentum of the car. However, by increasing the time interval over which the collision occurs (*i.e.*, by increasing the time over which the linear momentum of the car changes), the magnitude of the average net force exerted on the car and, therefore, on the driver of the car (assuming she used her seat belt) can be reduced. By increasing the time over which the car slows to a stop following a collision, the crumple zone decreases the magnitude of the forces acting on the driver and, thus, helps to protect the driver.

13-3 Galilean Transformations

The concept of relative descriptions of motion and velocity was first introduced in Section 2-6. The formal name given to this process of switching between reference frames for describing kinematics is a *Galilean transformation*. Let's consider the system consisting of two blocks shown in Figure 13.5.

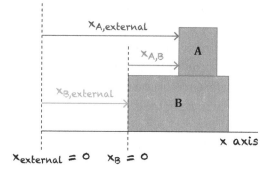

Figure 13.5: Measurements of the positions of two blocks relative to each other and to an external reference frame (dashed line).

The positions of the blocks on the *x*-axis can be measured using a variety of reference frames (*e.g.*, different origins). The reference frame $x_{external}$ is external to this system of blocks and has an origin on the *x*-axis of $x_{external} = 0$, as indicated by the dashed line on the far left in Figure 13.5. This external reference frame is constant regardless of the motion of the blocks. We can also use the location of block B to define the reference frame x_B whose origin is the location of block B on the *x*-axis. As block B moves, the location of $x_B = 0$ will also move. It follows from Figure 13.5 that we can relate the *x*-axis position of each of the blocks in the system by

$$x_{A,external} = x_{A,B} + x_{B,external}$$

As introduced previously in Section 2-6, in this equation, we use subscripts to denote both the block and the reference frame. Thus, $x_{A,B}$ is the position of block A in the reference frame of block B (*i.e.*, $x_{A,B}$ is the position of block A relative to block B). Similarly, $x_{A,external}$ is the position of block A relative to an external reference frame, and $x_{B,external}$ is the position of block B relative to an external reference frame. The velocities of the two blocks in our system can also be measured relative to each other or to an external reference frame, and these descriptions are related by

$$v_{A,external} = v_{A,B} + v_{B,external}$$

Of course, we could extend these definitions of relative position and velocity to systems consisting of more than two objects and to multidimensional descriptions of these vectors.

13-4 Linear Momentum Conservation

Since linear momentum is an extensive quantity, the linear momentum of a system of moving objects is the sum of the linear momenta of those objects (Equation 13-7). For this calculation, all of the velocity vectors are defined with respect to a reference frame that is external to the system.

$$\vec{p}_{system} = m_1\vec{v}_{1,external} + m_2\vec{v}_{2,external} + \ldots m_n\vec{v}_{n,external} \quad \rightarrow \quad \vec{p}_{system} = \sum_{i=1}^{n} m_i\vec{v}_{i,external} \qquad (13\text{-}7)$$

Consider the system shown in Figure 13.6 that consists of two blocks moving along a frictionless horizontal surface. The velocities of the blocks relative to the horizontal surface are also shown in Figure 13.6.

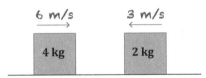

Figure 13.6. A system consisting of two blocks moving across a frictionless horizontal surface. The indicated velocities are relative to the horizontal surface.

The first step in determining the linear momentum of this system is to specify the reference frame with respect to which we will measure the velocities (and, hence, momenta) of the blocks that constitute the system. Let's choose the horizontal surface as the external reference frame for our calculation of the momentum of our system. Let's denote this as the x-axis with the positive direction pointing in the same direction as the velocity of the 4 kg block (Figure 13.7).

Since the speeds given for the blocks are relative to the horizontal surface, we have

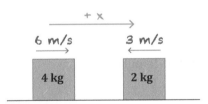

Figure 13.7. Definition of the reference frame for calculating the momentum of the system in Figure 13.6.

$$\vec{p}_{system} = \left(4\,\text{kg}\right)\left(6\frac{\text{m}}{\text{s}}\right) + \left(2\,\text{kg}\right)\left(-3\frac{\text{m}}{\text{s}}\right) \quad \rightarrow \quad \vec{p}_{system} = 18\frac{\text{kg m}}{\text{s}}$$

The momentum of the system can also be expressed in terms of the motion of the center of mass of the system. Recall from Section 10-2 that we defined the center of mass of a collection of objects to be

$$\vec{r}_{CM} = \frac{\displaystyle\sum_{i=1}^{n} m_i\vec{r}_i}{\displaystyle\sum_{i=1}^{n} m_i}$$

Let's now choose a reference frame external to our system for these measurements of position

$$\vec{r}_{CM,external} = \frac{\sum_{i=1}^{n} m_i \vec{r}_{i,external}}{\sum_{i=1}^{n} m_i}$$

(13-8)

If we assume that the masses of the objects in our system are constant in time, then differentiation of Equation 13-8 with respect to time gives us

$$\frac{d}{dt}\vec{r}_{CM,external} = \frac{\sum_{i=1}^{n} m_i \frac{d}{dt}\vec{r}_{i,external}}{\sum_{i=1}^{n} m_i} \quad \rightarrow \quad \frac{d}{dt}\vec{r}_{CM,external} = \frac{\sum_{i=1}^{n} m_i \vec{v}_{i,external}}{\sum_{i=1}^{n} m_i}$$

This equation can then be simplified using Equation 13-7 to give us

$$\frac{d}{dt}\vec{r}_{CM,external} = \frac{\vec{p}_{system}}{\sum_{i=1}^{n} m_i}$$

We can now define a new vector quantity called the velocity of the center of mass $\vec{v}_{CM}$ as the first derivative of the center of mass with respect to time.

$$\vec{v}_{CM} = \frac{d}{dt}\vec{r}_{CM}$$

With this definition, we have

$$\vec{v}_{CM,external} = \frac{\vec{p}_{system}}{\sum_{i=1}^{n} m_i} \quad \rightarrow \quad \vec{p}_{system} = \left(\sum_{i=1}^{n} m_i\right)\vec{v}_{CM,external}$$

$$\vec{p}_{system} = m_{total}\vec{v}_{CM,external}$$

(13-9)

The linear momentum of the system is simply the product of the total mass of the system and the velocity of the center of mass. Equation 13-9 also indicates that we can treat a system of moving objects as though all of the mass of the objects were concentrated at the center of mass of the system. This is the natural extension of the definition of center of mass introduced in Section 10-5.

Example 13-4:

Problem: What is the velocity of the center of mass of the system of blocks shown in Figure 13.6?

Solution: Starting with Equation 13-9 we have

$$\vec{p}_{system} = m_{total}\vec{v}_{CM,external} \quad \rightarrow \quad \vec{v}_{CM,external} = \frac{\vec{p}_{system}}{m_{total}}$$

From our previous calculation, we know that

$$\vec{p}_{system} = 18\frac{kg\,m}{s} \quad \rightarrow \quad \vec{v}_{CM,external} = \frac{18\dfrac{kg\,m}{s}}{6\,kg}$$

$$\vec{v}_{CM,external} = 3\frac{m}{s}$$

From the definition of the external reference frame for this problem (Figure 13.7), we know that the direction of the velocity of the center of mass of this system is to the right in Figure 13.6.

We can now build upon the system approach to using Newton's 2nd law introduced in Section 12-6 to rewrite Newton's 2nd law as

$$\left(\vec{F}_{external}\right)_{net} = \frac{d}{dt}\vec{p}_{system} \tag{13-10}$$

It follows from Equation 13-10 that since no net external force acts on an isolated system, the linear momentum of an isolated system is constant.

$$\left(\vec{F}_{external}\right)_{net} = 0 \quad \rightarrow \quad \frac{d}{dt}\vec{p}_{system} = 0$$

If a system's linear momentum is constant, we say that linear momentum is conserved for that system. Now imagine an open container sliding in a snow storm across a horizontal frozen lake. The ice on the lake can be assumed to be frictionless, and, thus, the container is an isolated system. The mass of the container increases as snow accumulates in it. Since linear momentum must be conserved[3], for this isolated system we have

$$\frac{d}{dt}\vec{p}_{system} = 0 \;\;\rightarrow\;\; \Delta\vec{p} = 0 \;\;\rightarrow\;\; \vec{p}_f = \vec{p}_i \;\;\rightarrow\;\; m_i\vec{v}_i = m_f\vec{v}_f$$

$$\vec{v}_f = \left(\frac{m_i}{m_f}\right)\vec{v}_i$$

Thus, the speed of the container must decrease as its mass increases. Furthermore, the acceleration of the container is also a function of the mass of the container.

$$\vec{a}_f = \frac{d\vec{v}_f}{dt} \;\;\rightarrow\;\; \vec{a}_f = -\left(\frac{m_i}{m_f^2}\right)\left(\frac{dm_f}{dt}\right)\vec{v}_i$$

The magnitude of the acceleration decreases as the mass of the container increases.

However, we will frequently be concerned with systems whose total mass is constant. It follows from Equation 13-10 that if the total mass of an isolated system remains constant, we have

$$\frac{d}{dt}\vec{p}_{system} = 0 \;\;\rightarrow\;\; m_{total}\frac{d}{dt}\vec{v}_{CM,external} = 0 \;\;\rightarrow\;\; \frac{d}{dt}\vec{v}_{CM,external} = 0$$

Therefore, the velocity of the center of mass of an isolated system will be constant.

Example 13-5:

Problem: Emily has a mass of 50 kg and is standing on the left end of a 15 m long and 575 kg perfectly level cart that has frictionless wheels and rolls on a horizontal and frictionless track; both Emily and the cart are initially at rest. Emily then starts to run along the cart toward the right end of the cart at a constant speed of 5 m/s relative to the cart. How far will Emily have run relative to the ground when she reaches the right end of the cart?

Solution: We can consider Emily and the cart together as a single system. This is an isolated system since there is no interaction between anything outside the system and either Emily or the cart (the cart is rolling along frictionless rails, *e.g.*). Therefore the momentum of the system will be conserved as Emily runs.

$$\Delta\vec{p}_{system} = 0 \;\;\rightarrow\;\; \vec{p}_{system,f} = \vec{p}_{system,i}$$

---

3   The linear momentum of the snow is directed along the vertical axis, which is perpendicular to the horizontal motion of the container. Thus, for the conservation of linear momentum along the horizontal axis, there is only the linear momentum of the container. The conservation of linear momentum associated with the vertical axis includes the linear momentum of the snow as well as the linear momentum of the Earth. But that's a separate problem to solve.

When writing expressions for the momenta of Emily and the cart, we will use the ground as our external reference frame. Since Emily and the cart were initially at rest, we have

$$\vec{p}_{system,i} = 0 \rightarrow m_{Emily} v_{Emily,ground} + m_{cart} v_{cart,ground} = 0$$

In writing this equation we will not include the subscript "f" to denote these angular momenta in order to simplify our nomenclature. Since we were given Emily's velocity relative to the cart, we need to use a Galilean transformation to determine Emily's velocity relative to the ground.

$$v_{Emily,ground} = v_{Emily,cart} + v_{cart,ground} \rightarrow v_{cart,ground} = v_{Emily,ground} - v_{Emily,cart}$$

Substitution yields

$$m_{Emily} v_{Emily, ground} + m_{cart}\left(v_{Emily\, ground} - v_{Emily,cart} \right) = 0$$

$$v_{Emily,ground} = \left(\frac{m_{cart}}{m_{cart} + m_{Emily}} \right) v_{Emily,cart}$$

Since velocity is a vector, we must specify a reference frame for its measurement. All of the motion occurs along 1-dimension, the horizontal direction, and we can define the positive direction for this axis to be the same as the direction of Emily's velocity relative to the cart. With this definition, we have

$$v_{Emily,ground} = \left(\frac{575\,kg}{575\,kg + 50\,kg} \right)\left(5\frac{m}{s} \right)$$

$$v_{Emily,ground} = 4.6\frac{m}{s}$$

The positive sign for our answer indicates that the direction of $v_{Emily,ground}$ is the same as the direction of $v_{Emily,cart}$, as expected. The magnitude of $v_{Emily,ground}$ is less than the magnitude of $v_{Emily,cart}$ since linear momentum conservation for this system requires that the cart moves backward as Emily moves forward.

Since Emily runs at a constant speed, we can use the constant acceleration kinematics equations to relate her velocity to her displacement.

$$\Delta x_{Emily,cart} = v_{Emily,cart} \Delta t \rightarrow \Delta t = \frac{\Delta x_{Emily,cart}}{v_{Emily,cart}} \rightarrow \Delta t = \frac{15\,m}{5\frac{m}{s}} \rightarrow \Delta t = 3s$$

Therefore,

$$\Delta x_{Emily,ground} = v_{Emily,ground}\Delta t \;\rightarrow\; \Delta x_{Emily,ground} = \left(4.6\frac{m}{s}\right)(3s)$$

$$\Delta x_{Emily,ground} = 13.8\,m$$

So, although Emily moved 15 m with respect to the cart, she moved only 13.8 m with respect to the ground since the cart was also moving with respect to the ground but in the opposite direction.

The solution for Example 13-5 can also be interpreted in terms of the center of mass of the system. Since Emily and the cart were initially at rest, the initial velocity of the center of mass of the system was

$$v_{CM,external} = 0$$

Since this is an isolated system, the velocity of the center of mass must be constant as Emily runs. Therefore, the velocity of the center of mass is always zero regardless of the motion of Emily and the cart. Furthermore, since the velocity of the center of mass is zero, the position of the center of mass will not change as Emily moves. The expression for the center of mass of the system is

$$x_{CM} = \frac{m_{Emily}x_{Emily,ground} + m_{cart}x_{cart,ground}}{m_{Emily}+m_{cart}} \;\rightarrow\; \Delta x_{CM} = \frac{m_{Emily}\Delta x_{Emily,ground} + m_{cart}\Delta x_{cart,ground}}{m_{Emily}+m_{cart}}$$

Hence,

$$v_{CM,external} = 0 \;\rightarrow\; \Delta x_{CM} = 0 \;\rightarrow\; m_{Emily}\Delta x_{Emily,ground} + m_{cart}\Delta x_{cart,ground} = 0$$

To test this prediction, let's determine $\Delta x_{cart,ground}$. We begin by calculating the velocity of the cart relative to the ground.

$$\vec{p}_{system,i} = 0 \;\rightarrow\; m_{Emily}v_{Emily,ground} + m_{cart}v_{cart,ground} = 0$$

$$v_{Emily,ground} = v_{Emily,cart} + v_{cart,ground} \;\rightarrow\; m_{Emily}\left(v_{Emily,cart}+v_{cart,ground}\right) + m_{cart}v_{cart,ground} = 0$$

$$v_{cart,ground} = -\left(\frac{m_{Emily}}{m_{Emily}+m_{cart}}\right)v_{Emily,cart} \;\rightarrow\; v_{cart,ground} = -\left(\frac{50\,kg}{575\,kg+50\,kg}\right)\left(5\frac{m}{s}\right)$$

$$v_{cart,ground} = -0.4\frac{m}{s}$$

As expected, the direction of $v_{cart,ground}$ is opposite the direction of $v_{Emily,ground}$. The distance travelled by the cart can be determined using our constant acceleration kinematics equations.

$$\Delta x_{cart,ground} = v_{cart,ground}\Delta t \quad \rightarrow \quad \Delta x_{cart,ground} = \left(-0.4\frac{m}{s}\right)(3s)$$

$$\Delta x_{cart,ground} = -1.2\,m$$

We can now solve for the change in the position of the center of mass of the system.

$$m_{Emily}\Delta x_{Emily,ground} + m_{cart}\Delta x_{cart,ground} = \left(50\,kg\right)\left(13.8\,m\right) + \left(575\,kg\right)\left(-1.2\,m\right)$$

$$m_{Emily}\Delta x_{Emily,ground} + m_{cart}\Delta x_{cart,ground} = 0$$

As predicted, the center of mass of the system has not changed since the system is isolated.

We can now, at last, return to the our discussion of the gravitational potential energy shared between the Earth and a small block that is initially held in place a short height above the ground (Section 3-5). Let's consider the Earth and the block to form an isolated system. Then, when the block is released and falls down toward the Earth, the center of mass of the system will not change, so the Earth will also move up towards the block. However, since the mass of the Earth is so much larger than the mass of the block, the displacement of the Earth will be much smaller than the displacement of the block[4].

As the Earth and the block move toward each other, the force of gravity between the Earth and the block will do work on both the Earth and the block[5]. It follows from the differences in the magnitudes of the displacements of the Earth and the block that the work done on the block by the force of gravity is larger than the work done on the Earth by the force of gravity (Section 7-5 and Section 9-4). Thus, the change in the kinetic energy of the Earth will be much smaller than the change in the kinetic energy of the block[6]; therefore, as proposed in Section 3-5, we can safely consider that all of the change in the gravitational potential energy of the system is converted into the kinetic energy of the block alone.

Example 13-6:

Problem: A woman initially at rest starts to run across a horizontal field. Compare the changes in linear momentum and kinetic energy for the woman and the Earth.

---

4   We could have obtained the same conclusion using a different application of Newton's 3rd law (Section 12-2). The magnitude of the force of gravity acting on the block is the same as the magnitude of the force of gravity acting on the Earth. However, since the mass of the Earth is so much larger than the mass of the block, the magnitude of the acceleration of the Earth will be much less than the magnitude of the acceleration of the block. Since the block has a larger acceleration, we know that it will cover a larger distance than the Earth during the time the block and the Earth come together.
5   From Newton's 3rd law (Section 12-2), we know that the magnitude of the gravitational force of the Earth on the block is equal to the magnitude of the gravitational force of the block on the Earth.
6   Newton's 2nd law (Equation 7.8).

Solution: From Newton's 3rd law, we know that the magnitude of the force of the woman on the Earth is the same as the magnitude of the force of the Earth on the woman and that these forces point in opposite directions. It follows that the change in the linear momentum of the woman is equal in magnitude but opposite in direction to the change in the linear momentum of the Earth.

Because the Earth is so much more massive than the woman, the magnitude of the acceleration of the Earth is much smaller than the magnitude of the acceleration of the woman. Therefore, the woman will always move a larger distance than the Earth will move. It follows that the work done by the Earth on the woman is larger than the work done by the woman on the Earth and, hence, that the change in the kinetic energy of the woman is much larger than the change in the kinetic energy of the Earth.

Running is, therefore, fairly efficient since the energy[7] expended by the runner to push on the Earth is converted almost entirely into the kinetic energy of the runner.

Similarly, it is *technically* incorrect to say that the Earth and the other planets orbit the Sun. Rather, the planets *and* the Sun are all orbiting around the center of mass of the solar system. Since the Sun is so much more massive than any of the planets, the center of mass of the solar system is very close to the geometric center of the Sun, and, thus, the motion of the Sun is very small. Nevertheless, it is the detection of such small wobbles in the position and/or velocity of other stars that has enabled astronomers to detect many exosolar planets.

13-5 Collisions and Explosions

In a *perfectly inelastic collision,* the colliding objects stick together and after the collision move together with a common final velocity. For example, consider the system shown in Figure 13.8 that consists of two blocks moving towards each other across a horizontal and frictionless surface.

In this system, the magnitude of $v_{A,i}$ is larger than the magnitude of $v_{B,i}$, so, eventually, the two blocks collide. The two blocks stick together after the collision and, subsequently, move with a common velocity. How is the final velocity of the combined object after the collision related to the velocities of the blocks before the collision?

Since the surface across which the blocks slide is frictionless, the blocks form an isolated system, and, therefore, linear momentum must be conserved during the collision. We could also conclude that linear momentum is conserved based upon Newton's 3rd law. When the two blocks come into contact with each other, they will exert forces on each other, which will, in turn, create impulses that can change the momenta of the blocks. However, according to Newton's

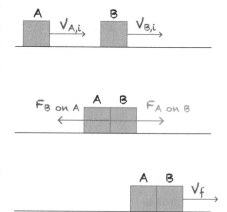

Figure 13.8: A perfectly inelastic collision between two objects. The indicated velocities are relative to the horizontal surface along which the blocks slide.

---

7   The energy obtained from digesting food or burning fat, for example.

3rd law, these forces and the associated impulses have the same magnitude but point in opposite directions. Therefore, the net impulse resulting from the collision is zero, and the linear momentum of the system will not change. Similarly, we could argue that since the forces that the blocks exert on each other are internal forces, they cannot affect the motion of the system (Section 12-6).

As before, we can express this requirement for linear momentum conservation mathematically as

$$\Delta \vec{p}_{system} = 0 \quad \rightarrow \quad \vec{p}_{system,f} = \vec{p}_{system,i}$$

Let's define the 1-dimensional external reference frame for our measurements of velocity (and linear momentum) to be the horizontal surface with a positive direction pointing in the same direction as $v_{A,i}$.

$$\vec{p}_{system,f} = \left(m_A + m_B\right)v_f$$

$$\vec{p}_{system,i} = m_A v_{A,i} + m_B v_{B,i}$$

Therefore,

$$\left(m_A + m_B\right)v_f = m_A v_{A,i} + m_B v_{B,i} \quad \rightarrow \quad v_f = \frac{m_A v_{A,i} + m_B v_{B,i}}{m_A + m_B}$$

Example 13-7:

Problem: Consider the system shown in Figure 13.6 that consists of two blocks moving along a frictionless horizontal surface. Assuming that the blocks undergo a perfectly inelastic collision determine the velocity of combined object after the collision.

Solution: We know that linear momentum must be conserved during the collision. Hence,

$$\Delta \vec{p}_{system} = 0 \quad \rightarrow \quad \vec{p}_{system,f} = \vec{p}_{system,i}$$

Let's adopt the same definition for a reference frame for this system that is shown in Figure 13.7. Since the speeds of the blocks in Figure 13.6 are relative to the horizontal surface (*i.e.*, to the external reference frame), we have

$$\vec{p}_{system,i} = \left(4\,kg\right)\left(6\frac{m}{s}\right) + \left(2\,kg\right)\left(-3\frac{m}{s}\right) \quad \rightarrow \quad \vec{p}_{system,i} = 18\frac{kg\,m}{s}$$

$$\vec{p}_{system,f} = \left(4\,kg + 2\,kg\right)v_f \quad \rightarrow \quad \vec{p}_{system,f} = \left(6\,kg\right)v_f$$

Hence,

$$\left(6\,kg\right)v_f = 18\frac{kg\,m}{s} \quad \rightarrow \quad v_f = 3\frac{m}{s}$$

The combined object created by the inelastic collision of the two blocks is moving in the positive direction (to the right in Figure 13.6). The final velocity of the combined blocks is the same as the velocity of the center of mass before the collision (Example 13-4), as it should be since linear momentum is conserved for this collision.

What happens to the energy in an inelastic collision? Let's consider the collision in Example 13-7. The only energy of interest to this system is the translational kinetic energy of the blocks[8]. Before the collision, the translational kinetic energy of the system is

$$K_i = \frac{1}{2}(4\,\text{kg})\left(6\frac{\text{m}}{\text{s}}\right)^2 + \frac{1}{2}(2\,\text{kg})\left(-3\frac{\text{m}}{\text{s}}\right)^2 \quad \rightarrow \quad K_i = 81\,\text{J}$$

After the collision, the translational kinetic energy of the system is

$$K_f = \frac{1}{2}(6\,\text{kg})\left(3\frac{\text{m}}{\text{s}}\right)^2 \quad \rightarrow \quad K_f = 27\,\text{J}$$

The translational kinetic energy after the collision is less than the translational kinetic energy before the collision. This result can be generalized as

Inelastic collisions result in energy being dissipated from the system.

But where does the energy go? Some of the kinetic energy is converted into the potential energy to deform the shapes of the objects and/or to make the objects stick together. Furthermore, although the system might be instantaneously isolated during the collision[9], eventually, there will be interactions with the outside environment that will dissipate energy from the system. For example, some of the energy will be dissipated as the kinetic energy of the air being pushed away from the collision, and some is dissipated as heat, which we will discuss in Chapter 15.

A collision in which objects bounce off each other, such as a rubber ball bouncing off of the floor, is an elastic collision. A *perfectly elastic collision* is a collision for which no energy is dissipated from the system. Let's consider the system shown in Figure 13.9 that consists of two blocks moving towards each

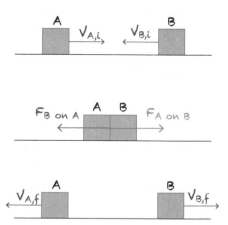

Figure 13.9: A perfectly elastic collision between two objects. All of the velocities are defined relative to the horizontal surface.

---

8   The blocks are moving along a horizontal surface, so there is no change in their gravitational potential energy.
9   The time interval over which the collision occurs is so short that there is simply no time for energy to be exchanged with the outside environment.

other on a horizontal and frictionless surface. What is the final velocity of each block if their collision is perfectly elastic?

The same reasoning that leads us to conclude that linear momentum is conserved during inelastic collisions indicates that linear momentum is also conserved during elastic collisions. Let's define the 1-dimensional reference frame for our measurements of velocity (and linear momentum) to be the horizontal surface with a positive direction pointing in the same direction as $v_{A,i}$.

$$\vec{p}_{system,f} = \vec{p}_{system,i} \quad \rightarrow \quad m_A v_{A,f} + m_B v_{B,f} = m_A v_{A,i} + m_B v_{B,i}$$

For perfectly elastic collisions, we also know that the energy of the system will remain constant. For our system, this requires that the initial and final kinetic energies are equal.

$$K_f = K_i \quad \rightarrow \quad \frac{1}{2}m_A v_{A,f}^2 + \frac{1}{2}m_B v_{B,f}^2 = \frac{1}{2}m_A v_{A,i}^2 + \frac{1}{2}m_B v_{B,i}^2$$

Solving these two equations allows us to determine the relationships between the initial and final velocities of the objects in the collision. It is often more convenient to express these relationships in terms of the initial and final linear momenta of the objects.

$$\vec{p}_{A,f} = \left(\frac{m_A - m_B}{m_A + m_B}\right)\vec{p}_{A,i} + \left(\frac{2m_A}{m_A + m_B}\right)\vec{p}_{B,i}$$

$$\vec{p}_{B,f} = \left(\frac{2m_B}{m_A + m_B}\right)\vec{p}_{A,i} + \left(\frac{m_B - m_A}{m_A + m_B}\right)\vec{p}_{B,i}$$

(13-11)

As expected, all of the momenta in Equation 13-11 must be measured relative to an external reference frame.

Example 13-8:

Problem: Consider the system shown in Figure 13.6 that consists of two blocks moving along a frictionless horizontal surface. Assuming that the blocks undergo a perfectly elastic collision determine the velocity of each block after the collision.

Solution: We can solve this problem using Equation 13-11. Let's adopt the same definition for a reference frame for this system, as shown in Figure 13.7. Since the speeds of the blocks in Figure 13.6 are relative to the horizontal surface, we have

$$p_{4kg,f} = \left(\frac{4\,kg - 2\,kg}{4\,kg + 2\,kg}\right)(4\,kg)\left(6\frac{m}{s}\right) + \left(\frac{2(4\,kg)}{4\,kg + 2\,kg}\right)(2\,kg)\left(-3\frac{m}{s}\right)$$

$$p_{4kg,f} = \left(8\frac{kg\,m}{s}\right) - \left(8\frac{kg\,m}{s}\right) \rightarrow p_{4kg,f} = 0 \rightarrow \left(4\,kg\right)v_{4kg,f} = 0$$

$$v_{4kg,f} = 0$$

$$p_{2kg,f} = \left(\frac{2\left(2kg\right)}{4\,kg + 2\,kg}\right)\left(4\,kg\right)\left(6\frac{m}{s}\right) + \left(\frac{2kg - 4\,kg}{4\,kg + 2\,kg}\right)\left(2\,kg\right)\left(-3\frac{m}{s}\right)$$

$$p_{2kg,f} = 16\frac{kg\,m}{s} + 2\frac{kg\,m}{s} \rightarrow p_{2kg,f} = 18\frac{kg\,m}{s} \rightarrow \left(2\,kg\right)v_{2kg,f} = 18\frac{kg\,m}{s}$$

$$v_{2kg,f} = 9\frac{m}{s}$$

The speed and the direction of the velocity of 2 kg block have changed, and the 4 kg block has stopped moving.

An explosion is another process that results from internal forces only, and, therefore, linear momentum is also conserved during an explosion. Indeed, one can think of an explosion as the opposite of an inelastic collision. Rather than objects colliding and sticking together, the objects in an explosion are initially together and then fly apart.

Example 13-9:

Problem: A two-stage rocket is traveling at 1200 m/s with respect to the Earth when the first stage runs out of fuel. Explosive bolts release the first stage and push it backward with a speed of 360 m/s relative to the second stage. The first stage is three times as massive as the second stage. What is the speed of the second stage with respect to the Earth after the separation?

Solution: Let's denote the masses of the two stages of the rocket as m_1 and m_2. The Galilean velocity transformation equation for the velocities of this system is

$$v_{1,Earth} = v_{1,2} + v_{2,Earth}$$

In this expression, $v_{1,Earth}$ and $v_{2,Earth}$ are the velocities of the 1st and 2nd stage relative to the Earth, respectively, and $v_{1,2}$ is the velocity of the first stage relative to the second state. The two stages of the rocket form our system, and we can consider the Earth as the external reference frame for our calculations. Since linear momentum is conserved during the explosion, we have

$$\Delta \vec{p}_{system} = 0 \quad \rightarrow \quad \vec{p}_{system,f} = \vec{p}_{system,i}$$

Let's define the positive direction for the 1-dimensional motion of the rocket to point in the same direction as the initial velocity of the rocket.

$$m_1 v_{1,Earth} + m_2 v_{2,Earth} = \left(m_1 + m_2\right)\left(1200\frac{m}{s}\right)$$

Substitution of our equation for the Galilean velocity transformation yields

$$m_1\left(v_{1,2} + v_{2,Earth}\right) + m_2 v_{2,Earth} = \left(m_1 + m_2\right)\left(1200\frac{m}{s}\right)$$

$$\left(m_2 + m_1\right)v_{2,Earth} = \left(m_1 + m_2\right)\left(1200\frac{m}{s}\right) - m_1 v_{1,2}$$

$$v_{2,Earth} = 1200\frac{m}{s} - \left(\frac{m_1}{m_1 + m_2}\right)v_{1,2}$$

Since the mass of the first stage is three times the mass of the second stage, we have

$$v_{2,Earth} = 1200\frac{m}{s} - \left(\frac{3m_2}{3m_2 + m_2}\right)v_{1,2} \quad \rightarrow \quad v_{2,Earth} = 1200\frac{m}{s} - \left(\frac{3}{4}\right)v_{1,2}$$

Finally, the direction of the $v_{1,2}$ must be negative, according to the reference frame of this system.

$$v_{2,Earth} = 1200\frac{m}{s} - \left(\frac{3}{4}\right)\left(-360\frac{m}{s}\right) \quad \rightarrow \quad v_{2,Earth} = 1200\frac{m}{s} + 270\frac{m}{s}$$

$$v_{2,Earth} = 1470\frac{m}{s}$$

Since any forces involved in an explosion can be treated as internal forces, we know that the velocity of the center of mass is not affected by an explosion.

Example 13-10:

Problem: A 30 kg artillery shell is fired with an initial speed of 70 m/s at a 45° angle above the ground. The shell explodes into two pieces 5 s after it was launched. One piece was five times heavier than the other. The heavier piece landed 200 m from the cannon. How far from the cannon did the lighter piece land? Ignore any effects of air resistance.

Solution: The center of mass of the artillery shell will continue to move in the same trajectory regardless of the explosion. Let's denote the horizontal axis for the motion of the projectile as the *x*-axis. The origin for this axis will be at the cannon, and the positive direction will point in the same direction as the initial horizontal component of the projectile's velocity. We can use the derivations in Section 4-4 to determine where the artillery shell would have landed.

$$\Delta x = \frac{2v_i^2 \sin\theta \cos\theta}{g} \quad \rightarrow \quad \Delta x = \frac{2\left(70\frac{m}{s}\right)^2 \sin 45° \cos 45°}{9.8\frac{m}{s^2}} \quad \rightarrow \quad \Delta x = 500\,m$$

This is the same as the location where the center of mass of the artillery shell landed.

$$\Delta x = x_{CM} \quad \rightarrow \quad x_{CM} = 500\,m$$

This position can also be expressed in terms of the final positions of the two fragments. Let's denote the position and mass of the lighter fragment as x_1 and m_1, respectively, and the position and mass of the heavier fragment as x_2 and m_2, respectively. With these definitions, the center of mass of the system is

$$x_{CM} = \frac{m_1 x_1 + m_2 x_2}{m_1 + m_2} \quad \rightarrow \quad x_{CM} = \frac{m x_1 + 5m(200\,m)}{m + 5m} \quad \rightarrow \quad x_{CM} = \frac{1}{6}\left(x_1 + 5(200\,m)\right)$$

Hence,

$$500\,m = \frac{1}{6}\left(x_1 + 5(200\,m)\right) \quad \rightarrow \quad 3000\,m = x_1 + 1000\,m$$

$$x_1 = 2000\,m$$

13-6 Conservation of Linear Momentum in Multiple Dimensions

Our preceding discussion of linear momentum conservation has been limited to 1-dimensional motion. For systems in which motion occurs in multiple dimensions, the separate components of the linear momentum along each coordinate axis of the reference frame must be conserved. Let's consider the system shown in Figure 13.10 in which a moving object explodes into three separate fragments that fly off in different directions.

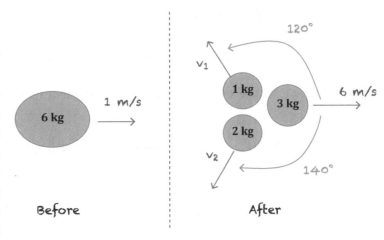

Figure 13.10: A system consisting of a single object that explodes into three separate pieces.

We can determine the speeds of the 1 kg and 2 kg fragments by applying the conservation of linear momentum to this system. Let's define an external reference frame for this system with an x-axis aligned parallel with the initial velocity of the 6 kg object. The positive direction for the x-axis points in the same direction as the initial velocity of the 6 kg object. The y-axis for this reference frame will be perpendicular to the x-axis with a positive direction pointing up in Figure 13.10. In Figure 13.11, the velocities of the fragments are plotted using this reference frame.
Linear momentum must be conserved during the explosion.

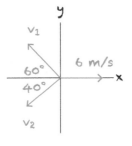

Figure 13.11: The velocities for the three fragments in Figure 13.10.

$$\Delta \vec{p}_{system} = 0 \quad \rightarrow \quad \vec{p}_{system,f} = \vec{p}_{system,i}$$

The initial linear momentum of the system is

$$\vec{p}_{system,i} = \left(6\,kg\right)\left(1\frac{m}{s}\right)\hat{x} \quad \rightarrow \quad \vec{p}_{system,i} = \left(6\frac{kg\,m}{s}\right)\hat{x}$$

The final linear momentum of the system is

$$\vec{p}_{system,f} = \left[\left(3kg\right)\left(6\frac{m}{s}\right) - \left(1kg\right)\left(v_1\right)\cos 60° - \left(2kg\right)\left(v_2\right)\cos 40°\right]\hat{x}$$
$$+ \left[\left(1kg\right)\left(v_1\right)\sin 60° - \left(2kg\right)\left(v_2\right)\sin 40°\right]\hat{y}$$

For linear momentum to be conserved, the individual components of the linear momentum along the x and y axes must be equal before and after the explosion. Let's start with the y-axis components of the linear momentum.

$$\left(\vec{p}_{system,f}\right)_y = \left(\vec{p}_{system,i}\right)_y \rightarrow \left(1\,kg\right)\left(v_1\right)\sin 60° - \left(2\,kg\right)\left(v_2\right)\sin 40° = 0$$

$$\left(1\,kg\right)\left(v_1\right)\sin 60° = \left(2\,kg\right)\left(v_2\right)\sin 40° \rightarrow v_1 = 1.48v_2$$

Next, let's solve for the x-axis components of the linear momentum.

$$\left(\vec{p}_{system,f}\right)_x = \left(\vec{p}_{system,i}\right)_x \rightarrow \left(3\,kg\right)\left(6\frac{m}{s}\right) - \left(1\,kg\right)\left(v_1\right)\cos 60° - \left(2\,kg\right)\left(v_2\right)\cos 40° = 3\frac{kg\,m}{s}$$

$$\left(1\,kg\right)\left(v_1\right)\cos 60° + \left(2\,kg\right)\left(v_2\right)\cos 40° = 18\frac{kg\,m}{s} - 3\frac{kg\,m}{s}$$

$$v_1 + 3.06v_2 = 30\frac{m}{s}$$

Hence,

$$v_1 = 30\frac{m}{s} - 3.06v_2 \rightarrow 1.48v_2 = 30\frac{m}{s} - 3.06v_2 \rightarrow 4.54v_2 = 30\frac{m}{s}$$

$$v_2 = 6.61\frac{m}{s}$$

Solving for v_1 then gives us

$$v_1 = 30\frac{m}{s} - 3.06v_2 \rightarrow v_1 = 30\frac{m}{s} - 3.06\left(6.61\frac{m}{s}\right) \rightarrow v_1 = 9.78\frac{m}{s}$$

Example 13-11:

Problem: Consider the system shown in Figure 13.12 in which a ball bounces off a rigid vertical wall in a perfectly elastic collision. The wall was initially at rest and can be considered to be infinitely massive when compared to the ball. What is the relationship between the initial and final velocities of the ball?

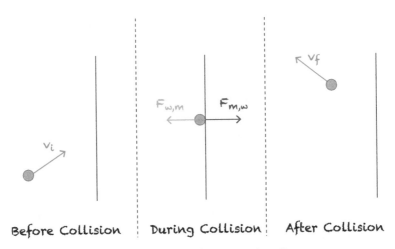

Figure 13.12: A ball bouncing off a vertical wall.

Solution: Let's define the horizontal direction of our reference frame to be the x-axis with the positive direction for the x-axis pointing to the right in Figure 13.12. The y-axis will be perpendicular to the x-axis with a positive direction pointing up in Figure 13.12. Since the action/reaction pair of forces between the ball and the wall occurs along the x-axis only, there will be no change in the y-axis component of the ball's linear momentum.

$$\left(\vec{p}_{ball,f}\right)_y = \left(\vec{p}_{ball,i}\right)_y \quad \rightarrow \quad \left(\vec{v}_{ball,f}\right)_y = \left(\vec{v}_{ball,i}\right)_y$$

Thus, the y-axis component of the ball's velocity is the same before and after the collision. The change in the x-axis component of the linear momentum of the ball can be found using Equation 13-11. Let's begin by rewriting this equation in terms of the masses of the ball and wall.

$$m_{ball}\left(\vec{v}_{ball,f}\right)_x = \left(\frac{m_{ball}-m_{wall}}{m_{ball}+m_{wall}}\right)m_{ball}\left(\vec{v}_{ball,i}\right)_x + \left(\frac{2m_{ball}}{m_{ball}+m_{wall}}\right)m_{wall}\left(\vec{v}_{wall,i}\right)_x$$

$$m_{wall}\left(\vec{v}_{wall,f}\right)_x = \left(\frac{2m_{wall}}{m_{ball}+m_{wall}}\right)m_{ball}\left(\vec{v}_{ball,i}\right)_x + \left(\frac{m_{wall}-m_{ball}}{m_{ball}+m_{wall}}\right)m_{wall}\left(\vec{v}_{wall,i}\right)_x$$

Simplifying these equations gives us

$$\left(\vec{v}_{ball,f}\right)_x = \left(\frac{m_{ball}-m_{wall}}{m_{ball}+m_{wall}}\right)\left(\vec{v}_{ball,i}\right)_x + \left(\frac{2m_{wall}}{m_{ball}+m_{wall}}\right)\left(\vec{v}_{wall,i}\right)_x$$

$$\left(\vec{v}_{wall,f}\right)_x = \left(\frac{2m_{ball}}{m_{ball}+m_{wall}}\right)\left(\vec{v}_{ball,i}\right)_x + \left(\frac{m_{wall}-m_{ball}}{m_{ball}+m_{wall}}\right)\left(\vec{v}_{wall,i}\right)_x$$

The limit of these equations for an infinitely massive wall is

$$m_{wall} = \infty \;\; \rightarrow \;\; \left(\vec{v}_{ball,f}\right)_x = -\left(\vec{v}_{ball,i}\right)_x + 2\left(\vec{v}_{wall,i}\right)_x$$

$$m_{wall} = \infty \;\; \rightarrow \;\; \left(\vec{v}_{wall,f}\right)_x = 0 - \left(\vec{v}_{wall,i}\right)_x$$

Finally, since the wall was initially at rest, its initial velocity was zero.

$$\left(\vec{v}_{wall,i}\right)_x = 0 \;\; \rightarrow \;\; \left(\vec{v}_{ball,f}\right)_x = -\left(\vec{v}_{ball,i}\right)_x$$

$$\left(\vec{v}_{wall,i}\right)_x = 0 \;\; \rightarrow \;\; \left(\vec{v}_{wall,f}\right)_x = 0$$

The x-axis component of the velocity of the ball has the same magnitude but an opposite direction after the collision.

The solution of Example 13-11 can also be expressed in terms of the angle of the velocity of the ball relative to the rigid wall. As shown in Figure 13.13, we can use the x-axis of the reference frame in Example 13-11 to define an axis normal to the surface of the rigid wall. Since the y-axis component of the velocity is the same before and after the collision, and only the direction of the x-axis component of the velocity has changed after the collision, the angle of incidence (θ_i in Figure 13.12) must be equal to the angle of reflection (θ_r).

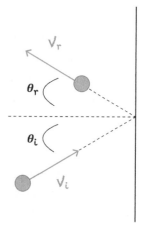

Figure 13.13: A ball bouncing off a vertical wall.

13-7 Work, Kinetic Energy, and Linear Momentum

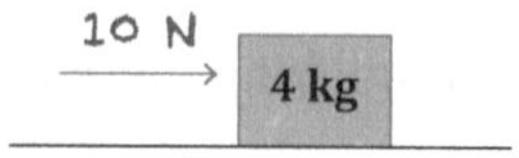

The result of a net force acting on an object can be a change in the object's kinetic energy, a change in object's linear momentum, or both, depending upon the time interval over which the force acts and the associated displacement of the object. Since the object's displacement is related to the time interval over which the force is acting through kinematics, it is not surprising that changes in kinetic energy and changes in linear momentum can also often be related to each other. Of course, since kinetic energy is a scalar, and linear momentum is a vector, there can be ambiguity in how to relate these changes. For example, let's reconsider Example 7-5 in which an object with mass m is moving along a 1-dimensional axis with a velocity of $+v$. Let's denote this 1-dimensional axis to be the x-axis of a reference frame. A net force then pushes on this object and, thereby, changes its velocity to $-v$. We

Figure 13.14: A block on a horizontal surface being pushed by a single horizontal force.

previously determined that the net work done by this force during this process was zero since the net displacement of the object during this process was zero; the distance travelled by the object as it slowed to a stop is exactly equal to the distance travelled by the object as it sped back up again. Hence, the change in the kinetic energy of the object is zero.

$$\Delta K = 0$$

The change in the object's linear momentum is not zero, however, but rather is equal to

$$\Delta \vec{p} = m\vec{v}_f - m\vec{v}_i \quad \rightarrow \quad \Delta \vec{p} = m\left[(-v)\hat{x}\right] - m\left[(v)\hat{x}\right] \quad \rightarrow \quad \Delta \vec{p} = (-2mv)\hat{x}$$

To put it another way, the external force did no work on the object but did impart an impulse to the object.

Nevertheless, although a *change* in an object's momentum cannot necessarily be directly related to a *change* in that object's kinetic energy, as shown in Section E-1, an object's kinetic energy can be expressed in terms of its linear momentum.

$$K = \frac{\vec{p} \cdot \vec{p}}{2m} = \frac{p^2}{2m} \qquad (13\text{-}12)$$

Example 13-12:

Problem: A block with a mass of 4 kg is initially at rest on a horizontal and frictionless surface. A constant 10 N external force is then applied to the block, as shown Figure 13.14. What is the linear momentum and kinetic energy of the block after the force has been applied for 10 s?

Solution: Let's define an x-axis to be parallel to the horizontal surface with the positive direction pointing in the same direction as that of the 10 N external force. Since this 10 N force is the net force acting on the object and is constant in time, we can determine the change in the linear momentum of the block using Newton's 2nd law (Equation 13-5).

$$\left(\Delta \vec{p}\right)_x = \left[(10\text{N})\hat{x}\right](10\text{s}) \quad \rightarrow \quad \left(\Delta \vec{p}\right)_x = (100\text{Nm})\hat{x}$$

Since the block started from rest, the final linear momentum of the block is equal to the change in the linear momentum of the block.

$$\vec{p}_i = 0 \quad \rightarrow \quad \vec{p}_f = \left(\Delta \vec{p}\right)_x \quad \rightarrow \quad \vec{p}_f = (100\text{Nm})\hat{x}$$

The final kinetic energy of the block can then be determined using Equation 13-12.

$$K_f = \frac{\vec{p}_f \cdot \vec{p}_f}{2m} \quad \rightarrow \quad K_f = \frac{\left[(100\,\text{Nm})\hat{x}\right] \cdot \left[(100\,\text{Nm})\hat{x}\right]}{2(4\,\text{kg})} \quad \rightarrow \quad K_f = 1250\,\text{J}$$

We can confirm that this answer is correct by independently calculating the change in the kinetic energy as the net work done by the external force using Equation 9.4.

$$\Delta K = \left(\vec{F}_{net}\right)_{avg} \cdot \Delta \vec{r} \quad \rightarrow \quad \Delta K = \left(F_{net}\right)_x \Delta x$$

The acceleration of the object can be determined from the net force using Newton's 2nd law.

$$\left(F_{net}\right)_x = ma_x \quad \rightarrow \quad a_x = \frac{\left(F_{net}\right)_x}{m} \quad \rightarrow \quad a_x = \frac{10\,\text{N}}{4\,\text{kg}} \quad \rightarrow \quad a_x = 2.5\frac{\text{m}}{\text{s}^2}$$

Since this acceleration is constant, the displacement of the object can be determined using a constant acceleration kinematics equation.

$$\Delta x = \frac{1}{2}a_x\left(\Delta t\right)^2 \quad \rightarrow \quad \Delta x = \frac{1}{2}\left(2.5\frac{\text{m}}{\text{s}^2}\right)\left(10\,\text{s}\right)^2 \quad \rightarrow \quad \Delta x = 125\,\text{m}$$

Hence,

$$\Delta K = \left(10\,\text{N}\right)\left(125\,\text{m}\right) \quad \rightarrow \quad \Delta K = 1250\,\text{J} \quad \rightarrow \quad K_f = 1250\,\text{J}$$

As expected, this is the same solution obtained earlier.

Unfortunately, Equation 13-12 is not generally valid for relating the total kinetic energy and total linear momentum of a system of moving objects. Consider the system shown in Figure 13.6 that consists of two blocks moving along a frictionless horizontal surface. As derived previously, the total linear momentum of this system is

$$\vec{p}_{system} = \left(4\,\text{kg}\right)\left(6\frac{\text{m}}{\text{s}}\right) + \left(2\,\text{kg}\right)\left(-3\frac{\text{m}}{\text{s}}\right) \quad \rightarrow \quad \vec{p}_{system} = 18\frac{\text{kg}\,\text{m}}{\text{s}}$$

The total kinetic energy of this system is

$$K_{system} = \frac{1}{2}\left(4\,kg\right)\left(6\frac{m}{s}\right)^2 + \frac{1}{2}\left(2\,kg\right)\left(-3\frac{m}{s}\right)^2 \;\rightarrow\; K_{system} = 81\,J$$

And, therefore,

$$\frac{\vec{p}_{system} \bullet \vec{p}_{system}}{2m} = \frac{\left(18\frac{kg\,m}{s}\right)^2}{2\left(4\,kg + 2\,kg\right)} \;\rightarrow\; \frac{\vec{p}_{system} \bullet \vec{p}_{system}}{2m} = 27\,J$$

$$\frac{\vec{p}_{system} \bullet \vec{p}_{system}}{2m} \neq K_{system}$$

Summary

- **Linear Momentum**: The product of an object's mass and velocity.

$$\vec{p} = m\vec{v}$$

- **If the linear momentum of an object is linearly dependent upon time, then the acceleration of the object will be constant.** If the linear momentum is linearly dependent upon the position of the object, then the acceleration will not be constant.
- **Newton's 2nd law:** The net force acting on an object is equal to the time rate of change of that object's linear momentum.

$$\vec{F}_{net} = \frac{d\vec{p}}{dt}$$

For systems of constant mass, we can express Newton's 2nd law as

$$\vec{F}_{net} = m\vec{a}$$

- **Impulse:** The integral of a force with respect to time

$$\vec{J} = \int \vec{F}\,dt$$

According to Newton's 2nd law, the net impulse acting on a system is equal to the change in the system's linear momentum.

$$\vec{J}_{net} = \int \vec{F}_{net}\, dt = \Delta\vec{p}$$

- **The linear momentum of a system of moving objects is the sum of the momenta of those objects.**

$$\vec{p}_{system} = \sum_{i=1}^{n} m_i \vec{v}_{i,external}$$

The linear momentum of a system can also be expressed in terms of the velocity of the center of mass of the system.

$$\vec{p}_{system} = m_{total}\, \vec{v}_{CM,external}$$

- **The linear momentum of an isolated system is constant.** This is equivalent to stating that the velocity of the center of mass of an isolated system is constant.
- **Linear momentum is conserved in both elastic and inelastic collisions.** This is a direct consequence of Newton's 3rd law.
- **No energy is dissipated during a perfectly elastic collision, but energy is dissipated during a perfectly inelastic collision.**
- **The kinetic energy of an object can be expressed in terms of its linear momentum.**

$$K = \frac{\vec{p}\cdot\vec{p}}{2m} = \frac{p^2}{2m}$$

However, this equation may not hold for a system of moving objects.

Problems

1. A 4 kg object is moving in 1-dimension along the x-axis. The linear momentum of the object increases with the position of the object, according to the following equation:

$$p(x) = 6\frac{\text{kg}\,\text{m}}{\text{s}} + \left(3\frac{\text{kg}}{\text{s}}\right)x$$

At $t = 0$ s the object is at $x = 0$ m. Where is the object at $t = 4$ s?

2. A 2 kg object is moving in 1-dimension along the x-axis. The linear momentum of the object is increasing in time, according to the following equation:

$$p(t) = 2\frac{kgm}{s} + \left(4\frac{kgm}{s^2}\right)t$$

At $t = 0$ s, the object is at $x = 0$ m. Where is the object at $t = 5$ s?

3. A 0.2 kg block and a 20 kg block, respectively, can both slide without friction on a horizontal surface. Equal forces are used to push both blocks forward for a time of 1 s starting from rest. After the force is removed at $t = 1$ s, which block has the larger magnitude of linear momentum? Which block has a larger kinetic energy?

4. A 2 kg object with a velocity of -10 m/s is subject to the force shown in the figure at right. The final velocity of the object is +20 m/s. What is the value of F_{max}?

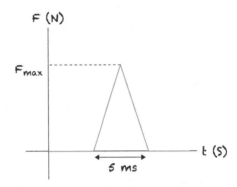

5. A 2 kg block is moving with a velocity of +1 m/s when it is subjected to the force shown in the figure at right. What is the velocity of the object after the force ends?

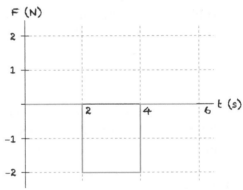

6. An open hopper railcar is rolling without friction in a thunderstorm and accumulates rainwater inside its bay. As the railcar collects rainwater, will the speed of the railcar increase, decrease, or stay the same? Will the magnitude of the linear momentum of the railcar increase, decrease, or stay the same? Will the kinetic energy of the railcar increase, decrease, or stay the same? Eventually the rain stops. The vents in the bottom of the railcar then open, allowing the water to pour out of the railcar. As the water leaves the car, will the speed of the railcar increase, decrease, or stay the same? Will the magnitude of the linear momentum of the railcar increase, decrease, or stay the same? Will the kinetic energy of railcar increase, decrease, or stay the same?

7. Three identical train cars, coupled together, are rolling with a speed of 2 m/s. A fourth identical car moving in the same direction at 4 m/s catches up with the three and couples with them to make a four-car train. What is the speed of the four-car train?

8. A woman is swimming in a pool. Compare the changes in linear momentum and kinetic energy for the woman and the water.

9. An object that was initially at rest explodes into three fragments. A 5 kg fragment is moving to the right. A 2 kg fragment is moving to the left with twice the speed of the 5 kg fragment. In which direction is the third fragment moving?

10. Two blocks are moving along a horizontal frictionless surface, as shown in the figure at right. The 4 kg block is moving to the right with a speed of 6 m/s, and the 2 kg block is moving to the left with a speed of 3 m/s. The two blocks collide perfectly inelastically and then continue to move together along the surface and then up a 30° frictionless ramp. How high up the ramp does the combined object move (*i.e.*, what is Δs in the figure)?

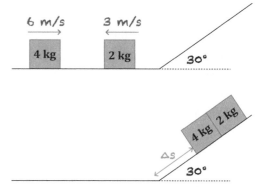

11. A 3 kg rifle fires a 10 g bullet. The velocity of the bullet (relative to the rifle) is +600 m/s. What is the velocity of the rifle (relative to the ground)? The rifle's velocity is commonly referred to as the recoil of the rifle.

12. Object 1 and object 2 in the figure at right have the same initial speed and collide inelastically with each other. If the mass of object 2 is three times the mass of object 1, what will be the final speed of the combined object after the collision?

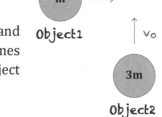

13. A 4 kg block sliding across a frictionless and horizontal surface with an initial speed of 5 m/s collides perfectly elastically with a second 4 kg block that is initially at rest. What are the velocities of the blocks after the collision?

14. Aerospace engineers often use the gravitational "slingshot effect" to accelerate spacecraft. In this procedure, the spacecraft partially orbits a massive planet and is accelerated by the planet's gravity to a larger speed, as shown in the figure at right. If we model this interaction as a 1-dimensional perfectly elastic collision, what is the final speed of the spacecraft shown in the figure? You may assume that the planet is infinitely massive compared to the spacecraft.

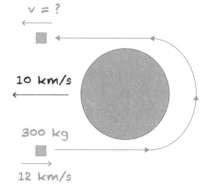

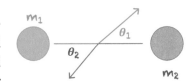

15. The two objects shown in the figure at right collide perfectly elastically with each other. Object 1 has a mass of 0.4 kg and an initial kinetic energy of 100 J. Object 2 has a mass of 0.6 kg and an initial kinetic energy of 112 J. After the collision, object 2 has a kinetic energy of 95 J and is now moving at an angle of θ_2 relative to its original direction of motion. What is the angle θ_2?

16. Two blocks with masses of 1 kg and 2 kg, respectively, are initially held together in place, as shown in the figure at right. The massless spring between the two blocks has a spring constant of k = 150 N/m and is initially compressed by 10 cm. You can assume that both masses are initially at rest. When the blocks are released, the spring expands and pushes the two blocks apart. What is the speed of the 2 kg block? You may assume that the surface is horizontal and frictionless.

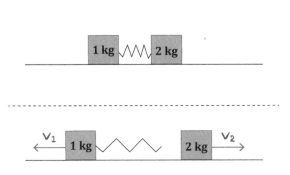

CHAPTER FOURTEEN
Angular Momentum

L inear momentum and translational kinetic energy are intrinsic properties of a translation-ally moving object (or system of objects). Similarly, an object (or system of objects) that is experiencing circular or rotational motion will possess both rotational kinetic energy and angular momentum. As we will see in this chapter, the same applications of Newton's 2nd and 3rd laws applied to linear momentum in the preceding chapter can be applied to angular momentum.

14-2 Angular Momentum

The angular momentum of an object is determined from the linear momentum of the object using Equation 14-1.

$$\vec{L} = \vec{r} \times \vec{p} \qquad (14\text{-}1)$$

In Equation 14-1, $\vec{p}$ is the linear momentum of the object, and $\vec{r}$ is the position of the object relative to the axis of rotation; in other words, the vector $\vec{r}$ points from the axis of rotation to the object[1]. Angular momentum is, thus, a vector quantity whose magnitude has units of $\frac{\text{kg}\,\text{m}^2}{\text{s}}$. The magnitude of the angular momentum vector can be obtained using Equation 14-2 (see Section B-7).

$$L = \left\lVert \vec{L} \right\rVert = rp\sin\theta \qquad (14\text{-}2)$$

In Equation 14-2, the angle θ is the angle between the position $\vec{r}$ and the linear momentum $\vec{p}$ of the object, as shown in Figure 14.1.

---

1 This is similar to the definition in Equation 10-3. Namely, the vector $\vec{r}$ always points out from the center of the circle.

It follows from the definition of angular momentum in Equation 14-1 that any object possessing linear momentum might also have angular momentum depending upon the location of an axis of rotation *regardless of whether the object is actually undergoing rotational or circular motion around that axis.* We need only specify a *potential* axis of rotation to determine the angular momentum of the object.

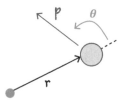

Figure 14.1: The angular momentum of an object is calculated from the distance between the object and the axis of rotation (red circle) and the orientation of the object's linear momentum relative to this axis.

Example 14-1:

Problem: What is the angular momentum with respect to the origin of an object located at

$$\vec{r} = \left(1\,\text{m}\right)\hat{x} + \left(2\,\text{m}\right)\hat{y} \text{ and moving with linear momentum } \vec{p} = \left(8\frac{\text{kgm}}{\text{s}}\right)\hat{x} + \left(6\frac{\text{kgm}}{\text{s}}\right)\hat{y} \text{ ?}$$

Solution: From Section B-7, we know that we can express Equation 14-1 as

$$\vec{r} \times \vec{p} = \begin{vmatrix} \hat{x} & \hat{y} & \hat{z} \\ r_x & r_y & r_z \\ p_x & p_y & p_z \end{vmatrix} \rightarrow \vec{L} = \begin{vmatrix} \hat{x} & \hat{y} & \hat{z} \\ 1\text{m} & 2\text{m} & 0 \\ 8\frac{\text{kgm}}{\text{s}} & 6\frac{\text{kgm}}{\text{s}} & 0 \end{vmatrix}$$

$$\vec{L} = \left(0 - 0\right)\hat{x} + \left(0 - 0\right)\hat{y} + \left(6\frac{\text{kgm}^2}{\text{s}} - 16\frac{\text{kgm}^2}{\text{s}}\right)\hat{z}$$

$$\vec{L} = \left(-10\frac{\text{kgm}^2}{\text{s}}\right)\hat{z}$$

The angular momentum is oriented in the negative direction of the z-axis and has a magnitude of 10 kgm²/s.

Example 14-2:

Problem: A 2 kg point particle is moving clockwise around a circle of radius 2.5 m with a constant tangential speed of 4 m/s. What is the magnitude of the angular momentum of the particle?

Solution: As shown in Figure 14.2, the angle between $\vec{r}$ and $\vec{p}$ for this object is 270°.

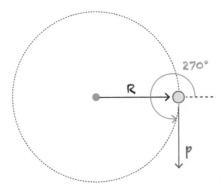

Figure 14.2: The orientation of the position and linear momentum vectors for the point particle in Example 14-2.

According to Equation 14-2, the magnitude of the angular momentum is

$$L = rp\sin\theta \quad \to \quad L = rmv\sin 270° \quad \to \quad L = -rmv$$

$$L = -(2.5\,\text{m})(2\,\text{kg})\left(4\,\frac{\text{m}}{\text{s}}\right) \quad \to \quad L = -20\,\frac{\text{kgm}^2}{\text{s}}$$

The magnitude of the angular momentum is $20\dfrac{\text{kgm}^2}{\text{s}}$.

The negative sign in our solution to Example 14-2 demonstrates that we can use the $(\pm)$ sign convention for circular and rotational motion (Section 5-2) to denote the direction of the angular momentum. Thus, *a positive angular momentum is associated with counterclockwise motion, and a negative angular momentum is associated with clockwise motion*. This notation for the direction of angular momentum also conveniently follows directly from the $\sin\theta$ term in Equation 14-2 (see Section B-7).

The angular momentum of a system of objects moving together as one rigid system can be determined using Equation 14-3.

$$\vec{L} = I\vec{\omega} \tag{14-3}$$

The expression for angular momentum in Equation 14-3 can be understood as the natural circular/rotational motion analog of the expression for linear momentum in Equation 13-1; recall from Chapter 5 that moment of inertia is the circular/rotational motion equivalent of mass, and angular velocity is the circular/rotational motion analog of velocity.

Example 14-3:

Problem: Two point particles with masses of 2 kg and 4 kg are connected by a rigid but massless rod of length 3 m and are freely rotating with an angular speed of 5 rad/s. What is the magnitude of the angular momentum for this rotation?

Solution: Because the system is freely rotating, it will be rotating around its center of mass since that will correspond to the minimum kinetic energy of the rotation[2]. To determine the center of mass of this system, let's define a 1-dimensional reference frame with an origin at the 4 kg particle and a positive direction pointing toward the 2 kg particle; we can denote this as the x-axis. The center of mass of the system can then be found using Equation 10-1.

$$x_{CM} = \frac{(2\text{kg})(3\text{m})+(4\text{kg})(0\text{m})}{2\text{kg}+4\text{kg}} \quad \rightarrow \quad x_{CM} = 1\text{m}$$

The center of mass is thus 1 m from the 4 kg particle and 2 m from the 2 kg particle. Since these are point particles the moment of inertia of this system is

$$I = (2\text{kg})(2\text{m})^2 + (4\text{kg})(1\text{m})^2 \quad \rightarrow \quad 12\text{kgm}^2$$

The magnitude of the angular momentum for this rotation can be determined using Equation 14-3.

$$L = I\omega \quad \rightarrow \quad L = (12\text{kgm}^2)\left(5\frac{\text{rad}}{\text{s}}\right)$$

$$L = 60\frac{\text{kgm}^2}{\text{s}}$$

From Equation 14-3, we see that the direction of the angular momentum of an object is the same as the direction of the object's angular velocity. Furthermore, since the direction of an object's angular momentum is perpendicular to the direction of that object's linear velocity (Equation 14-1), it follows that the direction of an object's angular velocity is also perpendicular to the direction of that object's linear velocity. Indeed, $\vec{\omega}$ is perpendicular to the plane formed by the vectors $\vec{r}$ and $\vec{v}$.

The easiest method for determining the direction of $\vec{\omega}$ is using the right-hand rule. Curl the fingers of your right hand in the direction of the angular rotation and the thumb of your right hand will point in the direction of $\vec{\omega}$, which is the same as the direction of $\vec{L}$ (Figure 14.3).

---

2   See Section 10-2.
3   See Section B-7.

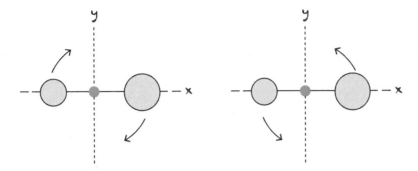

Figure 14.3: The direction of $\vec{\omega}$ for the rotation of this system can be determined using the right-hand rule. The axis of rotation for the system (red circles) is at the origin of a right-handed coordinate system[3]. The direction of $\vec{\omega}$ is in the $-\hat{z}$ direction for the rotation on the left and in the $+\hat{z}$ direction for the rotation on the right.

14-3 Newton's 2nd Law with Angular Momentum

The equivalent expression of Newton's 2nd law that relates the net torque acting on an object to the rate of change of that object's angular momentum is shown in Equation 14-4.

$$\vec{\tau}_{net} = \frac{d}{dt}\vec{L} \tag{14-4}$$

Example 14-4:

Problem: A constant 10 N force is applied tangentially to a uniformly dense solid disk to cause the disk to rotate counterclockwise. The mass and radius of the disk are 4 kg and 0.5 m, respectively. If the disk starts from rest, what is the final angular momentum of the disk after the force has been applied for 5 s?

Solution: Starting with Equation 14-4 we have

$$\tau_{net} = \frac{d}{dt}L \quad \rightarrow \quad \tau_{net}\,dt = dL \quad \rightarrow \quad \int \tau_{net}\,dt = \int dL \quad \rightarrow \quad \int \tau_{net}\,dt = \Delta L$$

The torque can be found using Equation 10-4. Since the force is being applied tangentially and causes the disk to rotate counterclockwise, we have

$$\tau = R_{disk}F$$

Hence,

$$\Delta L = \int R_{disk}F\,dt \quad \rightarrow \quad \Delta L = R_{disk}F\int dt \quad \rightarrow \quad \Delta L = R_{disk}F\Delta t$$

Substitution gives us

$$\Delta L = \left(0.5\,\text{m}\right)\left(10\,\text{N}\right)\left(5\,\text{s}\right) \quad \rightarrow \quad \Delta L = 25\,\text{Nms} \quad \rightarrow \quad L_f - L_i = 25\,\text{Nms}$$

$$L_f - 0 = 25\,\text{Nms} \quad \rightarrow \quad L_f = 25\frac{\text{kgm}^2}{\text{s}}$$

If the moment of inertia of the object is constant in time, then Equation 14-4 simplifies to Equation 14-5, which is the same as Equation 10-7.

$$\tau_{net} = I\alpha \qquad \qquad \textbf{(14-5)}$$

14-4 Angular Momentum Conservation

We know from Equation 14-4 that if no net torque acts on a system, the angular momentum of that system must be constant. For an object or a system of objects moving together as a rigid system, we can express this condition as

$$\vec{\tau}_{net} = 0 \quad \rightarrow \quad \frac{d}{dt}\vec{L} = 0 \quad \rightarrow \quad \frac{d}{dt}\left(I\vec{\omega}\right) = 0$$

$$I_f\vec{\omega}_f = I_i\vec{\omega}_i \qquad \qquad \textbf{(14-6)}$$

Consider an ice skater who is spinning about a fixed axis with an angular velocity of 0.2 rad/s. Her arms are outstretched and her moment of inertia is 1 kgm². When she pulls her arms in toward her chest, her moment of inertia decreases to 0.5 kgm². Since the ice is effectively frictionless, the skater's angular momentum must be conserved as she pulls her arms in. Thus, from Equation 14-6 we have

$$\vec{\omega}_f = \frac{I_i}{I_f}\vec{\omega}_i \quad \rightarrow \quad \vec{\omega}_f = \frac{1\,\text{kgm}^2}{0.5\,\text{kgm}^2}\vec{\omega}_i \quad \rightarrow \quad \vec{\omega}_f = 2\vec{\omega}_i$$

When she pulls her arms in, the magnitude of her angular velocity doubles.

Now, imagine a physics student sitting on a stool that can freely rotate on frictionless bearings around a vertical axis passing through the center of the stool (and, thus, through the student as well). The student is stationary and holding a rotating object, such as a spinning top or a rotating bicycle wheel. The direction of the angular momentum of rotating object is directed upwards from the ground along a vertical axis parallel to the axis of rotation of the stool (*i.e.,* when viewed from above, this object is rotating counterclockwise[4]). The total angular momentum of the isolated system consisting of the student and the rotating object is[5]

$$\vec{L}_{system,i} = \vec{L}_{student,i} + \vec{L}_{object,i} \quad \rightarrow \quad \vec{L}_{system,i} = I_{student}\,\vec{\omega}_{student,i} + I_{object}\,\vec{\omega}_{object,i}$$

Since the student is not moving, her angular velocity is zero.

$$\vec{\omega}_{student,i} = 0 \quad \rightarrow \quad \vec{L}_{system,i} = I_{object}\,\vec{\omega}_{object,i}$$

Now, the student inverts the rotating object so that it is rotating clockwise (*i.e.,* the angular velocity of the object is changed from $\vec{\omega}_{object,i}$ to $-\vec{\omega}_{object,i}$). Since the system is isolated, the total momentum of the system must remain the same after she inverts the object. Hence,

$$\vec{L}_{system,f} = \vec{L}_{system,i} \quad \rightarrow \quad I_{student}\,\vec{\omega}_{student,f} + I_{object}\,\vec{\omega}_{object,f} = I_{object}\,\vec{\omega}_{object,i}$$

$$\vec{\omega}_{object,f} = -\vec{\omega}_{object,i} \quad \rightarrow \quad I_{student}\,\vec{\omega}_{student,f} + I_{object}\left(-\vec{\omega}_{object,i}\right) = I_{object}\,\vec{\omega}_{object,i}$$

$$I_{student}\,\vec{\omega}_{student,f} = 2I_{object}\,\vec{\omega}_{object,i} \quad \rightarrow \quad \vec{\omega}_{student,f} = \left(\frac{2I_{object}}{I_{student}}\right)\vec{\omega}_{object,i}$$

When she inverts the rotating object, she will start to rotate counterclockwise[6].

Example 14-5:

Problem: A 424 kg circular merry-go-round with a radius of 4.4 m is mounted horizontally on a frictionless axle. Katherine has a mass of 32 kg and is standing at the edge of the merry-go-round (4.4 m away from the axis of rotation). Both Katherine and the merry-go-round are at rest, but then Katherine starts to walk along the edge of the merry-go-round with a speed of 5 m/s relative to the merry-go-round. What is the angular speed of the merry-go-round relative to the ground? You can model the merry-go-round as a uniformly dense solid disk.

Solution: Because the axle is frictionless, the system of Katherine and the merry-go-round can be considered to be isolated. Thus, angular momentum of this system with respect to

---

4   This follows from the right-hand rule in Section 14-2.
5   We assume that the initial and final moments of inertia of the student and the rotating object are the same.
6   This is a very fun demonstration, so make sure your professor uses it.

an external reference frame (such as the ground) will be conserved. We can also model Katherine as a point particle[7]. Since Katherine and the merry-go-round were at rest, we have

$$L_{system,i} = L_{system,f} \quad \rightarrow \quad 0 = L_{Katherine,ground} + L_{merry-go-round,ground}$$

In writing this equation we will not include the subscript "f" to denote these angular momenta in order to simplify our nomenclature. Substitution of the Equation 14-3 gives us

$$0 = I_{Katherine,ground}\omega_{Katherine,ground} + I_{merry-go-round,ground}\omega_{merry-go-round,ground}$$

$$0 = m_{Katherine}R^2_{merry-go-round}\omega_{Katherine,ground} + \frac{1}{2}m_{merry-go-round}R^2_{merry-go-round}\omega_{merry-go-round,ground}$$

$$0 = 2m_{Katherine}\omega_{Katherine,ground} + m_{merry-go-round}\omega_{merry-go-round,ground}$$

Through a Galilean transformation, we know that

$$\omega_{Katherine,ground} = \omega_{Katherine,merry-go-round} + \omega_{merry-go-round,ground}$$

Substitution of this transformation then yields

$$0 = 2m_{Katherine}\left(\omega_{Katherine,merry-go-round} + \omega_{merry-go-round,ground}\right) + m_{merry-go-round}\omega_{merry-go-round,ground}$$

$$0 = 2m_{Katherine}\omega_{Katherine,merry-go-round} + \left(2m_{Katherine} + m_{merry-go-round}\right)\omega_{merry-go-round,ground}$$

$$\omega_{merry-go-round,ground} = -\frac{2m_{Katherine}}{2m_{Katherine} + m_{merry-go-round}}\omega_{Katherine,merry-go-round}$$

Because Katherine is walking along the edge of the merry-go-round, the direction of her velocity is tangential to the direction of her position. We can relate her tangential velocity to her angular velocity using Equation 5.4.

$$v_{Katherine,merry-go-round} = R_{merry-go-round}\omega_{Katherine,merry-go-round}$$

Therefore,

$$\omega_{merry-go-round,ground} = -\left(\frac{2m_{Katherine}}{2m_{Katherine} + m_{merry-go-round}}\right)\left(\frac{v_{Katherine,merry-go-round}}{R_{merry-go-round}}\right)$$

---

7   We will often model people as point particles. This follows from applying the parallel axis theorem to the person (Equation D-8) under the assumption that the size of the person is small compared to the radius of their circular motion. See also the discussion at the end of Section 5-5.

$$\omega_{merry-go-round,ground} = -\left(\frac{2(32\,kg)}{2(32\,kg)+424\,kg}\right)\left(\frac{5\frac{m}{s}}{4.4\,m}\right)$$

$$\omega_{merry-go-round,ground} = -0.15\frac{rad}{s}$$

The negative sign indicates that the direction of the angular velocity of the merry-go-round is opposite the direction of Katherine's angular velocity. In other words, if Katherine is walking counterclockwise, the merry-go-round will be moving clockwise.

Angular momentum, like linear momentum, is also conserved in collisions and explosions. For example, let's consider what happens when a person running in a straight line jumps onto the outer rim of a merry-go-round that was at rest. We will assume that the merry-go-round rotates on a frictionless axle so that the person and the merry-go-round form an isolated system. The merry-go-round will start to rotate after the person jumps onto it, and, we can argue, this occurs because the person exerts a net force, and, hence, a net torque, on the merry-go-round. We could also determine a quantitative relationship between the linear momentum of the running person and the angular momentum of the merry

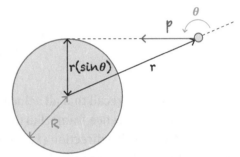

Figure 14.4: A person (indicated by the small circle) running toward a merry-go-round with radius R.

go round by applying the conservation of momentum to the inelastic collision of the person and the merry-go-round. Recall from Equation 14-1 that any object with linear momentum may also have angular momentum depending upon the potential axis of rotation that we choose. Therefore, even though the person is initially running in a straight line, we can, nevertheless, ascribe to her angular momentum with respect to the axis of rotation of the merry-go-round.

Using Equation 14-2 and Figure 14.4 we can calculate the magnitude of this angular momentum to be

$$L = rp\sin\theta \quad \rightarrow \quad L = p(r\sin\theta) \quad \rightarrow \quad L = pR$$

The merry-go-round was at rest, so the initial angular momentum of the system is simply the angular momentum of the person.

$$L_{system,i} = pR \quad \rightarrow \quad L_{system,i} = m_{person}v_{person,i}R$$

After the collision, both the person and the merry-go-round are moving with the same angular velocity. If we model the person as a point particle and the merry-go-round as a uniformly dense solid disk, the total moment of inertia of the system would be

$$I = m_{person}R^2 + \frac{1}{2}m_{merry-go-round}R^2$$

And, hence, the final angular momentum of this system would be

$$L_{system,f} = I\omega_f \quad \rightarrow \quad L_{system,f} = \left(m_{person}R^2 + \frac{1}{2}m_{merry-go-round}R^2\right)\omega_f$$

Since momentum is conserved for the collision, we have

$$L_{system,f} = L_{system,i} \quad \rightarrow \quad m_{person}v_{person,i}R = \left(m_{person}R^2 + \frac{1}{2}m_{merry-go-round}R^2\right)\omega_f$$

$$\omega_f = \left(\frac{m_{person}}{m_{person} + \frac{1}{2}m_{merry-go-round}}\right)\left(\frac{v_{person,i}}{R}\right)$$

Of course, we also recall that all velocities in equations for momentum conservation must be relative to an external reference frame. Furthermore, this solution indicates that the merry-go-round would rotate in the positive direction (*i.e.*, counterclockwise) after the collision. This is consistent with the arrangement of the system in Figure 14.4.

Example 14-6:

Problem: A block of mass m is sliding along a horizontal frictionless surface when it collides perfectly elastically with the bottom tip of a uniformly dense rigid rod of length L and mass $2m$. The rod is pivoted about a frictionless axle through one end and, initially, hangs straight down and is at rest. What is the speed of the block after the collision if the speed of the block before the collision is v_0?

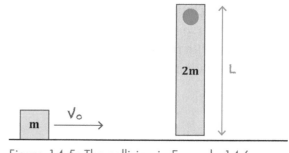

Figure 14.5: The collision in Example 14-6

Solution: Because the collision is perfectly elastic, we can apply both the conservation of momentum and the conservation of energy. We start with the conservation of momentum, which, in this case, is angular momentum.

$$\Delta L = 0 \quad \rightarrow \quad L_f = L_i$$

Before the collision, only the block is moving. Hence, the initial angular momentum of the system is

$$L_{system,i} = mv_0L$$

After the collision, both the block and the rod may be moving. We can, thus, express the final angular momentum of the system in terms of the translational velocity of the block, which we will denote as v, and the angular velocity of the rod, which we will denote as ω.

$$L_{system,f} = mvL + I\omega$$

Hence,

$$mvL + I\omega = mv_0L$$

The moment of inertia of the rod is found in Table D-2.

$$I = \frac{1}{3}(2m)L^2 \quad \rightarrow \quad I = \frac{2}{3}mL^2$$

Substitution yields

$$mvL + \frac{2}{3}mL^2\omega = mv_0L \quad \rightarrow \quad \omega = \frac{3}{2}\left(\frac{v_0 - v}{L}\right)$$

Since the collision is perfectly elastic, we can derive another equation relating ω and v by applying the conservation of energy to the collision. Specifically, during the collision the total kinetic energy of the system must be constant.

$$\Delta K_{rot} + \Delta K = 0 \quad \rightarrow \quad \left(\frac{1}{2}I\omega^2 - 0\right) + \left(\frac{1}{2}mv^2 - \frac{1}{2}mv_0^2\right) = 0$$

Thus, we have

$$mL^2\omega^2 + mv^2 - mv_0^2 = 0 \quad \rightarrow \quad \omega^2 = \frac{\left(v_0^2 - v^2\right)}{L^2}$$

Combining these two equations yields

$$\frac{\left(v_0^2 - v^2\right)}{L^2} = \left(\frac{3}{2}\left(\frac{v_0 - v}{L}\right)\right)^2 \quad \rightarrow \quad \frac{\left(v_0^2 - v^2\right)}{L^2} = \frac{9\left(v_0 - v\right)^2}{4L^2} \quad \rightarrow \quad v_0^2 - v^2 = \frac{9}{4}\left(v_0 - v\right)^2$$

$$4v_0^2 - 4v^2 = 9v_0^2 - 18v_0v + 9v^2 \quad \rightarrow \quad 13v^2 - 18v_0v + 5v_0^2 = 0$$

Solving this equation gives us

$$v = \frac{18v_0 \pm \sqrt{\left(-18v_0\right)^2 - 4\left(13\right)\left(5v_0^2\right)}}{2\left(13\right)} \quad \rightarrow \quad v = \frac{18v_0 \pm 8v_0}{26}$$

There two solutions are $v = v_0$ and $v = \left(\dfrac{5}{13}\right)v_0$. The first solution implies that the collision never occurred, so the only the second solution can be correct.

$$v = \left(\frac{5}{13}\right)v_0$$

14-5 Work, Rotational Kinetic Energy, and Angular Momentum

The rotational kinetic energy of an object can be expressed in terms of the angular momentum of the object, as shown in Equation 14-7.

$$K_{rot} = \frac{\vec{L} \cdot \vec{L}}{2I} = \frac{L^2}{2I} \qquad\qquad (14\text{-}7)$$

Let's consider the system shown in Figure 14.6 that consists of a point particle of mass m constrained to move on a frictionless surface in a horizontal circle of radius R by a massless string. The tangential speed of the particle is constant and denoted by v.

The magnitude of the angular momentum of this point particle can be found using Equation 14-2.

$$L = rp\sin\theta \quad \rightarrow \quad L = Rmv\sin 270° \quad \rightarrow \quad L = -Rmv$$

The rotational kinetic energy of the point particle can then be determined using Equation 14-7; the moment of inertia for this point particle is mR^2.

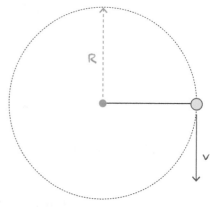

Figure 14.6: A point particle experiencing circular motion.

$$K_{rot} = \frac{(-Rmv)^2}{2(mR^2)} \quad \rightarrow \quad K_{rot} = \frac{1}{2}mv^2$$

The same solution is obtained using Equation 5.6 and Equation 5.10.

$$K_{rot} = \frac{1}{2}I\omega^2 \quad \rightarrow \quad K_{rot} = \frac{1}{2}(mR^2)\left(-\frac{v}{R}\right)^2 \quad \rightarrow \quad K_{rot} = \frac{1}{2}mv^2$$

Now, let's imagine that someone at the origin of the circle in Figure 14.6 pulls on the string and decreases the radius of the circular motion of the particle by a factor of 2 (*i.e.*, the radius decreases from R to $R/2$). The tension in the rope will not exert a torque on the particle since its level arm is zero[8].

Since no net torque is acting on the particle, we know from Newton's 2nd law (Equation 14-4) that the angular momentum of the particle will be constant. However, in order for the angular momentum to remain constant, the tangential speed of the particle must increase as the radius of the circle decreases.

$$L_f = L_i \quad \rightarrow \quad R_f m v_f = R_i m v_i \quad \rightarrow \quad v_f = \left(\frac{R_i}{R_f}\right)v_i$$

If the radius decreases by a factor of 2, the tangential speed must increase by a factor of 2.

$$v_f = \left(\frac{R}{\frac{1}{2}R}\right)v \quad \rightarrow \quad v_f = 2v$$

Hence, the rotational kinetic energy of the object must have increased by a factor of 4.

$$K_{rot,f} = \frac{1}{2}mv_f^2 \quad \rightarrow \quad K_{rot,f} = \frac{1}{2}m(2v)^2 \quad \rightarrow \quad K_{rot,f} = 4\left(\frac{1}{2}mv^2\right)$$

$$K_{rot,f} = 4K_{rot,i}$$

From Newton's 2nd law, we know that work must have been done on the particle for the particle's rotational kinetic energy to increase. Although this work did not result from the torque associated with the tension in the string, it, nevertheless, resulted from this force. Specifically, it is associated with the tension acting over a radial displacement of the particle.

---

8   In other words, since the angle between the tension force and the position vector is 180°, the torque associated with the tension must be zero, according to Equation 10-4.

14-6 The Fictitious Coriolis Force

In addition to the fictitious centrifugal force, circular or rotational motion also gives rise to a second fictitious force known as the coriolis force.

$$\vec{F}_{coriolis} = -2m\left(\vec{\omega} \times \vec{v}\right)$$

(14-8)

In Equation 14-8, the mass and velocity of the object experiencing the fictitious coriolis force are denoted by m and $\vec{v}$, respectively, and the angular velocity of the rotating reference frame is denoted by $\vec{\omega}$. The derivation of Equation 14-8 is, unfortunately, beyond the scope of this book[9].

Example 14-7:

Problem: A 2 kg block is sliding with a speed of 0.5 m/s across the surface of disk rotating counterclockwise around an axis through its center and perpendicular to the plane of the disk, as shown in Figure 14.7. The angular speed of the disk is 1 rad/s.

What is the magnitude and direction of the fictitious coriolis force?

Solution: The fictitious coriolis force can be determined using Equation 14-8. Let's begin by specifying a reference frame for this system in which the x-axis is aligned parallel to the initial velocity of the block. The positive direction for the x-axis points in the same direction as that of the initial velocity of the block, as shown in Figure 14.8 The y-axis of this reference frame will be perpendicular to the x-axis with a positive direction pointing up in Figure 14.7. This reference frame is shown in Figure 14.8.

Figure 14.7: A block sliding across the surface of a rotating disk. The disk is rotating counterclockwise around an axis (red circle) through its center and perpendicular to the plane of the disk.

---

9   You should feel inspired to take additional physics courses so that you can learn how to derive this equation.

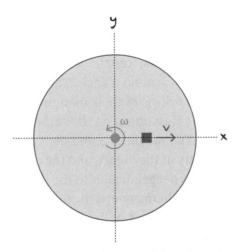

Figure 14.8: Definition of the reference frame for Example 14-7.

According to these definitions, the angular velocity of the disk[10] and the velocity of the block in Figure 14.7 are

$$\vec{\omega} = \left(1\frac{\text{rad}}{\text{s}} \right)\hat{z} \qquad \vec{v} = \left(0.5\frac{\text{m}}{\text{s}} \right)\hat{x}$$

Therefore, the fictitious coriolis force is

$$\vec{F}_{coriolis} = -2\left(2\text{kg}\right)\left[\left(1\frac{\text{rad}}{\text{s}} \right)\hat{z}\right]\times\left[\left(0.5\frac{\text{m}}{\text{s}} \right)\hat{x}\right] \quad \rightarrow \quad \vec{F}_{coriolis} = -\left(2\text{N}\right)\left(\hat{z}\times\hat{x}\right)$$

$$\vec{F}_{coriolis} = -\left(2\text{N}\right)\hat{y}$$

The direction of the fictitious coriolis force is shown in Figure 14.9.

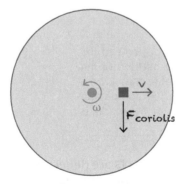

Figure 14.9: The direction of the fictitious coriolis force acting on the block.

10   We are using the right-hand rule introduced in Section 14-2.

In Section 11-5, we described the fictitious centrifugal force *"felt"* by objects on the surface of the Earth due to the rotation of the Earth around its axis. This fictitious centrifugal force acts on all objects on the surface of the Earth regardless of their motion and always pushes the objects away from the surface of the Earth. However, if an object on the surface of the Earth is moving, it will also experience a fictitious coriolis force. The magnitude and direction of this fictitious force depends upon the mass of the object, the velocity of the object, and the component of angular velocity of the Earth at the location of the object that is perpendicular to the surface of the Earth (Equation 14-8)[11]. As shown in Figure 14.10, in the northern hemisphere, the direction of this component of the angular velocity of the Earth points out from the surface of the Earth, and, in the southern hemisphere, the direction of this component of the angular velocity of the Earth points in toward the center of the Earth.

As shown in Figure 14.11, in the northern hemisphere, all moving objects appear to be deflected to the right because of the fictitious coriolis force.

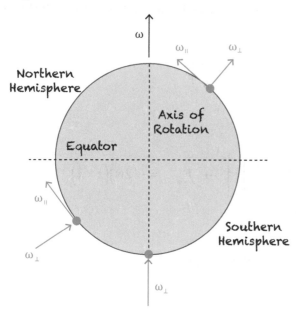

Figure 14.10: The direction of components of the angular velocity of the Earth at the surface of the Earth. The component of ω parallel to the surface of the Earth is denoted as $\omega_{\parallel}$, and the component of ω perpendicular to the surface of the Earth is denoted as $\omega_{\perp}$.

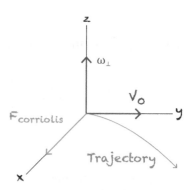

Figure 14.11: The direction of the fictitious coriolis force on an object moving in the northern hemisphere. In this reference frame, the z-axis is perpendicular to the surface of the Earth with a positive direction pointing up from the surface of the Earth.

In the southern hemisphere, all moving objects are deflected to the left. Furthermore, the magnitude of the fictitious coriolis force depends upon the latitude of the object; magnitude is strongest at the poles and weakest at the equator.

---

11   The component of the angular velocity parallel to the surface of the Earth will cause a component of the fictitious coriolis force to be directed perpendicular to the surface of the Earth. The magnitude of this component will be much smaller than the magnitude of the force of gravity and, thus, can be ignored just as the fictitious centrifugal force can also be ignored.

As with the fictitious centrifugal force discussed in Section 11-5, the magnitude of the fictitious coriolis force is small due to the small angular velocity of the Earth[12]. For example, although it is often falsely claimed that the rotational motion of water draining from a sink results from the fictitious corilois force, in reality, this motion is dominated by other factors. Indeed, the effects of the fictitious corilois force can usually be seen only when an object is moving over a very large distance, thus, providing enough time for the acceleration associated with the fictitious corilois force to significantly change the direction of the object's velocity. A good example of such a situation is the rotational motion associated with wind blowing across the surface of the Earth. In the northern hemisphere, the rightward deflection of the wind blowing toward the center of a hurricane results in the storm's counterclockwise rotation (see Figure 14.12). In contrast, in the southern hemisphere, the wind is deflected to the left, and the resulting storms rotate clockwise (see Figure 14.12).

Figure 14.12: The fictitious coriolis force is partly responsible for the rotational motion of large, low-pressure storms on Earth. In the northern hemisphere, the fictitious coriolis force causes a counterclockwise rotation of these storms, as seen in the satellite image on the left of Hurricane Isabel in 2003 (http://visibleearth.nasa.gov/view.php?id=68479). The fictitious coriolis force acts in the opposite direction in the southern hemisphere, as seen in the satellite image on the right of Cyclone Inigo in 2003. (http://visibleearth.nasa.gov/view_rec.php?id=5161).

14-7 Hamiltonian Mechanics

Translational kinetic energy and rotational kinetic energy can be written in terms of linear momentum and angular momentum, respectively, using Equation 13-12 and Equation 14-7. This means that the total energy of a system can be written in terms of the momenta and positions of the objects in the system. For example, the total energy of a 1-dimensional simple harmonic oscillator can be written as

---

12   For this reason, we can also ignore the effect of the fictitious coriolis force and treat the surface of the Earth as an inertial reference frame.

$$E = \frac{1}{2}mv_x^2 + \frac{1}{2}kx^2 \quad \rightarrow \quad E = \frac{p_x^2}{2m} + \frac{1}{2}kx^2$$

We have included the subscript "x" with the velocity and linear momentum variables to remind us that these variables are associated with changes in the x-axis position of the oscillator[13]. The total energy of an isolated system is also referred to as the Hamiltonian[14] for the system[15] and is denoted by the variable H. Thus, for this isolated system

$$H = E \quad \rightarrow \quad H = \frac{p_x^2}{2m} + \frac{1}{2}kx^2$$

Throughout this book, we have repeatedly differentiated an equation for the energy of a system to determine the acceleration of that system. This included differentiation with respect to the position of an object in the system, with respect to the velocity of an object in the system, or with respect to time. In Hamiltonian mechanics, the equations describing the motion of a system are found through differentiation of the Hamiltonian of the system with respect to position and momentum. For the isolated 1-dimensional simple harmonic oscillator, these equations are

$$\frac{\partial p_x}{\partial t} = -\frac{\partial H}{\partial x}$$

$$\frac{\partial x}{\partial t} = \frac{\partial H}{\partial p_x}$$

Hence,

$$\frac{\partial p_x}{\partial t} = -\frac{\partial}{\partial x}\left(\frac{p_x^2}{2m} + \frac{1}{2}kx^2\right) \quad \rightarrow \quad \frac{\partial p_x}{\partial t} = -kx$$

$$\frac{\partial x}{\partial t} = \frac{\partial}{\partial p_x}\left(\frac{p_x^2}{2m} + \frac{1}{2}kx^2\right) \quad \rightarrow \quad \frac{\partial x}{\partial t} = \frac{p_x}{m}$$

If the mass of the oscillator is constant, then

$$\frac{\partial p_x}{\partial t} = \frac{\partial}{\partial t}(mv) \quad \rightarrow \quad \frac{\partial p_x}{\partial t} = ma_x \quad \rightarrow \quad ma_x = -kx \quad \rightarrow \quad a_x = -\frac{k}{m}x$$

$$\frac{\partial x}{\partial t} = \frac{mv_x}{m} \quad \rightarrow \quad \frac{\partial x}{\partial t} = v_x$$

Thus, through the application of Hamilton's equations, we have derived the same equations of motion for this system that we had previously derived using our energy-based approach[16].

---

13   See Section 6-3.
14   This function is named in honor of William Rowan Hamilton
15   The Hamiltonian for a non-isolated system is more complicated.
16   See Section 6-3.

For systems with angular momentum, the corresponding Hamilton's equations are

$$\frac{\partial L_\theta}{\partial t} = -\frac{\partial H}{\partial \theta}$$

$$\frac{\partial \theta}{\partial t} = \frac{\partial H}{\partial L_\theta}$$

In these equations, we have included the subscript θ with the variable for angular momentum to remind us that angular momentum is associated with changes in the angular position θ of the pendulum.

Example 14-8:

Problem: Use Hamilton's equations to determine the equations of motion for an isolated physical pendulum.

Solution: The Hamiltonian for this isolated system is equal to the total energy of the system.

$$H = \frac{L_\theta^2}{2I} - mgL\cos\theta$$

Hence,

$$\frac{\partial L_\theta}{\partial t} = -\frac{\partial H}{\partial \theta} \quad \rightarrow \quad \frac{\partial L_\theta}{\partial t} = -\frac{\partial}{\partial \theta}\left(\frac{L_\theta^2}{2I} - mgL\cos\theta\right) \quad \rightarrow \quad \frac{\partial L_\theta}{\partial t} = -mgL\sin\theta$$

$$\frac{\partial \theta}{\partial t} = \frac{\partial H}{\partial L_\theta} \quad \rightarrow \quad \frac{\partial \theta}{\partial t} = \frac{\partial}{\partial L_\theta}\left(\frac{L_\theta^2}{2I} - mgL\cos\theta\right) \quad \rightarrow \quad \frac{\partial \theta}{\partial t} = \frac{L_\theta}{I}$$

Since the moment of inertia of the physical pendulum is constant, we have

$$L_\theta = I\omega \quad \rightarrow \quad \frac{\partial L_\theta}{\partial t} = \frac{\partial(I\omega)}{\partial t} \quad \rightarrow \quad I\alpha = -mgL\sin\theta \quad \rightarrow \quad \alpha = -\frac{mgL}{I}\sin\theta$$

$$L_\theta = I\omega \quad \rightarrow \quad \frac{\partial \theta}{\partial t} = \frac{I\omega}{I} \quad \rightarrow \quad \frac{\partial \theta}{\partial t} = \omega$$

As expected, these are the same equations we have derived previously (Section 10-6).

In general, the Hamiltonian for a system can be expressed in terms of the positions of the objects in the system and the momenta of the objects associated with changes in those positions. For example, the linear momentum of the 1-dimensional harmonic oscillator is associated with changes in the position of the oscillator along the *x*-axis. Similarly, the angular momentum of the physical pendulum is associated with changes in the angular position of the pendulum. Hamilton's equations can, then, be applied to each of these "*coupled*" positions and momenta for a system to determine the equations describing the motion of the system.

Hamilton's equations are more broadly applicable than the energy-based approach we have been using since they combine two different intrinsic properties of a system (energy and momentum) into a single description of the motion of the system. Indeed, rather than determining the acceleration of a system, as we have calculated through differentiation of the equation of the energy of the system, the application of Hamilton's equations gives us equations for how the position and momentum of the system change with time. For this reason, the Hamiltonian for a system is the starting point for describing the dynamics of that system. This is true for classical mechanics, quantum mechanics, and the wider world of theoretical physics.

Summary

- **Angular Momentum:** The cross product (or vector product) of an object's position and linear momentum.

$$\vec{L} = \vec{r} \times \vec{p}$$

The angular momentum of a system of objects moving together as one rigid system is the product of the moment of inertia and angular velocity of the system.

$$\vec{L} = I\vec{\omega}$$

- **The rotational kinetic energy of an object can be expressed in terms of the object's angular momentum and moment of inertia.**

$$K_{rot} = \frac{\vec{L} \cdot \vec{L}}{2I} = \frac{L^2}{2I}$$

- **Newton's 2nd law:** The net torque acting on an object is equal to the time rate of change of that object's linear angular momentum.

$$\vec{\tau}_{net} = \frac{d}{dt}\vec{L}$$

For systems of constant moment of inertia, we can express Newton's 2nd law as

$$\vec{\tau}_{net} = I\vec{\alpha}$$

- **The angular momentum of an isolated system is constant.**

- **Angular momentum is conserved in both elastic and inelastic collisions.** This is a direct consequence of Newton's 3rd law.
- **A fictitious coriolis force appears to act inside non-inertial reference frames undergoing circular or rotational motion.**

Problems

1. A spacecraft is in a perfectly circular orbit around the Earth. What is magnitude of the torque that the Earth's gravitational field exerts on the spaceship? How does the spaceship's angular momentum change with time?

2. A 2 m long and 6 kg thin rod is rotating around its center of mass with an angular velocity of 2 rad/s. What is the magnitude of the rod's angular momentum?

3. The three point masses shown in the figure at right are connected by rigid but massless rods and are all freely rotating in space with an angular speed of 1.5 rad/s. What is the magnitude of the angular momentum of this system for this rotation?

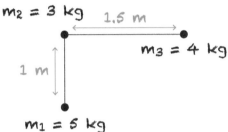

4. What is the magnitude of the angular momentum of a 40 g ball flying through the air and spinning at 4300 rpm? The ball can be modelled as a uniformly dense sphere with a radius of 2.5 cm.

5. You are walking around a perfectly circular track with a radius of 20 m. What is the magnitude of the angular momentum associated with your motion if your mass is 70 kg, and you complete 1 revolution of the track in 30 min?

6. A person with a mass of 52 kg runs with a speed of 6.8 m/s jumps onto the outer rim of a merry-go-round. The merry-go-round has a radius of 1.5 m and can be modelled as a large disk. The merry-go-round was initially at rest before the person jumped onto it and rotates at 1.3 rad/s immediately after the person jumps on. What is the mass of the merry-go-round?

7. A 50 kg person stands at the edge of a 7.4 m diameter circular platform that is mounted horizontally on a frictionless axle and has a total mass of 300 kg. The platform is at rest, but when the person begins running at a speed of 10 m/s (with respect to the platform) around its edge, the platform begins to rotate in the opposite direction. What is the magnitude of the speed of the person with respect to the ground? You can model the platform as a circular disk.

8. A solid disk is rotating around an axis through its center of mass and perpendicular to its plane. A thin ring with the same mass and radius is dropped straight down onto the disk, as shown in the figure at right. Friction causes the ring to accelerate until it is riding on the disk without slipping. What is the ratio of the final angular velocity of the two masses together to the initial angular velocity of the disk?

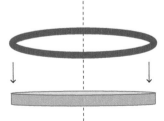

CHAPTER FIFTEEN
Heat and the 1st Law of Thermodynamics

15-1 Introduction

U p to this point, we have focused on mechanical descriptions of systems consisting of only a few objects. In the remaining two chapters of this book, we will turn our attention to systems consisting of very large number of objects. Fortunately, the same energy-based approaches we have been using can be readily scaled to describe the behavior of these much larger systems. However, since complete kinematic descriptions of each object in a large system are often impractical, if not impossible, we will, instead, employ statistical descriptions of these systems as a whole. This is a natural extension of the system approach to Newton's 2nd law introduced in Section 12-6 and is the foundation of an entire field of physics called statistical mechanics. The basic postulates and approaches of statistical mechanics and the associated thermodynamics will be the subject of the remainder of this book.

15-2 Microscopic vs. Macroscopic

We begin by making a distinction between the sizes of the systems and/or the properties of these systems that we are describing. We will use the term *microscopic* to describe a system that consists of only a few objects or a system whose physical size is small (*e.g.,* roughly the dimensions of a single molecule). We will use the term *macroscopic* to describe a system that consists of a large number of objects (*e.g.,* the number of molecules of air in the room) or a system whose physical size is large (*e.g.,* visible without the use of a microscope). For example, a block sliding across a frictionless horizontal surface would be considered a macroscopic system; whereas, the atoms that constitute that block would be a microscopic system. Similarly we can now make a distinction between microscopic and macroscopic descriptions of our system. For example, the magnitude of the movements of the atoms within a block relative to each other would be a microscopic description of the block; whereas, the volume of the block would be a macroscopic description. Thus, macroscopic parameters characterize the system as a whole and provide a statistical description of ensemble behavior of the microscopic objects that constitute the system.

15-3 Statistical Descriptions of Systems

Let's consider the macroscopic system shown in Figure 15.1 that consists of two blocks connected by a massless rope that passes over a massive but frictionless pulley.

The equation for the energy of this system is the sum of the kinetic and potential energies of the objects in the system.

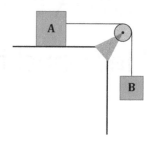

Figure 15.1: A macroscopic system consisting of two blocks attached by a rope.

$$E = K_A + K_B + \left(K_{rot}\right)_{pulley} + \left(U_g\right)_A + \left(U_g\right)_B + \left(U_g\right)_{pulley}$$

We have previously shown that through differentiation of this equation for the energy of the system we can determine kinematic equations that relate the position, velocity, and acceleration of the objects in the system. We can generalize this approach by calculating the energy of a macroscopic system of N blocks as a summation of the kinetic and potential energies of each block in the system[1]. If we use subscripts to denote these blocks, then we can express the total energy of the system as

$$E = \sum_{i=1}^{N} E_i \quad \rightarrow \quad E = \sum_{i=1}^{N} K_i + \left(K_{rot}\right)_i + U_i \tag{15-1}$$

In Equation 15-1, E_i is the total energy of the ith block in the system, K_i is the translational kinetic energy of the ith block in the system, $(K_{rot})_i$ is the rotational kinetic energy of the ith block in the system, and Ui is the total potential energy of the ith block in the system, which is a sum of all the possible potential energies (gravitational, spring, *etc.*)[2].

Now, let's consider a macroscopic system that consists of a 100 ml of water in a sealed container. Rather than a collection of blocks, this system consists of approximately 10^{24} molecules of water. Each of these molecules will have kinetic energies and potential energies, and each molecule can interact with other molecules in the system (*e.g.*, through collisions). The energy of this system is simply the sum of the kinetic and potential energies of all these molecules of water (Equation 15-1). Sadly, however, the sheer number of terms in this summation makes this approach impractical. Furthermore, even if you had a computer powerful enough to perform all calculations in Equation 15-1 for this system and the associated differentiation necessary for calculating the kinematics of the molecules of water, you would still be unable to apply this approach. Such a complete deterministic description of this system is impossible because of the limitations imposed by quantum mechanics on the ability to precisely determine the position and velocity of an object[3].

---

1   Recall from Section 1-6 that energy is an extensive quantity.
2   It is, of course, possible that these potential energies might result from interactions between the objects in the system. If that was the case, then the single summation in Equation 15-1 would need to be replaced by a double summation over the pairs of objects whose interaction generates the potential energy.
3   According to the Heisenberg uncertainty principle, it is not possible to precisely determine both the position and the velocity of an object.

We can, however, derive a valid *statistical description* of the ensemble system of water molecules that includes a representation of the average behavior of the individual molecules. If we could follow an individual molecule of water in the system for a long enough period of time, that molecule would eventually have been located in all possible positions in the container and would eventually have had all possible kinetic energies. Naturally, while we are following one specific molecule of water, all of the other molecules of water are also moving around in the container and, thus, also eventually experiencing all possible positions and kinetic energies. Given the very large number of water molecules in our system we can reasonably argue that at any instant of time all possible positions and kinetic energies are associated with at least one molecule of water.

This argument is fundamental to the statistical descriptions of macroscopic systems. It can be more generally expressed as

If the number of objects in a system is large enough, then all possible positions and kinetic energies accessible to the objects in the system will be associated with at least one object in the system.

It follows that a system is equally likely to be found with its microscopic constituent objects in any of the possible configurations that are compatible with the macroscopic parameters of the system. Let's refer to each configuration of the microscopic objects in the system as a **thermodynamic state** (or, simply, *state*) of the system.

Thermodynamic state: A configuration of the microscopic constituent objects in a macroscopic system. Thermodynamic states can be characterized using the associated macroscopic parameters of the entire system.

For example, each distribution of the molecules of water would constitute a state of the system. Furthermore, each configuration of the molecules of water that would correspond to a total volume of 100 ml would be called an **accessible state** for the system.

Accessible state: A state that is compatible with the macroscopic parameters of the system.

If the volume of the water remains constant, then each of the accessible states of the system is equally probable. In other words, if we could identify and label the individual molecules of water in this system, there would be an equal probability of each molecule to be found in any of the possible positions within the solution of water and moving with any of the possible velocities such that the total volume of the water was 100 ml. We define a system to be in *thermal equilibrium* if the probability of finding a system within any of its accessible states is constant in time.

In thermal equilibrium, the probability of finding a system in any of its accessible states is independent of time. Furthermore, each of the accessible states of a system is equally probable when the system is in thermal equilibrium.

Since systems in equilibrium are equally likely to be found in any of their accessible states, we can define the average energy for a system E_{avg} to be equal to the product of the number of objects in the system N and the average energy of each object in the system $\left(E_i\right)_{avg}$.

$$E_{avg} = N\left(E_i\right)_{avg} \tag{15-2}$$

Strictly speaking, Equation 15-2 will be valid only for systems consisting of large numbers of objects like our system of water molecules. For all of the thermodynamic systems we will consider in Chapter 15 and Chapter 16, this condition can be assumed to be satisfied.

Finally, we can define the set of parameters necessary to define the thermodynamic state of a system to be *state variables*.

State variables: The set of parameters required to define a thermodynamic state.

State variables are parameters that can be measured directly in the laboratory (*e.g.*, volume) or that can be inferred from such measurements. Although the appropriate set of state variable varies between systems, each system is defined by a specific set of relationships between its corresponding state variables. We refer to these relationships as the **equations of state** for the system.

Equation of state: An expression of the relationship between the state variables for a system.

In addition to volume, the energy, temperature, and pressure of a system are common state variables found in equations of state.

15-4 Heat and Temperature

In the previous chapters, we have focused on mechanical interactions (*i.e.*, work) as the mechanism by which systems exchange energy with the external environment. For example, as a block slides across a horizontal surface, its kinetic energy will be dissipated to the environment through the work done by the force of kinetic friction acting on the block. We will now turn our attention to non-mechanical interactions through which systems can exchange energy with their environment. We refer to the change in energy associated with these interactions as **heat**.

Heat: A change in energy associated with a non-mechanical[4] interaction. Heat is denoted by the variable Q. The unit of heat is the joule (J).

There are three non-mechanical interactions associated with heat. *Conduction* is a transfer of energy between two objects that are in contact with one another. Conduction is the exchange of heat that occurs when you accidentally touch a hot stove and burn your hand. *Convection* is the transfer of energy between two objects mediated by a fluid. It is through the convection associated with the large-scale currents in the Earth's oceans that the warmth of the Earth's oceans at the equator is

---

4 Non-mechanical interactions are often also referred to as thermal interactions.

transferred toward the poles. Finally, *radiation* is the transfer of energy between two objects through electromagnetic radiation. The warmth you feel on your skin when exposed to the Sun results from radiation from the Sun.

We can further define two systems as being in **thermal equilibrium** if there is no *net* heat exchanged between them. Another useful definition of thermal equilibrium is that the temperatures of the systems are the same.

Thermal equilibrium: Two systems are said to be in thermal equilibrium if they have the same temperature. No net heat is exchanged between systems in thermal equilibrium.

We are very familiar with using temperature as a measure of hot and cold. Not surprisingly, however, the quantity *temperature* has a specific scientific definition[5]. In addition to its formal definition, temperature can also be defined is in terms of thermal equilibrium. Specifically, two systems are said to have the same temperature if they are in thermal equilibrium with each other. This *equivalence definition of temperature* is commonly expressed as the **zeroth law of thermodynamics**.

Zeroth law of thermodynamics: If system A has the same temperature as system C, and system B has the same temperature as system C, then system A has the same temperature as system B.

Zeroth law of thermodynamics: If system A is in thermal equilibrium with system C, and system B is in thermal equilibrium with system C, then system A is in thermal equilibrium with system B.

We will use the variable T for temperature, and the SI unit of temperature is the kelvin (K). Please note that the ° symbol is typically not used when using the unit K. In Equation 15-3, the relationships between measurements of temperature using kelvins, °C (denoted as T_C in Equation 15-3), and °F (denoted as T_F in Equation 15-3) are shown.

$$T = T_C + 273.15° \qquad T_F = \frac{9}{5}T_C + 32° \qquad T = \frac{5}{9}\left(T_F - 32°\right) + 273.15° \qquad \textbf{(15-3)}$$

We can think of temperature as an intrinsic property of a system, similar to how kinetic energy, potential energy, and momentum are intrinsic properties of a system.

15-5 The 1st Law of Thermodynamics

The 1st law of thermodynamics is an expression of energy conservation. The relationship between the changes in the kinetic and potential energies of a system and the work done on that system by external non-conservative forces was given in Equation 7.10 as

$$\Delta K + \sum_i \Delta U_i = \left(W_{net}\right)_{non-conservative}$$

---

5   We will learn this definition is Section 16-7.

We can now include changes in the energy of the system due to heat exchanged with the environment.

$$\Delta K + \sum_i \Delta U_i = \left(W_{net} \right)_{non-conservative} + Q \tag{15-4}$$

In Equation 15-4, the variable Q denotes heat absorbed by the system. Thus, a positive value for Q denotes heat absorbed by the system from the environment, and a negative value for Q denotes heat released by the system to the environment.

From Newton's 3rd law, we know that any external force exerted by the environment on a system is accompanied by a reaction force exerted by the system back on the environment. Since these two forces have the same magnitude but act in opposite directions, we know that works associated with these forces are related by

$$W_{environment\ on\ system} = -W_{system\ on\ environment}$$

We can, therefore, rewrite Equation 15-4 in terms of the work done by the system on the environment, denoted simply as W, rather than the work done on the system by the environment (*i.e.*, by the external non-conservative forces).

$$W_{system\ on\ environment} = W \;\rightarrow\; \left(W_{net} \right)_{non-conservative} = -W$$

With this definition, we can express the 1st law of thermodynamics (Equation 15-4) as Equation 15-5.

$$\Delta K + \sum_i \Delta U_i = Q - W \;\rightarrow\; \Delta E = Q - W \tag{15-5}$$

The 1st law of thermodynamics can be represented pictorially in Figure 15.2.

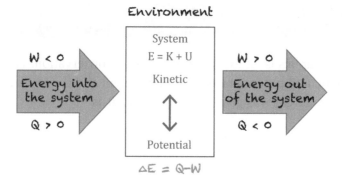

Figure 15.2: The 1st law of thermodynamics

Please note that in Figure 15.2 the variable W denotes the work done *by the system*. This definition of this variable is different from what was used in Figure 3.4, where W denoted the work done on the system, but this definition is more common and arguably more convenient for thermodynamic descriptions of systems.

Example 15-1:

Problem: Through the interaction with the outside environment, a system's energy increases by 10 J while it absorbs 6 J of heat. What is the associated work done by the system on the environment?

Solution: From Equation 15-5, we have

$$\Delta E = Q - W \quad \rightarrow \quad W = Q - \Delta E \quad \rightarrow \quad W = 6J - 10J$$

$$W = -4J$$

The system did -4 J of work on the environment, and, thus, the environment did +4 J of work on the system. In other words, the environment exerted a net external force on the system that did 4 J of work and, hence, increased the energy of the system. This could be an external push, for example, that increased the kinetic energy of the system.

15-6 Heat Capacity and Equipartition Theorem

In Section 1-4, we presented the 2nd law of thermodynamics as a requirement that systems always arrange themselves in order to minimize their total potential energy. Another way of stating the 2nd law of thermodynamics is that energy in the form of heat always flows from systems at higher temperature to systems at lower temperature[6]. Furthermore, it must be the case that when a system absorbs heat, its temperature increases, and when a system releases heat, its temperature decreases[7]. The proportionality between heat absorbed or released by a system and the change in the temperature of the system is the *heat capacity* of the system. Heat capacity has the units of J/K, is always a positive number[6], and will be denoted as C. The heat capacity of a system depends upon both the composition of the system (*e.g.*, the system is 10 kg of solid lead bricks, the system is a liter of liquid water, *etc.*) and the temperature of the system. Heat capacity is defined in terms of the

---

6   We will discuss this further in Chapter 16.

7   If this were not true, hot systems would always get hotter when they release heat, and cold systems would always get colder when they absorb heat. Under these conditions, systems at initially different temperatures would always move away from, rather than toward, thermal equilibrium.

infinitesimal change in temperature dT associated with an absorption/release of an infinitesimal heat $đQ$[8], as shown in Equation 15-6.

$$đQ = C(dT) \qquad \textbf{(15-6)}$$

If the temperature change is small enough such that the heat capacity is constant, then

$$\int đQ = \int C dT \quad \rightarrow \quad \int đQ = C \int dT \quad \rightarrow \quad Q = C(\Delta T) \qquad \textbf{(15-7)}$$

Example 15-2:

Problem: Through the interaction with its environment, a system's energy increases by 10 J while it absorbs 6 J of heat. What is the change in the temperature of the system if the heat capacity of the system is a constant 0.5 J/K?

Solution: Using Equation 15-7 we have

$$Q = C(\Delta T) \quad \rightarrow \quad \Delta T = \frac{(6 \text{J})}{\left(0.5 \dfrac{\text{J}}{\text{K}}\right)}$$

$$\Delta T = 12\text{K}$$

Example 15-3:

Problem: Two objects, A and B, initially at 200 K and 300 K, respectively, are brought into contact with each other. The heat capacity of the object A is a constant 2 J/K, and the heat capacity of object B is a constant 6 J/K. Through the exchange of heat, the two objects eventually obtain a common final temperature. What is this final temperature? How much heat was exchanged during the process of obtaining the final temperature?

Solution: Since the heat capacities of the two objects are constant, we can express the heat absorbed/released by the objects using Equation 15-7.

$$Q_A = C_A(\Delta T_A) \qquad Q_B = C_B(\Delta T_B)$$

---

8   See Appendix F.

The heat absorbed by one object must be released by the other object. Thus,

$$Q_A = -Q_B \;\rightarrow\; C_A\left(\Delta T_A\right) = -C_B\left(\Delta T_B\right) \;\rightarrow\; C_A\left(T_{F,A} - T_{i,A}\right) = -C_B\left(T_{F,B} - T_{i,B}\right)$$

Lastly, because the final temperatures of the objects are the same at equilibrium, we have

$$T_{F,A} = T_{F,B} = T_F \;\rightarrow\; C_A\left(T_F - T_{i,A}\right) = -C_B\left(T_F - T_{i,B}\right) \;\rightarrow\; C_A T_F - C_A T_{i,A} = C_B T_{i,B} - C_B T_F$$

$$\left(C_A + C_B\right)T_F = C_B T_{i,B} + C_A T_{i,A} \;\rightarrow\; T_F = \frac{C_B T_{i,B} + C_A T_{i,A}}{C_A + C_B}$$

$$T_F = \frac{\left(6\dfrac{J}{K}\right)(300K) + \left(2\dfrac{J}{K}\right)(200K)}{2\dfrac{J}{K} + 6\dfrac{J}{K}}$$

$$T_F = 275K$$

The heat exchanged was

$$Q_A = C_A\left(\Delta T_A\right) \;\rightarrow\; Q_A = \left(2\frac{J}{K}\right)(275K - 200K)$$

$$Q_A = 150J$$

Equation 15-5 demonstrates that systems can exchange energy with their environments through heat as well as work. While we know from Newton's 2nd law that the net work done on a system is equal to the change kinetic energy of the system, it is not immediately clear how the absorption or release of heat by a system affects the energy of that system. For example, what happens to the 6 J of energy absorbed as heat by the system in Example 15-1? Does it go into the kinetic energy of the system, into the potential energy of the system, or into both energies?

The simplest answer to these questions is that the change in temperature associated with the absorption or release of heat (Equation 15-6) can be related with a change in the average energy of the system, which we can represent as a change in the average energy of each object in the system

(Equation 15-2). The specific partitioning of this change in average energy among the potential and kinetic energies of the objects in the system follows the equipartition theorem.

Equipartition theorem: A mean value of $\frac{1}{2}k_BT$ is associated with each quadratic term[9] in the expression for the energy of a system at equilibrium.

The constant k_B in the equipartition theorem is the Boltzmann constant.

$$k_B = 1.38 \times 10^{-23}\,\frac{J}{K}$$

Let's consider the system shown in Figure 15.3 that consists of a block attached to a horizontally-mounted spring. We will assume that the horizontal surface along which the block moves is frictionless.

Figure 15.3: A 1-dimensional simple harmonic oscillator.

We know from Section 6-3 that this system is a 1-dimensional simple harmonic oscillator with an energy given by the equation

$$E = \frac{1}{2}mv_x^2 + \frac{1}{2}kx^2$$

The average energy of this system would, therefore, be

$$E_{avg} = \left(\frac{1}{2}mv_x^2\right)_{avg} + \left(\frac{1}{2}kx^2\right)_{avg}$$

And, thus, from the equipartition theorem, we know that

$$E_{avg} = \frac{1}{2}k_BT + \frac{1}{2}k_BT \quad \rightarrow \quad E_{avg} = k_BT$$

Example 15-4:

Problem: Consider a system consisting of N small molecules in a three dimensional box. How does the average translational kinetic energy of this system depend upon the temperature of the system? You may assume that N is sufficiently large enough that Equation 15-2 can be used.

---

9   We have learned three quadratic energy terms: translational kinetic energy ($\frac{1}{2}mv^2$), rotational kinetic energy ($\frac{1}{2}I\omega^2$), and spring potential energy ($\frac{1}{2}k(l-l_0)^2$).

Solution: The molecules can move in three dimensions, so the equation for the translational kinetic energy of the ith molecule is[10]

$$K_i = \frac{1}{2}mv_{x,i}^2 + \frac{1}{2}mv_{y,i}^2 + \frac{1}{2}mv_{z,i}^2$$

In this equation, the x, y, and z axis denote a right-handed coordinate system (Section B-7). The average translational kinetic energy of the ith molecule is

$$\left(K_i\right)_{avg} = \left(\frac{1}{2}mv_{x,i}^2\right)_{avg} + \left(\frac{1}{2}mv_{y,i}^2\right)_{avg} + \left(\frac{1}{2}mv_{z,i}^2\right)_{avg}$$

From the equipartition theorem, we have

$$\left(K_i\right)_{avg} = \frac{1}{2}k_BT + \frac{1}{2}k_BT + \frac{1}{2}k_BT \quad \rightarrow \quad \left(K_i\right)_{avg} = \frac{3}{2}k_BT$$

The average translational kinetic energy of the system of N molecules can then be found using Equation 15-2.

$$K_{avg} = \frac{3}{2}Nk_BT$$

15-7 The Equation of State of an Ideal Gas

An ideal gas is defined as a system of molecules of gas that possess only translational kinetic energy. We ignore any potential energy resulting from the interactions of the gas molecules with themselves or with the environment external to the system. Since the only energy of an ideal gas is translational kinetic energy, it follows from the equipartition theorem that the energy of the ideal gas is a function of the temperature of the gas only; in other words, the energy of an ideal gas is independent of the volume of the gas.

Since the molecules of an ideal gas have translational kinetic energy, they will be moving around inside the container holding the gas. As they move, they will continually collide both with each other and with the walls of the container. All of the collisions between molecules of the gas

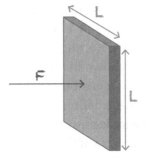

Figure 15.4: Pressure is defined as the ratio of the magnitude of the force to the area on which the force is acting.

---

10   Furthermore, the object's motion along each dimension is independent of its motion along the other dimensions.

will not affect any of the macroscopic parameters of the gas (*e.g.*, its center of mass) since they are associated with forces internal to the system (Section 12-5). However, the collisions of the molecules with the walls of the container will result in a net force being exerted on the walls of the container and, thus, on the environment external to the system. We can quantify this force as a macroscopic parameter called pressure.

The pressure associated with a force acting on a surface is defined as the ratio of the magnitude of the force to the area of the surface.

For example, the force in Figure 15.4 is acting on a square surface with sides of length L. The pressure of this force is, thus,

$$P = \frac{F}{A} \quad \rightarrow \quad P = \frac{F}{L^2}$$

The SI unit of pressure is the pascal, denoted by the symbol Pa.

$$1\,\text{Pa} = 1\frac{\text{N}}{\text{m}^2} \quad \rightarrow \quad 1\,\text{Pa} = 1\frac{\text{kg}}{\text{m}\,\text{s}^2}$$

The pressure of the ideal gas is associated with the impulses resulting from the collisions of the molecules of the gas with the surfaces of the container (Section 13-2). From Newton's 2nd law, we know that the magnitudes of these impulses are related to the magnitudes of the changes in the momenta of the molecules of the gas during these collisions. Therefore, since the kinetic energy and, hence,

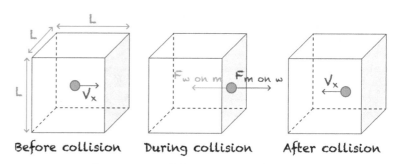

Before collision   During collision   After collision

Figure 15.5: The pressure of the gas results from the impulse associated with the collisions of molecules of the gas with the walls of the container. The container is a cube with sides of length L.

the magnitude of the momentum of the molecules of the ideal gas are functions of the temperature of the gas, it follows that the pressure of the gas must also be a function of temperature.

To determine this relationship between pressure and temperature, let's consider the simple system shown in Figure 15.5, which consists of a single molecule of gas bouncing back and forth along one dimension between two parallel walls of a cubic container with sides of length L.

Let's define the dimension for the motion of the molecule of gas to be the *x*-axis. The collisions of the molecule of gas with the wall will be perfectly elastic, so we can use Equation 13-11 to relate the momenta of the molecule of gas before and after the collision. Since the mass of the wall can be safely considered to be infinite compared to the mass of the molecule of gas, we have[11]

$$\vec{v}_{molecule,f} = -\vec{v}_{molecule,i}$$

---

11   See Example 13-11.

Therefore, the magnitude of the change in momentum following each collision with the wall will be

$$\Delta p_x = m\left(\Delta v_x\right) \quad \rightarrow \quad \Delta p_x = 2mv_x$$

In this equation, we have denoted the mass of the molecule of gas as m. During each collision, the molecule of gas will exert a force on the wall ($F_{m\,on\,w}$ in Figure 15.5), which, according to Newton's 3rd law, will be associated with a force of equal magnitude that the wall exerts on the molecule of gas ($F_{w\,on\,m}$ in Figure 15.5). It is the magnitude of these forces that gives rise to the pressure of the gas.

From Newton's 2nd law, we know that the magnitude of $F_{w\,on\,m}$ is equal to the time rate of change of the momentum of the molecule of gas. Each collision of the molecule of gas with the wall will give rise to a change of momentum of $2mv_x$ and the time between collisions with the same wall is simply twice the width of the cube divided by the speed of the molecule of gas. Therefore,

$$\frac{\Delta p_x}{\Delta t} = \frac{2mv_x}{\dfrac{2L}{v_x}} \quad \rightarrow \quad \frac{\Delta p_x}{\Delta t} = \frac{mv_x^2}{L}$$

This rate of change in momentum is, then, equal to the magnitude of the force exerted by the wall on the molecule of gas, which, according to Newton's 3rd law, is equal to the magnitude of the force of the molecule of gas on the wall.

$$F_{w\,on\,m} = \frac{mv_x^2}{L} \quad \rightarrow \quad F_{m\,on\,w} = \frac{mv_x^2}{L}$$

The pressure exerted by this molecule of gas on the walls of the container is simply the magnitude of this force divided by the area of the walls. Since the container is cubic, this area is L^2.

$$P = \frac{F_{m\,on\,w}}{L^2} \quad \rightarrow \quad P = \frac{\dfrac{mv_x^2}{L}}{L^2} \quad \rightarrow \quad P = \frac{mv_x^2}{L^3}$$

The quantity L^3 in this equation is simply the volume of the container V.

$$V = L^3 \quad \rightarrow \quad P = \frac{mv_x^2}{V}$$

To determine the total pressure resulting from all of the molecules of gas in the container, we need to sum the contributions from each individual molecule of gas. From the discussion in Section 15-3, it follows that the average pressure of the system of gas molecules is simply the product of the number of gas molecules and the average pressure of each individual molecule of gas.

$$P_{avg} = N\left(P_i\right)_{avg} \quad \rightarrow \quad P_{avg} = N\left(\frac{mv_x^2}{V}\right)_{avg} \quad \rightarrow \quad P_{avg} = N\frac{m}{V}\left(v_x^2\right)_{avg}$$

The average of the square of the speed of the individual gas molecules can be determined using the equipartition theorem (Example 15-4).

$$\left(\frac{1}{2}mv_x^2\right)_{avg} = \frac{1}{2}k_BT \quad \rightarrow \quad \frac{1}{2}m\left(v_x^2\right)_{avg} = \frac{1}{2}k_BT \quad \rightarrow \quad \left(v_x^2\right)_{avg} = \frac{k_BT}{m}$$

Hence,

$$P_{avg} = \frac{Nm\left(\dfrac{k_BT}{m}\right)}{V} \quad \rightarrow \quad P_{avg}V = Nk_BT \tag{15-8}$$

Equation 15-8 is the equation of state for an ideal gas since it expresses the relationship between the state variables (pressure, volume, temperature, and number of molecules) that define a thermo-dynamic state of the gas.

It is important to note that Equation 15-8 is applicable only when the assumptions included in its derivation are satisfied. Not only does the derivation of Equation 15-8 assume that the system is in thermal equilibrium at a constant temperature, but also that the walls of the container are fixed.

15-8 Work Done by an Ideal Gas

In our derivation of the equation of state for an ideal gas (Equation 15-8), we assumed that the walls of the container were fixed in place. However, if the walls were free to move, then the difference between the pressure of the gas inside the container and the pressure of the environment outside the container may cause the volume of the container to change. Furthermore, if the walls of the container are free to move, there will be an exchange of momentum and kinetic energy between the walls and the molecules of the gas with each collision between the walls and the molecules of gas. We can describe the effective transfer of energy as work done by the gas. This work will be positive if the volume of the container is increasing (*i.e.*, if there is a net transfer of energy from the gas to the walls) and negative if the volume of the container is decreasing (*i.e.*, if there is a net transfer of energy from the walls to the gas). The positive sign for this work associated with an increase in the volume of the container is also consistent with the definition of work in Section 9-5. Specifically, the work must be positive since the direction of the force of the gas on the walls (associated with the pressure of the gas) is in the same direction as the displacement of the walls of the container.

In Equation 15-9, we express the infinitesimal work dW^{12} associated with an infinitesimal change in volume of the gas dV.

$$dW = PdV \qquad\qquad \textbf{(15-9)}$$

In Equation 14-9, P is the pressure of the gas, which is assumed to be constant since the change in the volume of the gas is infinitesimally small. It follows from Equation 15-9 that the work done by a gas during a change in volume is the integral of the pressure of the gas with respect to the volume of the gas.

$$W = \int dW \quad \rightarrow \quad W = \int_{V_i}^{V_f} PdV$$

Hence, work is also the area under the curve of pressure versus volume (Figure 15.6).

Determining work through the integration of Equation 15-9 over a change in volume requires that we know how the pressure of the gas depends upon the volume of the gas. This is not generally known, however, and may even be impossible to describe analytically.

We can circumvent this process by changing the volume of the gas so slowly that the gas is always in thermal equilibrium, and, thus, the equation of state of the gas is always valid. We refer to all such slow changes of a system as **quasi-static** processes.

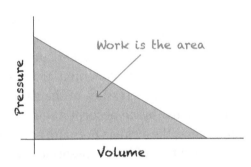

Figure 15.6: The work done by a gas during a change in its volume.

Quasi-static process: A process carried out so slowly that the system remains effectively at equilibrium throughout the process. Quasi-static processes are often also referred to as reversible processes.

Let's first consider the situation in which an ideal gas changes its volume quasi-statically while maintaining a constant temperature (*i.e.*, an isothermal process). Since this process is quasi-static, we can treat the gas as through it were continually in equilibrium and therefore use the equation of state of an ideal gas to relate the state variables of the system. The work done by the gas is therefore

$$W = \int dW \quad \rightarrow \quad W = \int_{V_i}^{V_f} P_{avg}\, dV \quad \rightarrow \quad W = \int_{V_i}^{V_f} \left(\frac{Nk_B T}{V} \right) dV$$

$$W = Nk_B T \int_{V_i}^{V_f} \frac{dV}{V} \quad \rightarrow \quad W = Nk_B T \ln\left(\frac{V_f}{V_i} \right)$$

---

12   See Appendix F.

As expected, if $V_f > V_i$, then $W > 0$ (work is positive if the gas expands) and if $V_f < V_i$, then $W < 0$ (work is negative if the gas is compressed).

If the gas changes its volume under conditions of constant pressure (*i.e.*, an isobaric process), then the work done by the gas is

$$W = \int dW \quad \rightarrow \quad W = \int_{V_i}^{V_f} P_{avg}\, dV \quad \rightarrow \quad W = P_{avg}\int_{V_i}^{V_f} dV \quad \rightarrow \quad W = P_{avg}\Delta V$$

For an ideal gas, this work can also be expressed in terms of the change in the temperature of the gas.

$$P_{avg}\Delta V = Nk_B\Delta T \quad \rightarrow \quad W = Nk_B\Delta T$$

Hence, if the volume increases, the temperature of the gas must have increased. This makes sense according to the 1st law of thermodynamics (Figure 15.2 and Equation 15-5). As the molecules of gas push the walls of the container outward (increasing the volume of the container), they transfer both kinetic energy and momentum to the walls and, as a result, their average kinetic energy decreases. In order for the pressure of the gas to remain constant, this decrease in kinetic energy must be compensated by an absorption of heat from the environment so that the average kinetic energy and, hence, the average pressure of the gas can remain constant. From Equation 15-7, we know that the absorption of heat is associated with an increase in temperature, and, hence, it follows that an isobaric expansion of a gas must be associated by an increase in the temperature of the gas.

Finally, let's consider the situation in which the volume of a gas changes without any heat exchanged with the outside environment. We refer to such a process as an adiabatic change in volume. For adiabatic processes, the change in the energy of the gas must equal the work done by the gas.

$$Q = 0 \quad \rightarrow \quad \Delta E = -W$$

Thus, an adiabatic expansion results in a decrease in the energy of a gas, and an adiabatic compression results in an increase in the energy of a gas.

Now, let's consider the processes shown in Figure 15.7. For both processes, the gas starts in state A corresponding to pressure P_1 and volume V_1 and ends in state C corresponding to a pressure P_2 and volume V_2. In one path, the gas first experiences a quasi-static isovolumetric increase in the pressure to state B. Since the volume is constant during this process, there is no work done by the gas. Next, the gas experiences a quasi-static isobaric expansion to state C during which it does work. The net work for this path from state A to state C is

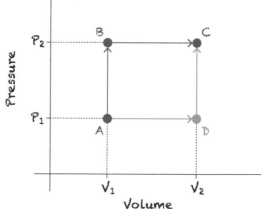

$$W_{ABC} = P_2\left(V_2 - V_1\right)$$

Figure 15.7: A system moves from state A to state C through different paths.

In a separate path, the gas first experiences a quasi-static isobaric expansion to state D during which it does work. The gas then experiences a quasi-static isovolumetric increase in the pressure to state C during which no work is done.

$$W_{ADC} = P_1\left(V_2 - V_1\right)$$

The work done by the gas in moving from state A to state C is clearly dependent upon the path taken with $W_{ABC} > W_{ADC}$. This simple example demonstrates that work is a path-dependent function and is, therefore, an inexact differential[13]. Through a similar calculation, we can show that $Q_{ABC} > Q_{ADC}$, thus, indicating that heat is also an inexact differential[13].

15-9 Heat Capacity Redux

According to the 1st law of thermodynamics, the change in the energy of a system is equal to the difference between the heat absorbed by the system and the work done by the system. For an ideal gas, we can write this relationship as

$$dE = đQ - đW \quad \rightarrow \quad dE = đQ - PdV \quad \rightarrow \quad đQ = dE + PdV$$

Substitution of the definition of the heat capacity in Equation 15-6 gives us

$$CdT = dE + PdV \quad \rightarrow \quad C = \frac{dE}{dT} + P_{avg}\frac{dV}{dT} \tag{15-10}$$

This heat capacity is called the heat capacity at constant pressure and is denoted by C_P.

$$C_P = \frac{dE}{dT} + P_{avg}\frac{dV}{dT}$$

If the volume of the system is constant during the change in temperature associated with the absorption/release of heat, then the heat capacity at constant volume, denoted by C_V, is applicable.

$$dV = 0 \quad \rightarrow \quad C_V = \frac{dE}{dT}$$

---

13   See Appendix F.

Example 15-5:

Problem: Let's model a solid as a 3-dimensional collection of N atoms. Each of the atoms in the solid is free to vibrate around its equilibrium location, and we can model these oscillations as simple harmonic motion (Section 6-7). What is the heat capacity of this system?

Solution: Since we can describe the motion of the atoms as simple harmonic motion, our system consists of a collection of N 3-dimensional harmonic oscillators. The equation for the energy of each oscillator (*i.e.*, for each atom in the solid) is

$$E_i = \frac{1}{2}mv_x^2 + \frac{1}{2}mv_y^2 + \frac{1}{2}mv_z^2 + \frac{1}{2}k_x x^2 + \frac{1}{2}k_y y^2 + \frac{1}{2}k_z z^2$$

According to the equipartition theorem, the average energy of each atom would be

$$\left(E_i\right)_{avg} = 6\left(\frac{1}{2}k_B T\right) \rightarrow \left(E_i\right)_{avg} = 3k_B T$$

Substitution of this result into Equation 15-2 gives us

$$E_{avg} = N\left(E_i\right)_{avg} \rightarrow E_{avg} = N\left(3k_B T\right) \rightarrow E_{avg} = 3Nk_B T$$

The heat capacity of the solid, which is a heat capacity at constant volume is, therefore,

$$C_V = \frac{dE_{avg}}{dT} \rightarrow C_V = \frac{d}{dT}\left(3Nk_B T\right)$$

$$C_V = 3Nk_B$$

This result is the Dulong-Petit law.

For an ideal gas, the only energy of the system is the translational kinetic energy of the molecules of the gas. We can determine the temperature dependence of the average value of these energies using the equipartition theorem (Example 15-4). Hence, for an ideal gas, the heat capacity at constant volume is

$$C_V = \frac{dK_{avg}}{dT} \quad \rightarrow \quad C_V = \frac{d}{dT}\left(\frac{3}{2}Nk_BT\right) \quad \rightarrow \quad C_V = \frac{3}{2}Nk_B$$

We can relate the heat capacity at constant pressure to the heat capacity at constant volume using the equation of state for the system. For an ideal gas, we have

$$P_{avg}V = Nk_BT \quad \rightarrow \quad V = \left(\frac{Nk_B}{P_{avg}}\right)T \quad \rightarrow \quad \frac{dV}{dT} = \frac{Nk_B}{P_{avg}}$$

$$C_P = \frac{3}{2}Nk_B + P_{avg}\left(\frac{Nk_B}{P_{avg}}\right) \quad \rightarrow \quad C_P = \frac{3}{2}Nk_B + Nk_B \quad \rightarrow \quad C_P = \frac{5}{2}Nk_B$$

When a system absorbs heat, the energy flowing into the system can be converted into work, an increase in the temperature of the system, or both. The larger the fraction of the energy that is partitioned into work the less the amount of energy that is available to increase the temperature of the system[14]. Thus, a system absorbing heat at constant pressure will have a smaller temperature change than if it was absorbing heat at constant volume. In other words, more heat must be absorbed by a system at constant pressure than at constant volume for the same change in temperature. It follows that C_P must be greater than C_V, as we have shown for the ideal gas.

15-10 Cyclic Processes with an Ideal Gas

We now turn our attention to an ideal gas that is undergoing a repeated cycle of pressure and volume changes. Let's consider the cycle shown in Figure 15.8.

The gas starts at point A corresponding to pressure P_1, volume V_1, and temperature T_A. The gas then undergoes a quasi-static isovolumetric increase in its pressure to arrive at point B, which corresponds to pressure P_2, volume V_1, and temperature T_B. Since the volume of the gas remained constant during this process, the gas did no work. The heat absorbed by the gas during this process is

$$Q_{AB} = C_V\left(T_B - T_A\right)$$

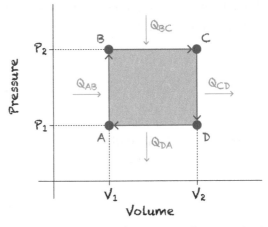

Figure 15.8: A cyclic process for an ideal gas. The net work done by the gas is the area enclosed by the path.

---

14   This is analogous to how changing the partitioning of a change in gravitational potential energy into different kinetic energies affects the acceleration of a system.

Since the process of moving from point A to point B was quasi-static we can relate T_A and T_B to the P_1, P_2, and V_1 using the equation of state of an ideal gas.

$$PV = Nk_B T \quad \rightarrow \quad P_2 V_1 - P_1 V_1 = Nk_B T_B - Nk_B T_A$$

$$\left(P_2 - P_1\right)V_1 = Nk_B\left(T_B - T_A\right) \quad \rightarrow \quad \left(T_B - T_A\right) = \frac{\left(P_2 - P_1\right)V_1}{Nk_B}$$

Hence,

$$Q_{AB} = C_V \frac{\left(P_2 - P_1\right)V_1}{Nk_B}$$

The system then undergoes a quasi-static isobaric expansion to point C. The work done by the system during this process is simply the area under the curve.

$$W_{BC} = P_2\left(V_2 - V_1\right)$$

The heat absorbed by the gas during this process is

$$Q_{BC} = C_P\left(T_C - T_B\right)$$

We can, again, use the equation of state to relate temperature to pressure and volume since this expansion was quasi-static.

$$Q_{BC} = C_P \frac{\left(V_2 - V_1\right)P_2}{Nk_B}$$

A similar set of calculations allows us to determine the heat and work associated with the other processes in the cycle.

$$W_{CD} = 0 \qquad Q_{CD} = C_V \frac{\left(P_1 - P_2\right)V_2}{Nk_B}$$

$$W_{DA} = P_1\left(V_1 - V_2\right) \qquad Q_{DA} = C_P \frac{\left(V_1 - V_2\right)P_1}{Nk_B}$$

The net work done by the system during this cycle is, thus,

$$W_{net} = W_{AB} + W_{BC} + W_{CD} + W_{DA} \quad \rightarrow \quad W_{net} = P_2\left(V_2 - V_1\right) + P_1\left(V_1 - V_2\right)$$

$$W_{net} = \left(P_2 - P_1\right)\left(V_2 - V_1\right)$$

The net work done by the gas is also the area enclosed by the path (Figure 15.8). Similarly, the net heat absorbed by the system during this cycle is

$$Q_{net} = Q_{AB} + Q_{BC} + Q_{CD} + Q_{DA}$$

$$Q_{net} = C_V \frac{\left(P_2 - P_1\right)V_1}{Nk_B} + C_P \frac{\left(V_2 - V_1\right)P_2}{Nk_B} + C_V \frac{\left(P_1 - P_2\right)V_2}{Nk_B} + C_P \frac{\left(V_1 - V_2\right)P_1}{Nk_B}$$

$$Q_{net} = \frac{\left(C_V - C_P\right)\left(P_1 - P_2\right)\left(V_2 - V_1\right)}{Nk_B}$$

Since our system is an ideal gas, we have

$$C_P = C_V + Nk_B \quad \rightarrow \quad C_V - C_P = -Nk_B$$

Substitution of this relationship gives us

$$Q_{net} = \frac{\left(-Nk_B\right)\left(P_1 - P_2\right)\left(V_2 - V_1\right)}{Nk_B} \quad \rightarrow \quad Q_{net} = \left(P_2 - P_1\right)\left(V_2 - V_1\right)$$

$$Q_{net} = W_{net}$$

The temperature of the gas at each point during the cycle is related to the pressure and volume of the gas at that point, according to the equation of state. Thus, the temperature of the gas at point A is the same before and after the system completes the cycle. Since energy is a state function for a system, the energy of the gas at the end of the cycle must equal the energy of the gas at the start of the cycle. This, of course, requires that $Q = W$ for the cycle (Equation 15-5), which we calculated.

Example 15-6:

Problem: An ideal gas is taken through the quasi-static cyclic process shown in Figure 15.9. The system begins in state A, then experiences an isovolumetric increase in pressure to state B, then an isothermal expansion to state C, and, finally, an isobaric compression back to state A.

What is the heat absorbed or released during each process of the cycle? What is the net work done by the gas during the cycle?

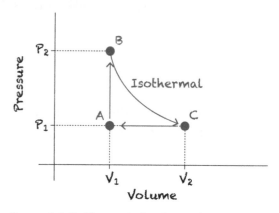

Figure 15.9: The cycle for Example 15-6.

Solution: Let's begin by defining the two temperatures of the system during this cycle. We will denote the temperature of the gas at state A to be T_1 and the temperature of the gas at state B and state C to be T_2.

$$T_A = T_1 \qquad T_B = T_C = T_2$$

There is no work done by the gas during the isovolumetric transition from state A to state B since the volume of the gas is constant during this process.

$$W_{AB} = 0$$

The heat associated with this process is

$$Q_{AB} = C_V\left(T_B - T_A\right) \quad \rightarrow \quad Q_{AB} = C_V\left(T_2 - T_1\right)$$

The work done by the gas during the isothermal transition from state B to state C is

$$W_{BC} = Nk_B T_B \ln\left(\frac{V_2}{V_1}\right) \quad \rightarrow \quad W_{BC} = Nk_B T_2 \ln\left(\frac{V_2}{V_1}\right)$$

Since this process is isothermal, the temperature of the gas is not changing, and, therefore, the energy of the gas is not changing. Thus, the gas must absorb energy from the environment to do the work associated with the increase in its volume.

$$Q_{BC} = Nk_B T_2 \ln\left(\frac{V_2}{V_1}\right)$$

Finally, for the isobaric compression of the gas from state C to state A, we have

$$W_{CA} = Nk_B\left(T_1 - T_2\right) \qquad Q_{CA} = C_P\left(T_1 - T_2\right)$$

Thus, heat is absorbed by the system when it transitions between state A and state B and between state B and state C, and heat is released by the system during the transition from state C to state A. Similarly, work is done by the system during the transition from state B to state C, and work is done on the system (negative work done by the system) during the transition from state C to state A.

The net heat absorbed by the gas during a complete cycle is

$$Q_{net} = Q_{AB} + Q_{BC} + Q_{CD}$$

$$Q_{net} = C_V\left(T_2 - T_1\right) + Nk_B T_2 \ln\left(\frac{V_2}{V_1}\right) + C_P\left(T_1 - T_2\right)$$

$$Q_{net} = \left(C_P - C_V\right)\left(T_1 - T_2\right) + Nk_B T_2 \ln\left(\frac{V_2}{V_1}\right) \quad \rightarrow \quad Q_{net} = Nk_B\left(T_1 - T_2\right) + Nk_B T_2 \ln\left(\frac{V_2}{V_1}\right)$$

$$Q_{net} = Nk_B\left(T_1 + T_2\left(\ln\left(\frac{V_2}{V_1}\right) - 1\right)\right)$$

Similarly, the net work done by the system during a complete cycle is

$$W_{net} = W_{AB} + W_{BC} + W_{CD}$$

$$W_{net} = Nk_B T_2 \ln\left(\frac{V_2}{V_1}\right) + Nk_B\left(T_1 - T_2\right) \quad \rightarrow \quad W_{net} = Nk_B\left(T_1 + T_2\left(\ln\left(\frac{V_2}{V_1}\right) - 1\right)\right)$$

In summary,

Process	Q	W
A to B	$C_V\left(T_2 - T_1\right)$	0
B to C	$Nk_B T_2 \ln\left(\dfrac{V_2}{V_1}\right)$	$Nk_B T_2 \ln\left(\dfrac{V_2}{V_1}\right)$
C to A	$C_P\left(T_1 - T_2\right)$	$Nk_B\left(T_1 - T_2\right)$

Entire Cycle	$Nk_B\left(T_1+T_2\left(\ln\left(\dfrac{V_2}{V_1}\right)-1\right)\right)$	$Nk_B\left(T_1+T_2\left(\ln\left(\dfrac{V_2}{V_1}\right)-1\right)\right)$

As expected, $Q_{net} = W_{net}$ for a complete cycle, so the temperature of the gas is the same at the start and end of a complete cycle. This is, of course, expected since energy is a state function and, for an ideal gas, depends upon only the temperature of the gas. Since the energy of the ideal gas must be the same at the start and end of a complete cycle, the temperature of the ideal gas must be the same at the start and end of a complete cycle.

15-11 Free Expansion

Consider the system shown in Figure 15.10 in which an ideal gas is initially restricted to half of the volume of a thermally and mechanically isolated container; a partition keeps the gas in only the left side of the container. The initial temperature, pressure, and volume of the gas are T, P_0, and V_0, respectively. When the partition is removed, the gas expands to fill the entire volume of the container. We refer to this process as a *free expansion*.

Since $Q = 0$ and $W = 0$ for this expansion, it follows that $\Delta E = 0$ for this expansion. Consequently, if the energy of the gas has not changed, then the temperature of the gas has not changed. Eventually, the gas will come to thermal equilibrium again at which point the volume of the gas has doubled to $2V_0$, and the pressure has decreased to $P_0/2$.

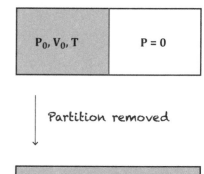

Figure 15.10: Free expansion of an ideal gas.

Why did the gas expand? There is no change in the potential energy of the gas associated with the expansion, so we cannot argue that expansion occurred to satisfy the principle of minimum potential energy. Furthermore, this expansion is irreversible since the gas will never spontaneously revert back to its original volume and pressure. Thus, we cannot argue that the expansion represents an equilibrium change in the state of the gas.

Of course, we can very easily explain why the gas expands in terms of the motion of the molecules of the gas. When the partition is removed, there is nothing preventing the molecules of gas from moving into the right-hand side of the container, and, thus, they will eventually fill the entire volume of the container. From the discussion of the statistical description of systems in Section 15-3, we can say that if given enough time, the molecules of the gas will eventually be evenly distributed among all possible accessible states (positions and velocities) of the entire container. We can, therefore, make a probability-based argument that the gas expanded simply because it is more likely to spread out among the entire accessible volume of the container rather than be confined to only a fraction of that volume. This probability-based explanation for the behavior of thermodynamic systems is the basis of a quantity known as entropy, which will be the subject of the next chapter.

Summary

- **If the number of objects in a system is large enough, then all possible positions and kinetic energies accessible to the objects in the system will be associated with at least one object in the system.**
- **Thermodynamic state:** A configuration of the microscopic constituent objects in a macroscopic system. Thermodynamic states can be characterized using the associated macroscopic parameters (*e.g.*, temperature, volume, pressure) of the entire system.
- **Accessible state:** A thermodynamic state that is compatible with the macroscopic parameters of the system.
- **State variables:** The set of parameters required to define a thermodynamic state.
- **Equation of state:** An expression of the relationship between the state variables for a system. For example, the equation of state for an ideal gas relates the pressure, volume, number of molecules, and temperature of the gas.

$$P_{avg}V = Nk_BT$$

- **In thermal equilibrium, the probability of finding a system in any of its accessible states is independent of time.**
- **In thermal equilibrium, all accessible states are equally probable.**
- **Thermal equilibrium:** Two systems are said to be in thermal equilibrium if they have the same temperature. No net heat is exchanged between systems in thermal equilibrium.
- **Heat:** A change in energy associated with a non-mechanical interaction. Heat is denoted by the variable Q.
- **The infinitesimal work dW associated with an infinitesimal change in volume dV is**

$$dW = PdV$$

- **The 1st law of thermodynamics:** The change in the energy of a system is equal to difference of the heat absorbed by the system and the work done by the system.

$$\Delta E = Q - W$$

- **The equipartition theorem:** A mean value of $\frac{1}{2}k_BT$ is associated with each quadratic term in the expression for the energy of a system at equilibrium.
- **Heat capacity:** The proportionality between infinitesimal heat absorbed or released by a system and the infinitesimal change in the temperature of the system.

$$C = \frac{dQ}{dT}$$

- The heat capacity of an ideal gas is

$$C = \frac{dE}{dT} + P_{avg}\frac{dV}{dT}$$

Problems

1. Through the interaction with its environment, a system's energy increases by 12 J while it does 4 J of work. What is the heat absorbed/released by the system?

2. Through the interaction with its environment, a system's energy increases by 12 J while it does 4 J of work. The heat capacity of the system is a constant 0.5 J/K. What is the change in the temperature of the system?

3. Two identical objects initially at 200 K and 300 K, respectively, are brought into contact with each other. The heat capacity of the objects is a constant 2 J/K. Through the exchange of heat, the two objects eventually obtain a common final temperature. What is this final temperature? How much heat was exchanged during the process of obtaining the final temperature?

4. An ideal gas with energy $E = \frac{3}{2} N k_B T$ is subjected to a cyclic, quasi-static (*i.e.*, reversible) process shown in the figure at right. What is the heat capacity at constant volume for this gas? What is the work done by the gas for one complete cycle? What is the heat absorbed by the gas for one full cycle?

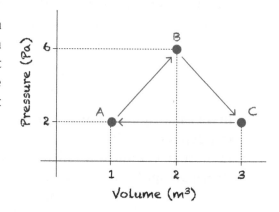

5. An ideal gas with energy $E = \frac{3}{2} N k_B T$ is subjected to a cyclic, quasi-static (*i.e.*, reversible) process shown in the figure at right. What is the net work done by the gas during one cycle? What is the difference in the energy of the gas between state C and state A? What is the heat absorbed by the gas in going from A to C via the path ABC?

6. 2*n* molecules of nitrogen gas and 6*n* molecules of hydrogen gas are inside a container and separated from each other by a valve. The entire container is thermally and mechanically isolated from the rest of the universe. The gases are initially at the same temperature, 300 K. If the valve is opened, the gases interact with each other to form ammonia (NH_3). What is the change in the temperature of the system if *n* molecules of ammonia are formed? You can treat the gases as ideal with heat capacities $C_V = \frac{3}{2} N k_B$ for N_2 and H_2 and $C_V = 3 N k_B$ for ammonia.

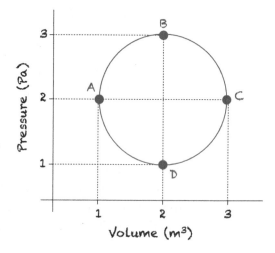

CHAPTER SIXTEEN
Entropy and the 2nd Law of Thermodynamics

We began this book with the principle of minimum potential energy: systems will always arrange themselves so as to minimize their total potential energy. We further indicated that it is the 2nd law of thermodynamics that justifies why systems behave this way. Indeed, it is the 2nd law of thermodynamics that ultimately explains why systems behave as they do even when there is no change in the energy of the system (such as in the free expansion of the gas in Section 15-11). As we shall see, rather than changes in the energy of a system, it is actually changes in the entropy of a system that affect the behavior of the system.

16-2 Entropy

The statistical definition of the entropy of a thermodynamic state is given in Equation 16-1[1].

$$S = k_B \ln \Omega \qquad \text{(16-1)}$$

In Equation 16-1, the entropy (S) is equal to the product of the Boltzmann constant (k_B) and the natural log of the multiplicity of the state (Ω). The multiplicity of a state is the number of configurations of the components of the system that all correspond to the same thermodynamic state (*i.e.*, to the same macroscopic parameters, such as temperature, pressure, and volume). As indicated in Equation 16-1, the units of entropy are J/K, and the largest entropy is associated with the state with the largest multiplicity.

Entropy is an intrinsic property of a system in the same way that energy and momenta are intrinsic properties of systems. Furthermore, since the entropy of a state is determined by the multiplicity of the state (Equation 16-1), it follows that entropy is a state function just like energy. In other words,

---

1 This same equation can be found on Ludwig Boltzmann's tombstone in Vienna.

the change in the entropy of a system associated with a change in the thermodynamic state of the system is independent of the path (*i.e.*, process) by which the change in entropy occurred. Finally, entropy is also an extensive parameter just like energy (Section 1-6).

To give this discussion more context, let's consider all the possible outcomes of flipping a coin 4 times; for example, the first flip might result in heads, but the next 3 might all be tails. In Table 16-1, the 16 possible outcomes are grouped together by the number of heads that occurred.

Table 16-1: The possible outcomes (heads is denoted by H, and tails is denoted by T) of flipping a coin 4 times.

Number of Heads	Associated Outcomes	Total Number of Outcomes
0	TTTT	1
1	HTTT THTT TTHT TTTH	4
2	HHTT THHT HTHT THTH HTTH TTHH	6
3	THHH HTHH HHTH HHHT	4
4	HHHH	1

It's clear from Table 16-1 that the largest number of outcomes is associated with 2 of the 4 flips being heads. We would, therefore, conclude that getting 2 heads is the most probable outcome[2].

This is the basis of the statistical definition of entropy. It is most probable to obtain 2 heads when flipping a fair coin 4 times since the largest fraction of the total outcomes corresponds to this result; the multiplicity associated with this result is the largest. When flipping a fair coin 4 times, the multiplicity for obtaining 2 heads ($\Omega = 6$) is larger than the multiplicity for obtaining 4 heads ($\Omega = 1$). Therefore, it is more likely that 2 heads will be obtained rather than 4 heads.

Furthermore, the probability of obtaining one outcome *relative* to the probability of obtaining another outcome is the ratio of the multiplicities of the outcomes.

$$\frac{P_A}{P_B} = \frac{\Omega_A}{\Omega_B}$$

(16-2)

In Equation 16-2, the subscripts A and B denote the possible outcomes or, more generally, accessible states of the system. For example, when flipping a fair coin 4 times, the ratio of the probability of getting 2 heads to the probability of getting 4 heads is

---

2   We assume that the coin is fair. That is, we assume that the probability of getting heads is equal to the probability of getting tails. In other words, each accessible state (each combination of heads and tails) is equally probable.

$$\frac{P_{2heads}}{P_{4heads}} = \frac{\Omega_{2heads}}{\Omega_{4heads}} \quad \rightarrow \quad \frac{P_{2heads}}{P_{4heads}} = \frac{6}{1} \quad \rightarrow \quad P_{2heads} = 6P_{4heads}$$

When flipping a coin 4 times, you are 6 times more likely to obtain 2 heads than to obtain 4 heads. Furthermore, according to Equation 16-1, we can say that the entropy associated with obtaining 2 heads is larger than the entropy associated with getting 1 head.

Example 16-1:

Problem: You flip a fair coin 3 times. How much more likely are you to obtain 2 heads than 3 heads?

Solution: The possible outcomes are shown in the table below.

Number of Heads	Associated Outcomes	Total Number of Outcomes
0	TTT	1
1	HTT THT TTH	3
2	HHT THH HHT	3
3	HHH	1

The ratio of the probability of getting 2 heads to the probability of getting 3 heads is

$$\frac{P_{2heads}}{P_{3heads}} = \frac{\Omega_{2heads}}{\Omega_{3heads}} \quad \rightarrow \quad \frac{P_{2heads}}{P_{3heads}} = \frac{3}{1}$$

$$P_{2heads} = 3P_{3heads}$$

You are 3 times more likely to get 2 heads than to get 3 heads.

Lastly, it is worth mentioning that people often incorrectly associate entropy with a measure of disorder. This cannot be true, of course, since disorder is subjective. Aside from Equation 16-1, entropy is best considered to be a measure of the number of ways that a system can be arranged given the constraint of a particular set of macroscopic properties for that system (*e.g.*, volume, temperature, or pressure). Of course, such calculations become intractable for large systems. Indeed, determining the multiplicity for each thermodynamic state for 1 liter of water (*i.e.*, enumerating the configurations of all possible positions and velocities of the water molecules for a given temperature of the water) would be nearly impossible.

16-3 The 2nd Law of Thermodynamics

Although direct calculations of the entropy of a system are often difficult (if not impossible), it is nevertheless straightforward to calculate *changes* in the entropy of a system. According to the 2nd law of thermodynamics, if a system undergoes a quasi-static process at constant temperature in which it absorbs an infinitesimal amount of heat, the infinitesimal change in the entropy of the system is

$$dS = \frac{dQ}{T} \qquad (16\text{-}3)$$

If the temperature of the system is constant as the heat is absorbed, then Equation 16-3 simplifies to Equation 16-4.

$$\int dS = \int \frac{dQ}{T} \quad \rightarrow \quad \int dS = \frac{1}{T}\int dQ \quad \rightarrow \quad \Delta S = \frac{Q}{T} \qquad (16\text{-}4)$$

Example 16-2:

Problem: One liter of water at 273 K is brought into contact with a large heat reservoir at 373 K. As a result of the interaction between the water and the reservoir, the temperature of the water will increase (*i.e.*, heat will flow from the reservoir to the water, thereby increasing the temperature of the water[3]). However, we will assume that the temperature of the reservoir remains constant. What has been the change in entropy of the water (ΔS_{water}), of the reservoir ($\Delta S_{reservoir}$), and of the entire system consisting of both water and heat reservoir (ΔS_{system}) when the water has reached 373 K? The heat capacity of the water has a constant a value of 4180 J/K during this process.

Solution: The changes in entropy can be calculated using Equation 16-3 and Equation 15-6. Since the heat capacity of the water is constant, we have

$$dQ_{water} = C_{water}dT \quad \rightarrow \quad dS_{water} = \frac{C_{water}dT}{T} \quad \rightarrow \quad \int dS_{water} = \int C_{water}\frac{dT}{T}$$

$$\Delta S_{water} = \int_{273K}^{373K} C_{water}\frac{dT}{T} \quad \rightarrow \quad \Delta S_{water} = C_{water}\int_{273K}^{373K}\frac{dT}{T} \quad \rightarrow \quad \Delta S_{water} = C_{water}\left(\ln T\Big|_{273K}^{373K}\right)$$

---

3   See Equation 15-6.

$$\Delta S_{water} = \left(4180\frac{J}{K}\right)\ln\left(\frac{373K}{273K}\right) \rightarrow \Delta S_{water} = 1305\frac{J}{K}$$

The entropy of the water has increased because the water has absorbed heat ($Q_{water} > 0$). Since the temperature of the reservoir remains constant, the change in the entropy of the reservoir can be found using Equation 16-4 and Equation 15-7.

$$\Delta S_{reservoir} = \frac{Q_{reservoir}}{T_{reservoir}} \rightarrow \Delta S_{reservoir} = \frac{-C_{water}\Delta T_{water}}{T_{reservoir}}$$

$$\Delta S_{reservoir} = \frac{-\left(4180\frac{J}{K}\right)(100K)}{373K} \rightarrow \Delta S_{reservoir} = -1121\frac{J}{K}$$

The entropy of the heat reservoir has decreased because it has released heat ($Q_{reservoir} < 0$). The total change in the entropy of the entire system is, thus,

$$\Delta S_{total} = \Delta S_{reservoir} + \Delta S_{water} \rightarrow \Delta S_{total} = -1121\frac{J}{K} + 1305\frac{J}{K}$$

$$\Delta S_{total} = 184\frac{J}{K}$$

The total entropy of the system has increased.

In addition to the definition of the change in entropy given in Equation 16-3, the 2nd law of thermodynamics also states that the entropy of an isolated system never decreases. Thus, for an isolated system, the change in entropy associated with any spontaneous process must be greater than or equal to zero.

$$\Delta S \geq 0 \qquad\qquad\qquad \textbf{(16-5)}$$

In Example 16-2, the change in the entropy of the system was positive indicating that if the water was brought into contact with the reservoir, heat would flow from the reservoir to the water, and the temperature of the water would increase. This process would happen spontaneously.

Indeed, the 2nd law of thermodynamics explains why heat always flows from an object at higher temperature to an object at lower temperature. Consider two objects, A and B, which are in thermal contact with each other but otherwise isolated from the outside environment. If an infinitesimal amount of heat flowed from object A to object B, the change in the entropy of the entire system consisting of both objects would be

$$\Delta S = \Delta S_A + \Delta S_B \quad \rightarrow \quad \Delta S = -\frac{đQ}{T_A} + \frac{đQ}{T_B}$$

The change in the entropy of object A is negative since it released heat, and the change in the entropy of object B is positive since it absorbed heat. In order for heat to spontaneously flow from object A to object B, the total change in the entropy of this system must be positive.

$$\Delta S > 0 \quad \rightarrow \quad -\frac{đQ}{T_A} + \frac{đQ}{T_B} > 0 \quad \rightarrow \quad \frac{đQ}{T_B} > \frac{đQ}{T_A} \quad \rightarrow \quad \frac{1}{T_B} > \frac{1}{T_A}$$

$$T_A > T_B$$

Hence, in order for heat to flow spontaneously from object A to object B, the temperature of object A must be larger than the temperature of object B.

There is no change in entropy for a reversible process (*i.e.,* there is no change in entropy for any process occurring at equilibrium).

$$\Delta S_{reversible} = 0 \quad \rightarrow \quad \Delta S_{equilibrium} = 0 \tag{16-6}$$

Now suppose the water in Example 16-2 had been heated by first bringing it into contact with a heat reservoir at 323 K and then, after its temperature had reached 323 K, with a heat reservoir at 373 K. What is the change in the entropy of the entire system during this process? Since entropy is a state function, the change in the entropy of the water is the same regardless of the path over which the heat was absorbed.

$$\Delta S_{water} = 1305 \frac{J}{K}$$

The change in the entropy of the 323 K reservoir is

$$\Delta S_{323K\,reservoir} = -\frac{Q_{323K\,reservoir}}{T_{323K\,reservoir}} \quad \rightarrow \quad \Delta S_{323K\,reservoir} = -\frac{C_{water}\Delta T_{water}}{T_{323K\,reservoir}}$$

$$\Delta S_{323K\,reservoir} = -\frac{\left(4180\frac{J}{K}\right)(50K)}{323K} \quad \rightarrow \quad \Delta S_{323K\,reservoir} = -647\frac{J}{K}$$

The change in the entropy of the 373 K reservoir is

$$\Delta S_{373K\,reservoir} = -\frac{Q_{373K\,reservoir}}{T_{373K\,reservoir}} \quad \rightarrow \quad \Delta S_{373K\,reservoir} = -\frac{C_{water}\Delta T_{water}}{T_{373K\,reservoir}}$$

$$\Delta S_{373K\,reservoir} = -\frac{\left(4180\dfrac{J}{K}\right)(50K)}{373K} \;\rightarrow\; \Delta S_{373K\,reservoir} = -560\frac{J}{K}$$

The total change in the entropy of the system is, thus,

$$\Delta S_{total} = \Delta S_{323K\,reservoir} + \Delta S_{373K\,reservoir} + \Delta S_{water} \;\rightarrow\; \Delta S_{total} = -647\frac{J}{K} - 560\frac{J}{K} + 1305\frac{J}{K}$$

$$\Delta S_{total} = 98\frac{J}{K}$$

The change in the entropy for the system is still positive; this positive change in entropy indicates that this process of heating the water would also happen spontaneously. More significantly, the change in entropy for this process of heating the water is closer to zero since this process more closely approximates a reversible process[4].

Finally, according to the 2nd law of thermodynamics, the entropy of an isolated system at equilibrium must be a maximum. This is the equivalent of saying that a system at equilibrium is most likely to be found in the accessible state[5] with the largest multiplicity (Equation 16-1).

16-4 Heat Engines

A heat engine is a device that absorbs heat from a high temperature reservoir, performs work, and then releases heat to a low temperature reservoir, as shown in Figure 16.1.

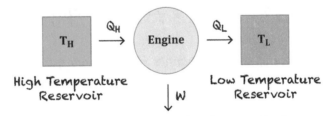

Figure 16.1: A heat engine absorbs heat Q_H from a reservoir at temperature T_H, performs work W, and then releases heat Q_L to a reservoir at temperature T_L.

From the 1st law of thermodynamics (Equation 15-5), the work done by the heat engine in Figure 16-1 is

$$W = Q_H - Q_L - \Delta E$$

In this equation, ΔE denotes the change in the energy of the engine. Now let's imagine that the heat engine functions ideally so that there is no change in its energy during its process of doing work

---

4   That is, a process occurring at equilibrium.
5   See Section 15-3.

(*e.g.*, there is no change in the temperature of the engine and no energy dissipated to the environment). For such an ideal heat engine, we have

$$\Delta E = 0 \quad \rightarrow \quad W = Q_H - Q_L$$

If the temperature of the engine is between the temperatures of the reservoirs, heat will spontaneously flow from the high temperature reservoir to the engine and from the engine to the low temperature reservoir. This will result in a decrease in the entropy of the high temperature reservoir and an increase in the entropy of the low temperature reservoir. Since the temperature of the engine does not change (*i.e.*, the engine is not absorbing any energy), the change in the entropy for the entire system is

$$\Delta S_{total} = \Delta S_{high\,temperature\,reservoir} + \Delta S_{low\,temperature\,reservoir}$$

$$\Delta S_{total} = -\frac{Q_H}{T_H} + \frac{Q_L}{T_L}$$

According to the 2nd law of thermodynamics (Equation 16-5) this change in the total entropy of the system must be greater than or equal to zero for the heat to flow spontaneously.

$$-\frac{Q_H}{T_H} + \frac{Q_L}{T_L} \ge 0 \quad \rightarrow \quad \frac{Q_L}{T_L} \ge \frac{Q_H}{T_H} \quad \rightarrow \quad Q_L \ge \frac{T_L}{T_H} Q_H$$

Hence, there is a limit to the work that can be done by the engine.

$$Q_H - W = Q_L \quad \rightarrow \quad Q_H - W \ge \frac{T_L}{T_H} Q_H \quad \rightarrow \quad W \le Q_H\left(1 - \frac{T_L}{T_H}\right)$$

It is, therefore, the 2nd law of thermodynamics (i.e., the concept of entropy) that not only explains how heat engines function but also places a limit on their efficiency.

Example 16-3:

Problem: An ideal heat engine absorbs heat from a 400 K reservoir and releases heat to a 100 K reservoir. If the engine absorbs 300 J of heat from the 400 K reservoir, what is the maximum work that can be done by the engine?

Solution: The maximum work done by the heat engine is

$$W \le Q_H\left(1 - \frac{T_L}{T_H}\right) \quad \rightarrow \quad W_{max} = Q_H\left(1 - \frac{T_L}{T_H}\right) \quad \rightarrow \quad W_{max} = (300J)\left(1 - \frac{100K}{400K}\right)$$

$$W_{max} = 225 \text{J}$$

Example 16-4:

Problem: The high and low temperature reservoirs of an ideal heat engine are initially at temperatures T_H and T_L, respectively. As a result of the operation of the heat engine, the high temperature reservoir cools and the low temperature reservoir heats until both have reached a common temperature, T_F, at which point the engine stops working. The heat capacities of the reservoirs are identical, denoted by C, and remain constant as the temperature of the reservoirs change. What is the maximum amount of work that can be obtained from this heat engine?

Solution: The total amount of work done by the engine can be determined from the 1st law of thermodynamics. The heat released by the high temperature reservoir is

$$Q_{high\,temperature\,reservoir} = C\left(T_H - T_F\right)$$

Similarly, the heat absorbed by the low temperature reservoir is

$$Q_{low\,temperature\,reservoir} = C\left(T_F - T_L\right)$$

Thus, the total work done by the engine is

$$W = Q_{high\,temperature\,reservoir} - Q_{low\,temperature\,reservoir}$$

$$W = C\left(T_H - T_F\right) - C\left(T_F - T_L\right) \quad \rightarrow \quad W = C\left(T_H + T_L - 2T_F\right)$$

We can now use the 2nd law of thermodynamics to determine the relationship between the initial and final temperatures of the reservoirs.

$$\Delta S_{total} \geq 0 \quad \rightarrow \quad \Delta S_{high\,temperature\,reservoir} + \Delta S_{low\,temperature\,reservoir} \geq 0$$

Since the heat capacities of the reservoirs are constant we have

$$dQ = CdT \rightarrow dS = \frac{CdT}{T} \rightarrow \int dS = \int C\frac{dT}{T} \rightarrow \int dS = C\int \frac{dT}{T}$$

$$\Delta S_{high\,temperature\,reservoir} = C\int_{T_H}^{T_F}\frac{dT}{T} \rightarrow \Delta S_{high\,temperature\,reservoir} = C\ln\left(\frac{T_F}{T_H}\right)$$

$$\Delta S_{low\,temperature\,reservoir} = C\int_{T_L}^{T_F}\frac{dT}{T} \rightarrow \Delta S_{high\,temperature\,reservoir} = C\ln\left(\frac{T_F}{T_L}\right)$$

Hence,

$$C\ln\left(\frac{T_F}{T_H}\right) + C\ln\left(\frac{T_F}{T_L}\right) \geq 0 \rightarrow C\ln\left(\frac{T_F^2}{T_H T_L}\right) \geq 0 \rightarrow \frac{T_F^2}{T_H T_L} \geq 0$$

$$T_F \geq \sqrt{T_H T_L}$$

Therefore, the largest amount of work that can be obtained from the engine is

$$W = C\left(T_H + T_L - 2T_F\right) \rightarrow T_F = \frac{T_H + T_L - \dfrac{W}{C}}{2} \rightarrow \frac{T_H + T_L - \dfrac{W}{C}}{2} \geq \sqrt{T_H T_L}$$

$$W \leq C\left(T_H + T_L - 2\sqrt{T_H T_L}\right) \rightarrow W \leq C\left(\sqrt{T_H} - \sqrt{T_L}\right)^2$$

$$W_{max} = C\left(\sqrt{T_H} - \sqrt{T_L}\right)^2$$

The efficiency of a heat engine is defined as the ratio of the work done by the engine to the heat absorbed by the engine.

$$\varepsilon = \frac{W}{Q_H} \rightarrow W = \varepsilon Q_H \qquad (16\text{-}7)$$

As derived above, the maximum efficiency obtained by an ideal engine is a simple function of the temperatures of the two reservoirs connected to the engine. All processes within the thermodynamic cycle of an ideal engine (absorbing heat, doing work, and releasing heat) are reversible[6], and the efficiency is

$$\varepsilon = 1 - \frac{T_L}{T_H}$$

Therefore, even an ideal engine will not be 100% efficient[7]. Unfortunately, a real engine is never as efficient as an ideal engine. Indeed, the efficiencies of most real engines are less than 40% since some of the energy absorbed by the engine is dissipated through friction forces or absorbed by the engine (thereby increasing both the temperature and the entropy of the engine). Indeed, the dissipation of energy by friction decreases the efficiency of the engine in the same way that the dissipation of energy by friction reduces the magnitude of the acceleration of a system of moving objects.

16-5 The Entropy of an Ideal Gas

The 1st law of thermodynamics is a statement of energy conservation. We can use the 2nd law of thermodynamics (Equation 16-3) to express the 1st law of thermodynamics as a relationship between changes in energy and changes in entropy[8].

$$dE = đQ - đW \;\; \rightarrow \;\; dE = TdS - PdV \tag{16-8}$$

As discussed in Section 15-7, the energy of an ideal gas is a function of the temperature of the gas only and can, therefore, be expressed in terms of the heat capacity of the gas at constant volume.

$$dE = C_V dT \;\; \rightarrow \;\; C_V dT = TdS - PdV \;\; \rightarrow \;\; dS = C_V \frac{dT}{T} + \frac{P}{T} dV$$

Intuitively, it makes sense that increasing the volume of a gas would increase the entropy of the gas. Specifically, an increase in the volume of the gas provides more potential positions for the molecules of the gas to be located. Indeed, there are more ways to distribute the molecules of a gas if the volume accessible to the molecules of gas increases. The increase in the entropy of the gas associated with an increase in temperature follows directly from the 2nd law of thermodynamics (Equation 16-3) and can also be understood in terms of the kinetic energy of the molecules of gas. We know from the equipartition theorem (Section 15-6) that the average kinetic energy of the molecules of gas increases with increasing temperature. Thus, an increase in the temperature of

---

6   $\Delta S = 0$ for the thermodynamic cycle of the ideal heat engine.

7   If connected to a low temperature reservoir at 0 K or a high temperature reservoir at ∞ K, the engine would be 100% efficient. However, such an engine would be impractical to construct.

8   In Equation 16-8, the only work that is considered is work associated with a change in volume. Furthermore, it is interesting to note that all terms in Equation 16-8 are exact differentials.

the gas results in a larger distribution of potential velocities for the molecules of gas and hence, a larger entropy.

We can now integrate this equation over a change in temperature and volume to determine the change in the entropy of the gas. Let's choose as the path of this integration (*i.e.*, the path over which the temperature and volume of the gas change) to be a reversible process. Specifically, let's assume that the changes in temperature and volume occur quasi-statically so that the overall process is reversible. Since the changes in pressure and volume occur quasi-statically, the gas is always in thermodynamic equilibrium during these processes. Under these conditions, we can use the equation of state of the gas (Equation 15-8) to relate the temperature, pressure, and volume of the gas.

$$P = \frac{Nk_B T}{V} \;\rightarrow\; dS = C_V \frac{dT}{T} + \frac{\left(\dfrac{Nk_B T}{V}\right)}{T} dV \;\rightarrow\; dS = C_V \frac{dT}{T} + Nk_B \frac{dV}{V}$$

Therefore,

$$\int dS = \int C_V \frac{dT}{T} + \int Nk_B \frac{dV}{V} \;\rightarrow\; \Delta S = C_V \int \frac{dT}{T} + Nk_B \int \frac{dV}{V}$$

$$\Delta S = C_V \ln\left(\frac{T_f}{T_i}\right) + Nk_B \ln\left(\frac{V_f}{V_i}\right) \tag{16-9}$$

Of course, since entropy is a state function, Equation 16-9 is valid whether or not the path taken by the gas is quasi-static[9].

Example 16-5:

Problem: An ideal gas with a heat capacity $C_V = \frac{3}{2} Nk_B$ experiences the changes in volume and pressure shown in Figure 16.2.

The gas starts in state A, undergoes an isovolumetric increase in pressure to state B, and then an isothermal expansion to state C. What is the change in the entropy of the gas between state A and state C?

Solution: The change in the entropy of the gas can be determined using Equation 16-9.

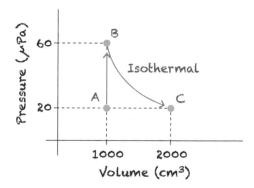

Figure 16.2: The thermodynamic cycle in Example 16-5.

---

9   This also follows from the fact that we can write the 1st law of thermodynamics in terms of state functions only, as shown in Equation 16-8.

$$\Delta S = \frac{3}{2} N k_B \ln\left(\frac{T_C}{T_A}\right) + N k_B \ln\left(\frac{V_C}{V_A}\right)$$

$$T = \frac{PV}{Nk_B} \quad \rightarrow \quad \Delta S = \frac{3}{2} N k_B \ln\left(\frac{P_C V_C}{P_A V_A}\right) + N k_B \ln\left(\frac{V_C}{V_A}\right)$$

The pressure at state C is the same as the pressure at state A.

$$P_C = P_A \quad \rightarrow \quad \Delta S = \frac{3}{2} N k_B \ln\left(\frac{V_C}{V_A}\right) + N k_B \ln\left(\frac{V_C}{V_A}\right) \quad \rightarrow \quad \Delta S = \left(\frac{3}{2}+1\right) N k_B \ln\left(\frac{V_C}{V_A}\right)$$

$$\Delta S = \frac{5}{2} N k_B \ln\left(\frac{V_C}{V_A}\right)$$

The change in the entropy of the gas, thus, depends upon the ratio of the volume of the gas at the two states. Hence,

$$\Delta S = \frac{5}{2} N k_B \ln\left(\frac{(2000\,\text{cm}^3)\left(\dfrac{1\text{m}}{100\text{cm}}\right)^3}{(1000\,\text{cm}^3)\left(\dfrac{1\text{m}}{100\text{cm}}\right)^3} \right)$$

$$\Delta S = \frac{5}{2} N k_B \ln(2)$$

Let's now return to the free expansion of an ideal gas introduced in Section 15-11. The change in the entropy of the gas experiencing the free expansion in Figure 15.10 would be

$$\Delta S = C_V \ln\left(\frac{T}{T}\right) + N k_B \ln\left(\frac{2V_0}{V_0}\right) \quad \rightarrow \quad \Delta S = 2 N k_B$$

Free expansion occurs spontaneously because the change in entropy associated with that process is positive.

16-6 Equilibrium Conditions

Let's imagine the situation shown in Figure 16.3 in which two systems, denoted as A and B, can interact with each other but are otherwise isolated from the outside environment.

$P_A,\ V_A,\ T_A$	$P_B,\ V_B,\ T_B$

The total energy and volume of the systems are

$$E_{total} = E_A + E_B \qquad V_{total} = V_A + V_B$$

Figure 16.3: Two systems, A and B, are in contact with each other but isolated from the outside environment.

The two systems can exchange energy with each other through heat and work; however, since the systems are isolated from outside environment, the total energy and volume of the systems must be constant. Thus, the sum of any infinitesimal exchange of energy or change of volume between the systems must equal zero.

$$dE_A + dE_B = 0 \quad \rightarrow \quad dE_A = -dE_B$$

$$dV_A + dV_B = 0 \quad \rightarrow \quad dV_A = -dV_B$$

When the two systems are in thermodynamic equilibrium, any change in the total entropy of the systems resulting from the systems exchanging energy with each other must be zero (Equation 16-6). Thus, for any process occurring at equilibrium

$$dS_{total} = 0 \quad \rightarrow \quad dS_A + dS_B = 0$$

Substitution of the 1st law of thermodynamics into this expression yields

$$\left(\frac{1}{T_A} dE_A + \frac{P_A}{T_A} dV_A \right) + \left(\frac{1}{T_B} dE_B + \frac{P_B}{T_B} dV_B \right) = 0$$

$$\left(\frac{1}{T_A}(-dE_B) + \frac{P_A}{T_A}(-dV_B) \right) + \left(\frac{1}{T_B} dE_B + \frac{P_B}{T_B} dV_B \right) = 0$$

$$\left(\frac{1}{T_B} - \frac{1}{T_A} \right) dE_B + \left(\frac{P_B}{T_B} - \frac{P_A}{T_A} \right) dV_B = 0$$

Since this equation must be valid for any change in energy or volume, the terms within both sets of parentheses must equal zero. It follows that at equilibrium, the following conditions must be satisfied

$$\frac{1}{T_B} - \frac{1}{T_A} = 0 \quad \rightarrow \quad T_A = T_B$$

$$\frac{P_B}{T_B} - \frac{P_A}{T_A} = 0 \quad \rightarrow \quad \frac{P_B}{T_B} - \frac{P_A}{T_B} = 0 \quad \rightarrow \quad \frac{1}{T_B}(P_B - P_A) = 0 \quad \rightarrow \quad P_B = P_A$$

At equilibrium, the pressure and temperature of the two systems must be the same. Indeed, it follows from the 1st and 2nd laws of thermodynamics that when two systems are brought into contact with each other, heat will flow from the system at higher temperature to the system at lower temperature until the two systems are at the same temperature. Similarly, the system at higher pressure will expand (and the system at lower pressure will compress) until the two systems have the same pressure.

It is, therefore, the entropy of a system (or collection of systems) that specifies the conditions for equilibrium.

16-7 General Thermodynamic Relationships

A complete description of the thermodynamics of a system can be obtained from an equation for the entropy of the system even when the system is not at equilibrium. As shown above, the 1st law of thermodynamics implies that entropy is a function of the energy and volume of a system.

$$dS = \frac{1}{T}dE + \frac{P}{T}dV \;\; \rightarrow \;\; dS = \left(\frac{\partial S}{\partial E}\right)_V dE + \left(\frac{\partial S}{\partial V}\right)_E dV$$

Hence, the temperature and the pressure of a system are defined in terms of the dependence of the entropy of the system on the energy and volume of the system, respectively.

$$\frac{1}{T} = \left(\frac{\partial S}{\partial E}\right)_V \;\; \rightarrow \;\; T = \left(\frac{\partial E}{\partial S}\right)_V \tag{16-10}$$

$$\frac{P}{T} = \left(\frac{\partial S}{\partial V}\right)_E \;\; \rightarrow \;\; P = T\left(\frac{\partial S}{\partial V}\right)_E \tag{16-11}$$

Example 16-6:

Problem: The entropy of a system is given by the following equation:

$$S = \chi V \sqrt{E}$$

In this equation, χ is a constant. What is the equation of state for this system? That is, what is the equation that relates the temperature, pressure, and volume of the system?

Solution: We begin with the definitions of temperature and pressure in Equation 16-10 and Equation 16-11.

$$\frac{1}{T} = \left(\frac{\partial S}{\partial E}\right)_V \quad \rightarrow \quad \frac{1}{T} = \frac{\chi V}{2}\sqrt{\frac{1}{E}} \quad \rightarrow \quad T = \frac{2}{\chi V}\sqrt{E}$$

$$P = T\left(\frac{\partial S}{\partial V}\right)_E \quad \rightarrow \quad P = T\chi\sqrt{E}$$

We can combine these expressions to determine the equation of state for the system.

$$T = \frac{2}{\chi V}\sqrt{E} \quad \rightarrow \quad E = \left(\frac{\chi V T}{2}\right)^2$$

$$P = T\chi\sqrt{E} \quad \rightarrow \quad E = \left(\frac{P}{T\chi}\right)^2$$

Hence,

$$\left(\frac{\chi V T}{2}\right)^2 = \left(\frac{P}{T\chi}\right)^2 \quad \rightarrow \quad P^2 = \frac{\chi^4 T^4 V^2}{4} \quad \rightarrow \quad P = \frac{\chi^2 T^2 V}{2}$$

Finally, it follows from the 1st and 2nd law of thermodynamics that the heat capacity of a system can also be expressed in terms of the entropy of the system.

$$C_V = T\left(\frac{\partial S}{\partial T}\right)_V \qquad \text{(16-12)}$$

$$C_P = T\left(\frac{\partial S}{\partial T}\right)_P \qquad \text{(16-13)}$$

Example 16-7:

Problem: The heat capacity at constant volume of a system at temperature T is given by

$$C_V = \lambda T^{\frac{3}{2}}$$

In this equation, λ is a constant. The entropy of this system is independent of the volume of the system and depends upon only the temperature of the system; the entropy of the system is S_0 at $T = 0$ K. What is the equation describing the entropy of this system as a function of temperature?

Solution: We begin with the definition of heat capacity in Equation 16-12. If the entropy of the system is a function of the temperature only, then

$$C_V = T\left(\frac{\partial S}{\partial T}\right)_V \rightarrow C_V = T\frac{dS}{dT} \rightarrow \frac{dS}{dT} = \frac{C_V}{T} \rightarrow dS = \frac{C_V}{T}dT$$

The entropy of the system can then be found through integration.

$$\int_{S_0}^{S} dS = \int_0^T \frac{C_V}{T}dT \rightarrow \int_{S_0}^{S} dS = \int_0^T \frac{\lambda T^{\frac{3}{2}}}{T}dT \rightarrow \int_{S_0}^{S} dS = \lambda \int_0^T T^{\frac{1}{2}}dT$$

$$S - S_0 = \lambda\left(\left.\frac{T^{\frac{3}{2}}}{\frac{3}{2}}\right|_0^T\right) \rightarrow S - S_0 = \frac{2\lambda}{3}\left(T^{\frac{3}{2}} - 0\right)$$

$$S = S_0 + \left(\frac{2\lambda}{3}\right)T^{\frac{3}{2}}$$

16-8 Diffusion and Boltzmann Factors

In addition to establishing the conditions for equilibrium, the 2nd law of thermodynamics also helps to explain how a system transitions to equilibrium[10]. For example, what would happen if you placed a drop of dye in a large container of water (*e.g.*, a bathtub[11])? The dye would slowly spread out until it filled the entire volume of the container. The concentration of the dye might still be largest at its initial location, but at least some dye would be found everywhere. We refer to this process of the dye spreading out in the container as *diffusion*.

---

10   We demonstrated in Section 16-3 that heat will always flow from high temperature to low temperature. Since heat capacity is always positive, this means that hot objects always cool, and cool objects always warm until they reach an equilibrium temperature with their environment.

11   Get your parents' permission first.

From a microscopic point of view, we could argue that diffusion occurs because the molecules of the dye have kinetic energy (from the equipartition theorem) and, thus, velocity. This velocity results in the molecules of dye moving around in the water, colliding with the molecules of the water, and, eventually, through this inherently random movement, filling the entire volume of the container. Indeed, if we model the energy of each molecule of the dye as only translational kinetic energy,[12] we have

$$K_{avg} = \frac{3}{2} k_B T$$

We can then relate this average kinetic energy to an average speed of the gas molecule.

$$\left(\frac{1}{2} m v^2 \right)_{avg} = \frac{3}{2} k_B T \quad \rightarrow \quad \frac{1}{2} m \left(v^2 \right)_{avg} = \frac{3}{2} k_B T \quad \rightarrow \quad \left(v^2 \right)_{avg} = \frac{3 k_B T}{m}$$

The square root of $\left(v^2 \right)_{avg}$ is a kind of average speed called the root-mean-square speed[13] that is denoted by v_{rms}.

$$v_{rms} = \sqrt{\frac{3 k_B T}{m}}$$

Hence, the average speed and, thus, the rate of diffusion depends upon the temperature of the solution. We can increase the rate of diffusion by increasing the temperature of the solution.

From a macroscopic point of view, we can argue that diffusion occurs because of the 2nd law of thermodynamics. There are simply more ways to distribute the molecules of dye over the entire volume of the container than to have all of the molecules of dye at only their initial place in container. Hence, the entropy of the system is largest when the dye molecules are spread out throughout the container. Diffusion is, thus, associated with an increase in the entropy of the system and, therefore, occurs spontaneously.

Indeed, we can quantify the probability that the molecules of dye will diffuse by comparing the entropies of two configurations of the molecules of dye. We begin with Equation 16-2 that relates the relative probability of these two configurations to the ratio of their multiplicities. Let's define state A to be when the molecules of dye are spread through the container and state B to be when the molecules of dye are concentrated at their initial location.

$$\frac{P_A}{P_B} = \frac{\Omega_A}{\Omega_B}$$

We can now use Equation 16-1 to express the multiplicities in terms of the entropies of the states.

---

12   See Example 15-4.
13   As the name implies, this value is determined by taking the square root of the mean of the square of the speeds.

$$S = k_B \ln \Omega \quad \rightarrow \quad \Omega = e^{\frac{S}{k_B}} \quad \rightarrow \quad \frac{P_A}{P_B} = \frac{e^{\frac{S_A}{k_B}}}{e^{\frac{S_B}{k_B}}} \quad \rightarrow \quad \frac{P_A}{P_B} = e^{\frac{S_A}{k_B} - \frac{S_B}{k_B}}$$

$$\frac{P_A}{P_B} = e^{\frac{S_A - S_B}{k_B}} \quad \rightarrow \quad \frac{P_A}{P_B} = e^{\frac{\Delta S_{AB}}{k_B}} \quad \rightarrow \quad P_A = P_B e^{\frac{\Delta S_{AB}}{k_B}} \tag{16-14}$$

Since the entropy of state A is much larger than the entropy of state B, ωS_{AB} is a positive number, and $P_A > P_B$. We can, therefore, state that since P_A is larger than P_B, the molecules of dye will eventually diffuse to fill the entire volume of the container. Interestingly, we do not argue that it is impossible for the molecules of the dye to remain in their initial location or to eventually all move back there after having diffused through the entire volume of the container; rather, we accept that the probability of such an occurrence is very small relative to other outcomes.

Now, let's imagine a different situation in which a system is in contact with a large heat reservoir. The system and the heat reservoir can exchange energy with each other, but both are unable to exchange any energy or do any work with the outside environment. Thus, the sum of the energy of the heat reservoir and the energy of the system are constant.

$$E_{reservoir} + E_{system} = \text{constant}$$

$$\Delta E_{reservoir} + \Delta E_{system} = 0 \quad \rightarrow \quad \Delta E_{reservoir} = -\Delta E_{system}$$

Furthermore, the temperature of the heat reservoir remains constant regardless of the heat it exchanges with the system. This can be accomplished if the energy of the heat reservoir is much, much larger than the energy of the system. Therefore, since entropy is a function of energy (Section 16-7), the total entropy of the system and the heat reservoir is approximately equal to the entropy of the heat reservoir.

$$S_{reservoir} \gg S_{system} \quad \rightarrow \quad S_{reservoir} \approx S_{total}$$

Let's now consider two separate accessible states for the system, denoted as A and B, that have total energies E_A and E_B, respectively. The ratio of the probability of finding the system in state A to the probability of finding the system in state B depends upon the difference in the total entropy of each state; the total entropy is the sum of the entropy of the system and the entropy of the reservoir. According to Equation 16-14, we have

$$\frac{P_A}{P_B} = e^{\frac{\Delta S_{reservoir} + \Delta S_{system}}{k_B}} \quad \rightarrow \quad \frac{P_A}{P_B} \approx e^{\frac{\Delta S_{reservoir}}{k_B}}$$

From the 1st law of thermodynamics, we can relate the difference in the entropy of the reservoir to a change in the energy of the reservoir[14].

$$\Delta E_{reservoir} = T\Delta S_{reservoir} \quad \rightarrow \quad \Delta S_{reservoir} = \frac{\Delta E_{reservoir}}{T} \quad \rightarrow \quad \frac{P_A}{P_B} \approx e^{\frac{\Delta E_{reservoir}}{k_B T}}$$

Finally, since the system and the reservoir are isolated from the outside environment, we have

$$\Delta E_{reservoir} = -\Delta E_{system} \quad \rightarrow \quad \frac{P_A}{P_B} \approx e^{\frac{-\Delta E_{system}}{k_B T}} \quad \rightarrow \quad \frac{P_A}{P_B} \approx e^{\frac{-(E_A - E_B)}{k_B T}}$$

Therefore the probability of finding a system in a particular state is proportional to both the energy of the state and the temperature of the system.

$$P_A \propto e^{\frac{-E_A}{k_B T}} \tag{16-15}$$

This exponential factor is referred to as the Boltzmann factor for the state. The temperature in Equation 16-15 is the temperature of the heat reservoir, which is equal to the temperature of the system since the system and the reservoir are in thermal equilibrium. The relative probability of finding a system in two different states is, thus, proportional to the ratio of the Boltzmann factors of the two states. Thus, this relative probability scales with the temperature of the system.

Example 16-8:

Problem: A system is in contact with a heat reservoir at 200 K. What is the ratio of the probability that the system is in a configuration with an energy of 10 pJ to the probability that the system is in a configuration with an energy of 20 pJ?

Solution: The ratio of the probabilities can be found using Equation 16-15.

$$P = e^{-\frac{\Delta E}{k_B T}} \quad \rightarrow \quad P = e^{-\frac{\left(10\times10^{-12}\,J - 20\times10^{-12}\,J\right)}{\left(1.38\times10^{-23}\,\frac{J}{K}\right)(200K)}} \quad \rightarrow \quad P = e^{3.6\times10^9}$$

The ratio of the probability of the system being in the lower energy state to the probability of the system being in the higher energy state is effectively infinite. In other words, the probability of the system being in the higher energy state is effectively zero.

---

14   The reservoir does no work, so from Equation 16-8 we have that dE = TdS.

It follows from Equation 16-15 that systems are always most likely to be found in the configuration with the lowest energy. Thus, it is the 2nd law of thermodynamics that justifies the principle of minimum potential energy introduced in Section 1-4.

16-9 Looking Ahead

In our energy-based approach to kinematics, we determined a description of the kinematics of a system (*e.g.*, the acceleration of the system) by differentiating an equation for the energy of the system with respect to the position of an object in the system (or with respect to time, *etc.*). In this chapter, we have shown that the equation for the entropy of a system can be differentiated to determine a description of the thermodynamics of a system. Similarly, just as it is changes in energy that are responsible for the kinematics of a system[15], ultimately, it is changes in entropy that

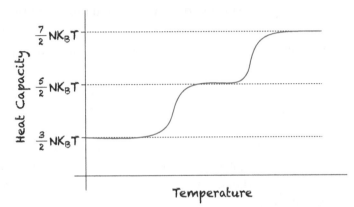

Figure 16.4: The heat capacity at constant volume of oxygen as a function of temperature.

drive the behavior of a system. Furthermore, although it is often too difficult to determine an equation for the entropy of a system using Equation 16-1, it is, nevertheless, straightforward to calculate changes in the entropy of a system using the 2nd law of thermodynamics (Equation 16-3). Typically, all that is needed for these calculations is heat capacity of the system, which can be readily measured.

Interestingly, despite our frequent assumptions to the contrary, heat capacity is always a function of temperature. Indeed, heat capacity increases with increasing temperature. Consider, for example, the heat capacity at constant volume of molecular oxygen (O_2) as a function of temperature (Figure 16-4).

At low temperatures, the heat capacity at constant volume of oxygen is $\frac{3}{2}Nk_B$, as expected from the equipartition theorem (Section 15-9). As the temperature increases, however, the heat capacity at constant volume suddenly increases to $\frac{5}{2}Nk_B$. We would argue, based upon the equipartition theorem, that this increase in the heat capacity is associated with the presence of additional terms in the equation for the energy of the gas. For example, if we included the energy associated with the rotational motion of the atoms within the molecule of oxygen, we would have.

$$K_i = \frac{1}{2}mv_x^2 + \frac{1}{2}mv_y^2 + \frac{1}{2}mv_z^2 + \frac{1}{2}I_y\omega_y^2 + \frac{1}{2}I_z\omega_z^2 \quad \rightarrow \quad \left(K_i\right)_{avg} = \frac{5}{2}k_BT$$

---

15   For example, systems always arrange themselves to minimize their potential energy.

In this equation, we have defined the *x*-axis to be the longitudinal axis of the molecule. The moment of inertia for this axis of rotation is much smaller than the moments of inertia for rotations around the perpendicular *y* and *z* axes. Thus, we ignore contributions to the kinetic energy for rotations around the *x*-axis. The average energy of a system of N molecules of oxygen and the associated heat capacity would, therefore, be

$$E_{avg} = N\left(K_i\right)_{avg} \quad \rightarrow \quad E_{avg} = \frac{5}{2}Nk_B T \quad \rightarrow \quad C_V = \frac{5}{2}Nk_B$$

Similarly, if we included the vibrational motion of the atoms around their equilibrium separation within the molecule, we would need to include the associated vibrational potential energies. Since these energies are also quadratic functions, the heat capacity of the gas would increase again.

$$E_{avg} = \frac{7}{2}Nk_B T \quad \rightarrow \quad C_V = \frac{7}{2}Nk_B$$

However, although the equipartition theorem can provide an energy-based interpretation of oxygen's different heat capacities, it cannot explain the temperature dependence of these heat capacities. That is, why do the rotational and vibrational energies contribute to the heat capacity only at higher temperatures?

Our first attempt to answer this question would likely involve using Boltzmann factors (Equation 16-15) to justify the temperature dependence of the probability of observing a molecule of oxygen with rotational or vibrational energy. However, this is ultimately unsatisfying as it cannot account for the abrupt transitions between the observed heat capacities shown in Figure 16.4. The ultimate answer to this question is that the rotational and vibrational motions of the oxygen molecule require a finite minimum amount of energy in order to be *"switched on."* This was one of the first discoveries that energy is quantized. Indeed, rather than having a continuous distribution of possible values, the energy of a system comes in discrete bunches only. This, in turn, brought about the development of quantum mechanics. These concepts also led to the development of statistical mechanics, which provides a framework for determining an equation for the entropy of a system from knowledge of the energies accessible to the system (*e.g.*, using Boltzmann factors). In this way, we end up back where we started again: with energy. If you can characterize the energy and entropy of a system, you can describe the system completely.

Summary

- **Entropy:** An intrinsic property of a system. Entropy is best considered to be a measure of the number of ways that a system can be arranged given the constraint of a particular set of macroscopic properties for that system (*e.g.*, volume, temperature, or pressure). The mathematical definition for the entropy of a system is

$$S = k_B \ln \Omega$$

- **The ratio of the multiplicities of two states is equal to the probability of obtaining (or observing) those two states.**

$$\frac{P_A}{P_B} = \frac{\Omega_A}{\Omega_B}$$

- **The 2nd law of thermodynamics:** The infinitesimal change in the entropy of a system associated with the absorption of an infinitesimal amount of heat through a quasi-static process is

$$dS = \frac{dQ}{T}$$

Furthermore, the entropy of an isolated system never decreases. Thus, for an isolated system, the change in entropy associated with any spontaneous process must be greater than or equal to zero.

$$\Delta S \geq 0$$

It follows that the entropy of a system must be a maximum when the system is at equilibrium. Finally, there is no change in entropy for a reversible process (*i.e.*, there is no change in entropy for any process occurring at equilibrium).

$$\Delta S_{reversible} = 0 \quad \rightarrow \quad \Delta S_{equilibrium} = 0$$

- **Heat engine:** A device that absorbs heat from a high temperature reservoir, performs work, and then releases heat to a low temperature reservoir. The efficiency of a heat engine is the ratio of the work done to the heat absorbed.

$$\varepsilon = \frac{W}{Q_H}$$

According to the 2nd law of thermodynamics, the maximum efficiency of an ideal heat engine is

$$\varepsilon \leq 1 - \frac{T_L}{T_H} \quad \rightarrow \quad \varepsilon_{max} = 1 - \frac{T_L}{T_H}$$

- **The 1st law of thermodynamics:** The entropy of a system can be written in terms of the energy and volume of the system.

$$dS = \left(\frac{\partial S}{\partial E}\right)_V dE + \left(\frac{\partial S}{\partial V}\right)_E dV$$

This form of the 1st law also provides the definitions of temperature and pressure for a system.

$$\frac{1}{T} = \left(\frac{\partial S}{\partial E}\right)_V \qquad P = T\left(\frac{\partial S}{\partial V}\right)_E$$

- **Heat capacity:** A measure of the dependence of the entropy of a system on the temperature of the system.

$$C_V = T\left(\frac{\partial S}{\partial T}\right)_V \qquad C_P = T\left(\frac{\partial S}{\partial T}\right)_P$$

- **The change in the entropy of an ideal gas associated with a change in the temperature and/or volume of the gas is given by the following equation**

$$\Delta S = C_V \ln\left(\frac{T_f}{T_i}\right) + Nk_B \ln\left(\frac{V_f}{V_i}\right)$$

- **The probability of finding a system in a particular state is proportional to both the energy of the state and the temperature of the system.**

$$P_A \propto e^{-\frac{E_A}{k_B T}}$$

This exponential factor is referred to as the Boltzmann factor for the state.

Problems

1. You flip a coin 5 times. What is the ratio of the probability of getting 3 heads to the probability of getting 4 heads? What is the ratio of the probability of getting 3 heads to the probability of getting 2 heads?

2. The low temperature reservoir for a heat engine is at 300 K. If the heat engine must do 200 J of work and can absorb a maximum of 500 J from the high temperature reservoir, what is the minimum required temperature for the high temperature reservoir?

3. A refrigerator is a heat engine running in reverse, as shown in the figure at right. Work that is done on the refrigerator enables it to absorb heat from a low temperature reservoir and release heat to a high temperature reservoir. Consider an ideal refrigerator connected to a

200 K reservoir and a 400 K reservoir. How much work would be required for this refrigerator to absorb 300 J of energy from the 200 K reservoir?

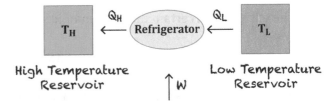

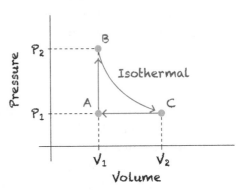

4. An ideal gas with energy $E = \frac{3}{2} N k_B T$ is taken through the quasi-static cyclic process shown in the figure at right. What is the change in entropy for each step in the cycle?

5. An ideal gas with energy $E = \frac{3}{2} N k_B T$ is subjected to a cyclic, quasi-static (*i.e.* reversible) process shown in the figure at right. What is the efficiency (ratio of work done to heat in) for this cycle? What is the change in entropy for each step in the cycle?

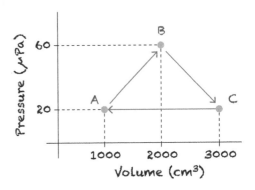

6. A cylindrical container 70 cm long is separated into two compartments by a movable partition that is originally clamped in position 20 cm from the right end. The right compartment is initially filled with one liter of helium gas at a pressure of 5 x 10⁶ Pa. The left compartment is filled with argon gas at 1 x 10⁶ Pa of pressure. Both of these gasses may be considered ideal. The cylinder is submerged in 1 liter of water, and the entire system is initially at the uniform temperature of 270 K. When the piston is unclamped, a new equilibrium situation is ultimately reached with the piston in a new position. The entire system is thermally and mechanically isolated, and you may ignore the heat capacities of the cylinder and the piston. What is the increase in the temperature of the water at the new equilibrium? How far from the left end of the cylinder will the piston come to rest? What is the increase of the total entropy of the system?

7. The entropy of a system is given by the following equation:

$$S = \mu E \sqrt{V}$$

In this equation, μ is a constant. Determine an equation of state for this system.

8. The entropy of a certain thermodynamic system is given by the following equation:

$$\lambda S^2 = NE + \gamma V^2$$

In this equation, N is the number of molecules in the system, and l and g are constants. Determine an equation of state for this system.

9. The equation for the entropy of a system of N molecules of an ideal gas is

$$S = Nk_B \left[\ln\left(\frac{V}{N}\right) + \frac{3}{2}\ln T + \sigma \right]$$

In this equation, σ is a constant that is independent of N, V, and T. What is the heat capacity at constant volume for this system? What is the heat capacity at constant pressure for this system?

10. A system is in contact with a heat reservoir at 4000 K. What is the ratio of the probability that the system is in a configuration with an energy of 5 pJ to the probability that the system is in a configuration with an energy of 10 pJ? What is this ratio if the temperature of the heat reservoir is 10^{12} K? What is this ratio if the temperature of the heat reservoir is infinite?

APPENDIX A

All measurements in this book will use the International System of Units (known by its French acronym SI); this system is commonly referred to as the metric system. There are seven base quantities that constitute the SI units.

Quantity	Unit Name	Unit Symbol
Length	meter	m
Time	second	s
Mass	kilogram	kg
Temperature	kelvin	K
Amount of Substance	mole	mol
Electric Current	ampere	A
Luminous Intensity	candela	cd

There are several additional SI units that are derived from this basis set. A few of the more common are shown in the table below.

Quantity	Unit Name	Unit Symbol	Derivation
Energy	joule	J	$1\,J = 1\dfrac{kg\,m^2}{s^2}$
Power	watt	W	$1\,W = 1\dfrac{kg\,m^2}{s^3}$
Force	newton	N	$1\,N = 1\dfrac{kg\,m}{s^2}$

Frequency	hertz	Hz	$1\,Hz = 1\dfrac{1}{s}$
Pressure	pascal	Pa	$1\,Pa = 1\dfrac{N}{m^2}$

The following prefixes can be used when describing very large or very small quantities.

Prefix	Symbol	Factor
tera	T	10^{12}
giga	G	10^{9}
mega	M	10^{6}
kilo	k	10^{3}
hecto	h	10^{2}
deca	da	10^{1}
deci	d	10^{-1}
centi	c	10^{-2}
milli	m	10^{-3}
micro	μ	10^{-6}
nano	n	10^{-9}
pico	p	10^{-12}

Thus, $9.5\,ns = 9.5\times10^{-9}\,s$ and $2.6\,MW = 2.6\times10^{6}\,W$.

A-2 Physical Constants

Quantity	Variable	Accepted Value
Gravitational Constant	G	6.67×10^{-11} Jm/kg^2 (or Nm^2/kg^2)
Avogadro Constant	N_A	6.02×10^{23} mol^{-1}
Universal Gas Constant	R	8.314 J/mol K
Boltzmann Constant	k_B	1.38×10^{-23} J/K
Mass of the Earth	M_E	5.98×10^{24} kg
Radius of the Earth	R_E	6.37×10^{6} m
Mass of the Sun	M_S	1.99×10^{30} kg

A-3 Useful Mathematics

Solution for a quadratic equation:

$$ax^2 + bx + c = 0 \quad \rightarrow \quad x = \frac{-b \pm \sqrt{b^2 - 4ac}}{2a}$$

Trigonometry

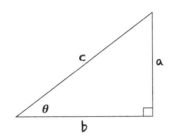

$$\sin\theta = \frac{a}{c}$$

$$\sin(-\theta) = -\sin\theta$$

$$\cos\theta = \frac{b}{c}$$

$$\cos(-\theta) = \cos\theta$$

$$\tan\theta = \frac{a}{b}$$

$$\tan(-\theta) = -\tan\theta$$

$$\sin(\theta \pm \varphi) = \sin\theta\cos\varphi \pm \cos\theta\sin\varphi$$

$$\cos(\theta \pm \varphi) = \cos\theta\cos\varphi \mp \sin\theta\sin\varphi$$

Calculus

$$\frac{d}{dx}x^n = nx^{n-1}$$

$$\frac{d}{dx}e^{ax} = ae^{ax}$$

$$\frac{d}{dx}\sin(ax) = a\cos(ax)$$

$$\frac{d}{dx}\cos(ax) = -a\sin(ax)$$

$$\frac{d}{dx}\tan(ax) = \frac{a}{\cos^2(ax)}$$

$$\frac{dy}{dx} = \frac{dy}{du}\frac{du}{dx}$$

$$\frac{d}{dx}\ln(ax) = \frac{1}{x}$$

$$\frac{d}{dx}a^x = a^x\ln a$$

$$\frac{d}{dx}\big(f(x)g(x)\big) = \left(\frac{df(x)}{dx}\right)g(x) + \left(\frac{dg(x)}{dx}\right)f(x)$$

APPENDIX B

B-1 Definition of Vectors

Vectors are mathematical quantities that are specified by both a magnitude (*i.e.*, a size) and a direction; examples of vector quantities include position, velocity, and acceleration. When expressing a vector, we must denote both the magnitude and the direction. The magnitude of a vector can be positive or zero, but it cannot be negative.

B-2 1-Dimensional Vectors

When expressing a 1-dimensional vector, a positive (+) or negative (−) sign is commonly used to denote the direction of the vector with respect to the origin of the corresponding coordinate axis (Figure B.1).

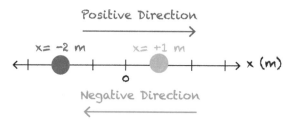

Figure B.1: Coordinate system for describing the position of an object using 1-dimensional vectors.

It is worth noting that the positive (+) sign is frequently omitted when writing 1-dimensional vectors.

B-3 General Descriptions of Vectors

Vector quantities are usually labeled with an arrow over their symbol, but this is sometimes neglected for 1-dimensional vectors. Using this notation, we can write the vector $\vec{A}$ with magnitude A and direction along $\hat{a}$ as

$$\vec{A} = A\hat{a} \ \rightarrow \ \hat{a} = \frac{\vec{A}}{A}$$

In this example, $\hat{a}$ denotes a *unit vector*, which points in the direction of $\vec{A}$ and has a magnitude of one. Unit vectors are denoted by the ^ symbol and are commonly used to express the components of a vector along the coordinate axis relevant to a particular problem. This is mathematically permissible since they have a magnitude of 1; in other words, they specify direction only.

B-4 Components and Decomposition

Working with vectors is made easier by expressing the vector in terms of its projections or components along a set of unit vectors (*i.e.*, its components along the axes of a coordinate system). We refer to this process as *decomposing* the vector. For example, in a standard Cartesian coordinate system, the vector $\vec{A}$ can also be written (or decomposed) as

$$\vec{A} = A_x \hat{x} + A_y \hat{y} + A_z \hat{z}$$

In this example, $\hat{x}, \hat{y},$ and $\hat{z}$ are the unit vectors pointing along the Cartesian $x, y,$ and z axes, respectively, and $A_x, A_y,$ and A_z are the components of the vector along those directions. These components can be positive, negative, or zero depending upon the orientation (*i.e.*, direction) of the vector with respect to the fixed Cartesian coordinates. When written this way, the magnitude of the vector $\vec{A}$, denoted by A or $\left\|\vec{A}\right\|$, can be expressed in terms of its components along the coordinate axes.

$$A = \left\|\vec{A}\right\| = \left(A_x^2 + A_y^2 + A_z^2\right)^{\frac{1}{2}} \tag{B-1}$$

It is worth noting that although the components of a vector can be either positive or negative, the magnitude of a vector is always positive (see Figure B.2).

The components of a vector can also be used to determine the angles between the vector and the coordinate axes. Consider the simple case of the 2-dimensional vector shown in Figure B.3.

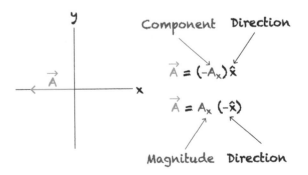

Figure B.2: The difference between describing a vector in terms of its components and magnitudes.

The following trigonometric identities apply to the vector shown in Figure B.3.

$$\sin\theta = \frac{A_y}{A} = \frac{A_y}{\|\vec{A}\|} = \frac{A_y}{\sqrt{A_x^2 + A_y^2}}$$

$$\cos\theta = \frac{A_x}{A} = \frac{A_x}{\|\vec{A}\|} = \frac{A_x}{\sqrt{A_x^2 + A_y^2}}$$

$$\tan\theta = \frac{A_y}{A_x}$$

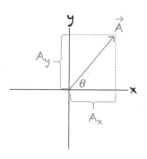

Figure B.3: A 2-dimensional vector with its components along both coordinate axes.

B-5 Simple Vector Mathematics

Expressing a vector in terms of its components (*i.e.*, decomposing the vector) simplifies vector arithmetic and calculus since all operations are carried out component by component.

Addition $\quad \vec{A} + \vec{B} = \left(A_x + B_x\right)\hat{x} + \left(A_y + B_y\right)\hat{y} + \left(A_z + B_z\right)\hat{z}$

Subtraction $\quad \vec{A} - \vec{B} = \left(A_x - B_x\right)\hat{x} + \left(A_y - B_y\right)\hat{y} + \left(A_z - B_z\right)\hat{z}$

Multiplication by a scalar $\quad c\vec{A} = \left(cA_x\right)\hat{x} + \left(cA_y\right)\hat{y} + \left(cA_z\right)\hat{z}$

Differentiation $\quad \frac{d}{dt}\vec{A} = \left(\frac{d}{dt}A_x\right)\hat{x} + \left(\frac{d}{dt}A_y\right)\hat{y} + \left(\frac{d}{dt}A_z\right)\hat{z}$

B-6 The Dot Product

The dot product (also called scalar product or the inner product) of two vectors is related to the magnitude of the projection of one vector onto the other; the dot product is, thus, a scalar quantity. The expression for the dot product of the two vectors $\vec{A}$ and $\vec{B}$ is

$$\vec{A} \cdot \vec{B} = AB\cos\theta \qquad\qquad \text{(B-2)}$$

The angle θ in this equation is the angle between the two vectors. The dot product is a commutative operation so $\vec{A} \cdot \vec{B} = \vec{B} \cdot \vec{A}$. Because the unit vectors of the standard Cartesian coordinate system are orthonormal, we have the following identities:

$$\hat{x} \cdot \hat{x} = 1 \quad \hat{y} \cdot \hat{y} = 1 \quad \hat{z} \cdot \hat{z} = 1$$

$$\hat{x} \cdot \hat{y} = 0 \quad \hat{x} \cdot \hat{z} = 0 \quad \hat{y} \cdot \hat{z} = 0$$

The dot product of a vector with itself is the square of the magnitude of that vector.

$$\vec{A} \cdot \vec{A} = \left(A_x \hat{x} + A_y \hat{y} + A_z \hat{z} \right) \cdot \left(A_x \hat{x} + A_y \hat{y} + A_z \hat{z} \right)$$

$$\vec{A} \cdot \vec{A} = A_x^2 \left(\hat{x} \cdot \hat{x} \right) + A_y^2 \left(\hat{y} \cdot \hat{y} \right) + A_z^2 \left(\hat{z} \cdot \hat{z} \right) + A_x A_y \left(\hat{x} \cdot \hat{y} \right) + A_x A_z \left(\hat{x} \cdot \hat{z} \right) +$$

$$A_y A_x \left(\hat{y} \cdot \hat{x} \right) + A_y A_z \left(\hat{y} \cdot \hat{z} \right) + A_z A_x \left(\hat{z} \cdot \hat{x} \right) + A_z A_y \left(\hat{z} \cdot \hat{y} \right)$$

$$\vec{A} \cdot \vec{A} = A_x^2 + A_y^2 + A_z^2 = A^2$$

Similarly,

$$\vec{A} \cdot \vec{B} = A_x B_x + A_y B_y + A_z B_z \tag{B-3}$$

B-7 The Cross Product

The cross product (or vector product) of two vectors $\vec{A}$ and $\vec{B}$ results in a new vector whose magnitude is the area of a parallelogram with $\vec{A}$ and $\vec{B}$ as its sides. The equation for the magnitude of this vector is

$$\left\| \vec{A} \times \vec{B} \right\| = AB \sin \theta \tag{B-4}$$

In Equation B-4, θ is the angle between the two vectors $\vec{A}$ and $\vec{B}$. By convention, the angle θ is always drawn *counterclockwise* from $\vec{A}$ and $\vec{B}$, as shown in Figure B.4.

The direction of the vector resulting from the cross product of $\vec{A}$ and $\vec{B}$ is determined using the right-hand rule. Point the figures of your right hand in the direction of the first vector in the cross product $\left(\vec{A} \right)$, bend them to point in the direction of the second vector in the cross product $\left(\vec{B} \right)$, and your thumb will then point in the direction of the resultant vector $\left(\vec{A} \times \vec{B} \right)$. Two examples of vector cross product are shown in Figure B.5.

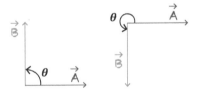

Figure B.4: The definition of the angle θ between the vectors $\vec{A}$ and $\vec{B}$ in the vector cross product $\vec{A} \times \vec{B}$.

Alternatively, for 3-dimensional vectors, the cross product of $\vec{A}$ and $\vec{B}$ can be calculated using a simple determinant.

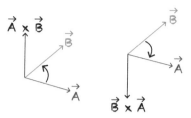

$$\vec{A} \times \vec{B} = \begin{vmatrix} \hat{x} & \hat{y} & \hat{z} \\ A_x & A_y & A_z \\ B_x & B_y & B_z \end{vmatrix}$$

$$\vec{A} \times \vec{B} = \left(A_y B_z - A_z B_y \right)\hat{x} + \left(A_z B_x - A_x B_z \right)\hat{y} + \left(A_x B_y - A_y B_x \right)\hat{z}$$

Figure B.5. The direction of the vector cross product determined using the right-hand rule.

Incidentally, we define a *right-handed coordinate system* in terms of the cross product of the associated unit vectors. For a right-handed system, we have

$$\hat{x} \times \hat{y} = \hat{z} \quad \hat{y} \times \hat{z} = \hat{x} \quad \hat{z} \times \hat{x} = \hat{y}$$

$$\hat{x} \times \hat{x} = 0 \quad \hat{y} \times \hat{y} = 0 \quad \hat{z} \times \hat{z} = 0$$

It's important to note that unlike the dot product the cross product is not commutative (see Figure B.5).

$$\vec{A} \times \vec{B} = -\vec{B} \times \vec{A}$$

APPENDIX C

Position

The position of an object is a vector quantity (often) denoted by $\vec{r}$.

$$\vec{r} = \left(x, y, z\right)$$

$$\vec{r} = x\hat{i} + y\hat{j} + z\hat{k}$$

$$\vec{r} = x\hat{x} + y\hat{y} + z\hat{z}$$

In this equation, the scalars x, y, and z are the components of the vector along the corresponding unit vector directions (*i.e.*, coordinate axes). These components can, of course, be time-dependent functions, which would result in the position being a function of time.

$$\vec{r}(t) = \left[x(t)\right]\hat{x} + \left[y(t)\right]\hat{y} + \left[z(t)\right]\hat{z}$$

Velocity

The velocity of an object is a vector quantity, denoted by $\vec{v}$, that is the first derivative of the position of the object with respect to time.

$$\vec{v} = \frac{d\vec{r}}{dt} \tag{C-1}$$

$$\vec{v} = \left(\frac{dx}{dt}\right)\hat{i} + \left(\frac{dy}{dt}\right)\hat{j} + \left(\frac{dz}{dt}\right)\hat{k} = v_x\hat{i} + v_y\hat{j} + v_z\hat{k}$$

$$\vec{v} = \left(\frac{dx}{dt}\right)\hat{x} + \left(\frac{dy}{dt}\right)\hat{y} + \left(\frac{dz}{dt}\right)\hat{z} = v_x\hat{x} + v_y\hat{y} + v_z\hat{z}$$

The speed of an object is the special name we give to the magnitude of the velocity of the object.

$$\left\| \vec{v} \right\| = \sqrt{\vec{v} \bullet \vec{v}} = v = \sqrt{v_x^2 + v_y^2 + v_z^2} \qquad \textbf{(C-2)}$$

Acceleration

The acceleration of an object is vector quantity, denoted by $\vec{a}$, that is the first derivative of the velocity of the object with respect to time.

$$\vec{a} = \frac{d\vec{v}}{dt} = \frac{d^2\vec{r}}{dt^2} \qquad \textbf{(C-3)}$$

$$\vec{a} = \left(\frac{d^2 x}{dt^2}\right)\hat{i} + \left(\frac{d^2 y}{dt^2}\right)\hat{j} + \left(\frac{d^2 z}{dt^2}\right)\hat{k} = a_x \hat{i} + a_y \hat{j} + a_z \hat{k}$$

$$\vec{a} = \left(\frac{d^2 x}{dt^2}\right)\hat{x} + \left(\frac{d^2 y}{dt^2}\right)\hat{y} + \left(\frac{d^2 z}{dt^2}\right)\hat{z} = a_x \hat{x} + a_y \hat{y} + a_z \hat{z}$$

We can also express the acceleration in terms of derivatives of the velocity (specifically, the components of the velocity).

$$\vec{a} = \left(\frac{dv_x}{dt}\right)\hat{i} + \left(\frac{dv_y}{dt}\right)\hat{j} + \left(\frac{dv_z}{dt}\right)\hat{k} = a_x \hat{i} + a_y \hat{j} + a_z \hat{k}$$

$$\vec{a} = \left(\frac{dv_x}{dt}\right)\hat{x} + \left(\frac{dv_y}{dt}\right)\hat{y} + \left(\frac{dv_z}{dt}\right)\hat{z} = a_x \hat{x} + a_y \hat{y} + a_z \hat{z}$$

The magnitude of the acceleration has no special name but is calculated in the same way as speed.

$$\left\| \vec{a} \right\| = a = \sqrt{a_x^2 + a_y^2 + a_z^2}$$

C-2 Expressions for Average Values

The expressions for the average acceleration and velocity are

$$\vec{a}_{avg} = \frac{\Delta \vec{v}}{\Delta t} = \frac{\vec{v}_f - \vec{v}_i}{t_f - t_i} \qquad\qquad \vec{v}_{avg} = \frac{\Delta \vec{r}}{\Delta t} = \frac{\vec{r}_f - \vec{r}_i}{t_f - t_i}$$

As expected, in the limit of small time intervals, the average and instantaneous value of acceleration and velocity are identical.

$$\lim_{\Delta t \to 0} \vec{a}_{avg} = \lim_{\Delta t \to 0} \frac{\Delta \vec{v}}{\Delta t} = \frac{d\vec{v}}{dt}$$

$$\lim_{\Delta t \to 0} \vec{v}_{avg} = \lim_{\Delta t \to 0} \frac{\Delta \vec{r}}{\Delta t} = \frac{d\vec{r}}{dt}$$

C-3 Constant Acceleration Equations

When the acceleration of the object is constant in time, we can derive simple expressions for the change of the object's velocity and position as a function of time.

$$\vec{a} = \frac{d\vec{v}}{dt} \;\to\; \vec{a}\,dt = d\vec{v} \;\to\; \int_{t_i}^{t_f} \vec{a}\,dt = \int_{\vec{v}_i}^{\vec{v}_f} d\vec{v} \;\to\; \vec{a}\int_{t_i}^{t_f} dt = \int_{\vec{v}_i}^{\vec{v}_f} d\vec{v}$$

$$\vec{a}\left(t_f - t_i\right) = \vec{v}_f - \vec{v}_i$$

$$\Delta \vec{v} = \vec{a}\Delta t \tag{C-4}$$

We could have also arrived at this result beginning with the definition of average acceleration because the magnitude of a constant acceleration will be equal to the magnitude of its average acceleration.

$$\vec{a}_{avg} = \frac{\Delta \vec{v}}{\Delta t} \;\to\; \vec{a}_{avg}\Delta t = \Delta \vec{v} \;\to\; \vec{a}\Delta t = \Delta \vec{v}$$

Rearrangement of this equation yields

$$\vec{v}_f = \vec{v}_i + \vec{a}\Delta t$$

The magnitude of the acceleration is, therefore,

$$a^2 = \vec{a}\cdot\vec{a} \;\to\; a^2 = \left(\frac{\Delta \vec{v}}{\Delta t}\right)\cdot\left(\frac{\Delta \vec{v}}{\Delta t}\right) \;\to\; a^2 = \frac{\left(\Delta \vec{v}\right)\cdot\left(\Delta \vec{v}\right)}{\left(\Delta t\right)^2} \;\to\; a^2 = \frac{\left(\Delta v\right)^2}{\left(\Delta t\right)^2}$$

We can continue this process to derive an expression for the displacement in position.

$$\vec{v} = \frac{d\vec{r}}{dt} \;\to\; \vec{v}\,dt = d\vec{r} \;\to\; \int_{t_i}^{t_f} \vec{v}(t)\,dt = \int_{\vec{r}_i}^{\vec{r}_f} d\vec{r}$$

We already know that $\vec{v}_f = \vec{v}_i + \vec{a}\Delta t$, so we can substitute $\vec{v}(t) = \vec{v}_i + \vec{a}(t - t_i)$ into our integral.

$$\int_{t_i}^{t_f} \vec{v}(t)\,dt = \int_{t_i}^{t_f} \left(\vec{v}_i + \vec{a}(t - t_i)\right)dt \quad \rightarrow \quad \int_{t_i}^{t_f} \vec{v}(t)\,dt = \vec{v}_i \int_{t_i}^{t_f} dt + \vec{a}\int_{t_i}^{t_f} (t - t_i)\,dt$$

Let's consider each integral separately.

$$\vec{v}_i \int_{t_i}^{t_f} dt = \vec{v}_i\, t\Big|_{t_i}^{t_f} \quad \rightarrow \quad \vec{v}_i \int_{t_i}^{t_f} dt = \vec{v}_i\left(t_f - t_i\right) \quad \rightarrow \quad \vec{v}_i \int_{t_i}^{t_f} dt = \vec{v}_i \Delta t$$

$$\vec{a}\int_{t_i}^{t_f} (t - t_i)\,dt = \vec{a}\int_{t_i}^{t_f} t\,dt - \vec{a}\int_{t_i}^{t_f} t_i\,dt$$

$$\vec{a}\int_{t_i}^{t_f} t\,dt = \vec{a}\,\frac{t^2}{2}\Big|_{t_i}^{t_f} \quad \rightarrow \quad \vec{a}\int_{t_i}^{t_f} t\,dt = \frac{\vec{a}}{2}\left(t_f^2 - t_i^2\right)$$

$$\vec{a}\int_{t_i}^{t_f} t_i\,dt = \vec{a}t_i \int_{t_i}^{t_f} dt \quad \rightarrow \quad \vec{a}\int_{t_i}^{t_f} t_i\,dt = \vec{a}t_i\, t\Big|_{t_i}^{t_f} \quad \rightarrow \quad \vec{a}\int_{t_i}^{t_f} t_i\,dt = \vec{a}t_i\left(t_f - t_i\right)$$

Thus,

$$\vec{a}\int_{t_i}^{t_f} \Delta t\,dt = \frac{\vec{a}}{2}\left(t_f^2 - t_i^2\right) - \vec{a}t_i\left(t_f - t_i\right)$$

$$\vec{a}\int_{t_i}^{t_f} \Delta t\,dt = \vec{a}\left(\frac{1}{2}t_f^2 - \frac{1}{2}t_i^2 - t_i t_f + t_i^2\right) \quad \rightarrow \quad \vec{a}\int_{t_i}^{t_f} \Delta t\,dt = \vec{a}\left(\frac{1}{2}t_f^2 + \frac{1}{2}t_i^2 - t_f t_i\right)$$

$$\vec{a}\int_{t_i}^{t_f} \Delta t\,dt = \frac{1}{2}\vec{a}\left(t_f^2 - 2t_f t_i + t_i^2\right) \quad \rightarrow \quad \vec{a}\int_{t_i}^{t_f} \Delta t\,dt = \frac{1}{2}\vec{a}\left(t_f - t_i\right)^2 \quad \rightarrow \quad \vec{a}\int_{t_i}^{t_f} \Delta t\,dt\, \frac{1}{2}\vec{a}\left(\Delta t\right)^2$$

And since $\int_{\vec{r}_i}^{\vec{r}_f} d\vec{r} = \vec{r}_f - \vec{r}_i = \Delta \vec{r}$, we have

$$\Delta \vec{r} = \vec{v}_i \Delta t + \frac{1}{2}\vec{a}\left(\Delta t\right)^2 \tag{C-5}$$

Thus, when the acceleration of the object is constant, we can readily calculate the changes in position and velocity that occur during a specific time interval.

We can combine Equation C-4 and Equation C-5 to derive another equation that relates velocity, position, and acceleration.

$$\Delta\vec{r} = \vec{v}_i\Delta t + \frac{1}{2}\vec{a}\left(\Delta t\right)^2 \quad \rightarrow \quad \vec{a}\cdot\Delta\vec{r} = \vec{a}\cdot\vec{v}_i\Delta t + \frac{1}{2}\vec{a}\cdot\vec{a}\left(\Delta t\right)^2$$

$$2\vec{a}\cdot\Delta\vec{r} = 2\vec{a}\cdot\vec{v}_i\Delta t + a^2\left(\Delta t\right)^2$$

Substitution of

$$\vec{a} = \frac{\vec{v}_f - \vec{v}_i}{\Delta t} \qquad a^2 = \frac{\left(\Delta v\right)^2}{\left(\Delta t\right)^2}$$

yields

$$2\vec{a}\cdot\Delta\vec{r} = 2\left(\frac{\vec{v}_f - \vec{v}_i}{\Delta t}\right)\cdot\vec{v}_i\Delta t + \left(\Delta v\right)^2$$

$$2\vec{a}\cdot\Delta\vec{r} = 2\vec{v}_f\cdot\vec{v}_i - \vec{v}_i\cdot\vec{v}_i + \left(\Delta\vec{v}\cdot\Delta\vec{v}\right)$$

$$2\vec{a}\cdot\Delta\vec{r} = 2\vec{v}_f\cdot\vec{v}_i - 2v_i^2 + \left(\vec{v}_f - \vec{v}_i\right)\cdot\left(\vec{v}_f - \vec{v}_i\right)$$

$$2\vec{a}\cdot\Delta\vec{r} = 2\vec{v}_f\cdot\vec{v}_i - 2v_i^2 + \vec{v}_f\cdot\vec{v}_f - 2\vec{v}_f\cdot\vec{v}_i + \vec{v}_i\cdot\vec{v}_i \quad \rightarrow \quad 2\vec{a}\cdot\Delta\vec{r} = v_f^2 - v_i^2$$

$$v_f^2 = v_i^2 + 2\vec{a}\cdot\Delta\vec{r} \tag{C-6}$$

These results also convey some fundamental physics. Kinematics allow us to calculate changes rather than absolute values. Likewise, it is the change in something that is, in some sense, physically real.

APPENDIX D

The simplest definition of the moment of inertia is that it is the rotational equivalent of mass. The larger the mass of an object, the larger the net force that is required to accelerate the object. Similarly, the larger the moment of inertia of an object, the larger the net torque that is required to rotate the object. Mathematically, we define the moment of inertia according to the following equation:

$$I = \int r^2 dm \qquad \text{(D-1)}$$

It is important to emphasize that the variable r in this equation, and the corresponding moment of inertia, depends upon the axis of rotation. In other words, the same object may have a different moment of inertia for different axes of rotation. The term dm in Equation D-1 is an infinitesimal amount of mass located at $\vec{r} = x\hat{x} + y\hat{y} + z\hat{z}$ from the axis of rotation. This integral is typically simplified by relating the dm term to a measure of distance, area, or volume using the appropriate mass density.

Table D-1. Variable substitutions for integrals involving differential mass.

Dimensionality of integral	Density used	Relation to dm
1 (linear integral)	λ (linear mass density)	$dm = \lambda \bullet dx$
2 (area integral)	σ (area mass density)	$dm = \sigma \bullet dA$
3 (volume integral)	ρ (volume mass density)	$dm = \rho \bullet dV$

For a collection of point particles or objects that can be treated as point particles, the moment of inertia can be calculated using a simpler equation:

$$I = m_1 r_1^2 + m_2 r_2^2 + \ldots \quad \rightarrow \quad I = \sum_i m_i r_i^2 \qquad \text{(D-2)}$$

In this equation, the moment of inertia is calculated as a sum of terms, each of which corresponds to a contribution from a different particle.

D-2 Sample Calculation of Moment of Inertia

Consider a thin rigid rod of length L and mass M, as shown in Figure D.1. This rod is uniformly dense meaning that the mass density of the rod is constant throughout the rod.

The moment of inertia of this rod for rotations about one end would be given by the equation:

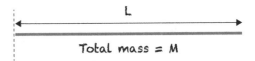

Figure D.1. A thin rod of uniform density with a length L and mass M is rotated around one of its ends.

$$I = \int r^2 dm$$

We can express the infinitesimal amount of mass in this equation in terms of the linear mass density of the rod and an infinitesimal distance along the rod (Figure D.2).

With this definition, the integral with respect to mass in Equation D-1 can be written as an integral with respect to the length of the rod.

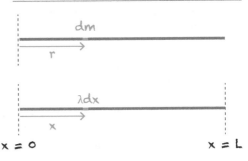

Figure D.2. Expressing a differential mass in terms of a mass density and a differential distance.

$$I = \int_0^L x^2 \lambda \, dx$$

Since the density of the rod is constant, this integral is straightforward to calculate.

$$I = \lambda \int_0^L x^2 \, dx \;\rightarrow\; I = \frac{\lambda L^3}{3}$$

The density of the rod is related to the mass and length of the rod through the following equation:

$$\lambda = \frac{M}{L}$$

Substitution of this definition into our equation for the moment of inertia of the rod then yields

$$I = \frac{L^3}{3}\left(\frac{M}{L}\right) \;\rightarrow\; I = \frac{1}{3}ML^2$$

D-3 Common Moments of Inertia

All moments of inertia are products of the mass of the object, the square of a geometric parameter (length, radius, *etc.*), and a constant. Consequently, the units of moment of inertia are kgm². Some common moments of inertia are:

Table D-2. Moments of Inertia

Object and Axis of Rotation	Moment of Inertia
Thin rod of uniform density with mass M and length L rotating around its center.	$I = \frac{1}{12}ML^2$
Thin rod of uniform density with mass M and length L rotating around one end.	$I = \frac{1}{3}ML^2$
Solid cylinder or disk of uniform density with mass M and radius R rotating around its center.	$I = \frac{1}{2}MR^2$
Cylindrical hoop with mass M and radius R rotating around its center.	$I = MR^2$
Solid sphere of uniform density with mass M and radius R rotating around its center.	$I = \frac{2}{5}MR^2$
Spherical shell or hollow sphere with mass M and radius R rotating around its center.	$I = \frac{2}{3}MR^2$

D-4 Definition of the Center of Mass

There are three definitions for the center of mass of an object:
1. The center of mass is the specific point at which you can balance an object. For objects that are uniformly dense (*i.e.*, have the same density everywhere), the center of mass is at the geometric center of the object.
2. For an object undergoing both rotational and translational motion, the center of mass is the point that moves in the same path that a non-rotating point particle with the same mass would move if it were subjected to the same net force.
3. An unconstrained object (*i.e.*, one not on an axle or pivot) on which there is no net force rotates about its center of mass. In other words, a freely rotating object will always rotate around its center of mass.

In addition to these definitions, we can define the center of mass mathematically according to the following equation:

$$\vec{r}_{CM} = \frac{\int \vec{r} \, dm}{M}$$

(D-3)

Or in component form as:

$$x_{CM} = \frac{\int x \, dm}{M} \qquad y_{CM} = \frac{\int y \, dm}{M} \qquad z_{CM} = \frac{\int z \, dm}{M}$$

In these equations, M is the total mass of the object, and dm is an infinitesimal amount of mass located at $\vec{r} = x\hat{x} + y\hat{y} + z\hat{z}$. As with the integral for moment of inertia, these integrals for center of mass are typically simplified by relating the dm term to a measure of distance, area, or volume using the appropriate mass density.

D-5 Applications of the Center of Mass

Consider a collection of n massive objects with a total mass M. The equation for the center of mass of this collection is

$$\vec{r}_{CM} = \frac{m_1 \vec{r}_1 + m_2 \vec{r}_2 + \ldots m_n \vec{r}_n}{M} \quad \rightarrow \quad \vec{r}_{CM} = \frac{\sum_{i=1}^{n} m_i \vec{r}_i}{M}$$

(D-4)

In Equation D-4, m_i and r_i are the mass and position of the ith object, respectively. If the objects are moving, then the center of mass may also be moving. We can describe this motion in terms of the velocity and acceleration of the center of mass.

$$\vec{v}_{CM} = \frac{d}{dt}\vec{r}_{CM} \quad \rightarrow \quad \vec{v}_{CM} = \frac{\sum_{i=1}^{n} m_i \frac{d}{dt}\vec{r}_i}{M} \quad \rightarrow \quad \vec{v}_{CM} = \frac{\sum_{i=1}^{n} m_i \vec{v}_i}{M}$$

(D-5)

$$\vec{v}_{CM} = \frac{\sum_{i=1}^{n} \vec{p}_i}{M} \quad \rightarrow \quad \vec{v}_{CM} = \frac{\vec{P}_{system}}{M}$$

$$\vec{a}_{CM} = \frac{d}{dt}\vec{v}_{CM} \quad \rightarrow \quad \vec{a}_{CM} = \frac{\sum_{i=1}^{n} m_i \frac{d}{dt}\vec{v}_i}{M} \quad \rightarrow \quad \vec{a}_{CM} = \frac{\sum_{i=1}^{n} m_i \vec{a}_i}{M} \quad \rightarrow \quad \vec{a}_{CM} = \frac{\vec{F}_{net}}{M}$$

Thus, we have simple relationships between the total linear momentum of the system and the velocity of the center of mass of the system and between the net force acting on a system and the acceleration of the center of mass of the system.

$$\vec{P}_{system} = M\vec{v}_{CM} \tag{D-6}$$

$$\vec{F}_{net} = M\vec{a}_{CM} \tag{D-7}$$

Because of these equations, it is clear that if no net force acts on a system, then the acceleration of the center of mass of the system will be zero. Furthermore, if the acceleration of the center of mass of the system is zero, then the velocity of the center of mass of the system is constant as is the total linear momentum of the system. This is the law of conservation of momentum.

D-6 Parallel Axis Theorem

If the moment of inertia for an object rotating around an axis passing through its center of mass is known, then the moment of inertia for this object rotating around any parallel axis of rotation can be determined using the parallel axis theorem.

$$I = I_{CM} + Md^2 \tag{D-8}$$

In Equation D-8, I_{CM} is the moment of inertia for the object if it was rotating around an axis through the center of mass, M is the mass of the object, and d is the distance between the actual axis of rotation and an axis passing through the center of mass.

For example, the parallel axis theorem can be used to determine the moment of inertia for a thin rod of uniform density rotated around one end (see Section D-2). From Table D-2, we know the moment of inertia for a thin rod of uniform density rotated around its center. Since the rod is uniformly dense, we know that this must be an axis through the center of mass of the rod.

$$I_{CM} = \frac{1}{12}ML^2$$

The distance from an axis through the center of mass of the rod and a parallel axis at one end of the rod must be L/2. Substitution of this distance into the parallel axis theorem then yields

$$I = \frac{1}{12}ML^2 + M\left(\frac{L}{2}\right)^2 \quad \rightarrow \quad I = \frac{1}{12}ML^2 + \frac{1}{4}ML^2$$

$$I = \frac{1}{3}ML^2$$

This is the same value that we calculated using Equation D-1.

D-7 Connection to Statistics

Consider a distribution of n measurements of a variable x (i.e., $x_1, x_2, ..., x_n$). The mean of this distribution will be

$$\overline{x} = \frac{x_1 + x_2 + ... + x_n}{n}$$

The variance (or dispersion) of the distribution will be

$$\overline{\left(\Delta x\right)^2} = \frac{\left(x_1 - \overline{x}\right)^2 + \left(x_2 - \overline{x}\right)^2 + ... + \left(x_n - \overline{x}\right)^2}{n}$$

The variance is a measure of the amount of scatter of values of the variable x around its mean value. The square root of the variance is the standard deviation of the distribution, which is often used as a measure of the error or uncertainty in the measurement of the mean.

Now, consider a slightly more abstract case in which the values of the variable x form a continuous distribution. If the probability of measuring a value of x between x and $x + dx$ is given by $p(x)$, then we have the following integral expressions for the mean and variance of the distribution of x.

$$\overline{x} = \frac{\int p(x) x \, dx}{\int p(x) dx}$$

$$\overline{\left(\Delta x\right)^2} = \frac{\int p(x)\left(x_i - \overline{x}\right)^2 dx}{\int p(x) dx}$$

We can then use these expressions to help us understand the mathematical basis for our expressions for the center of mass and moment of inertia of a distribution of mass. For such a distribution, the probability is directly proportional to the mass of the object, and, thus, the center of mass is the mathematical equivalent of the mean of the distribution of mass.

$$\overline{x} = \frac{\int p(x) x \, dx}{\int p(x) dx} \xrightarrow{p(x)dx=dm} x_{CM} = \frac{\int x \, dm}{\int dm} = \frac{\int x \, dm}{M}$$

Similarly, the moment of inertia is the equivalent of the variance of the distribution of mass.

$$\overline{\left(\Delta x\right)^2} = \frac{\int p(x)\left(x_i - \overline{x}\right)^2 dx}{\int p(x) dx} \xrightarrow{p(x)dx=dm} \frac{\int \left(x - \overline{x}\right)^2 dm}{\int dm} = \frac{I}{M}$$

In light of these equations, we can interpret the center of mass of a distribution of masses as the mean position of the masses and the moment of inertia as a measure of how those masses are distributed around this center of mass.

APPENDIX E

When the mass of the system is constant, Newton's 2nd law can be written as

$$\vec{F}_{net} = m\frac{d}{dt}\vec{v}$$

We then take the inner product of both sides of the equation with a differential change in position vector.

$$\vec{F}_{net} \cdot d\vec{r} = m\frac{d\vec{v}}{dt} \cdot d\vec{r} \quad \rightarrow \quad \vec{F}_{net} \cdot d\vec{r} = m\frac{d\vec{v}}{dt} \cdot \frac{d\vec{r}}{dt}dt \quad \rightarrow \quad \vec{F}_{net} \cdot d\vec{r} = m\frac{d\vec{v}}{dt} \cdot \vec{v}dt$$

We can simplify this expression further since

$$\frac{d}{dt}\left(\vec{v} \cdot \vec{v}\right) = \frac{d\vec{v}}{dt} \cdot \vec{v} + \vec{v} \cdot \frac{d\vec{v}}{dt} = 2\frac{d\vec{v}}{dt} \cdot \vec{v} \quad \rightarrow \quad \frac{d\vec{v}}{dt} \cdot \vec{v} = \frac{1}{2}\frac{d}{dt}\left(\vec{v} \cdot \vec{v}\right) = \frac{1}{2}\frac{d}{dt}\left(v^2\right)$$

Therefore,

$$\vec{F}_{net} \cdot d\vec{r} = \frac{1}{2}\frac{d}{dt}\left(v^2\right)dt = \frac{m}{2}d\left(v^2\right) = d\left(\frac{1}{2}mv^2\right)$$

If we integrate both sides, we have

$$\int \vec{F}_{net} \cdot d\vec{r} = \int d\left(\frac{1}{2}mv^2\right) = \Delta\left(\frac{1}{2}mv^2\right) = \Delta K$$

The left-hand side of this equation is simply the net work done on the system. Hence, Newton's 2nd law can be equivalently expressed as

$$W_{net} = \Delta K$$

We can derive a similar expression starting with the more general expression of Newton's 2nd law that relates the net force to a change in momentum.

$$\vec{F}_{net} = \frac{d}{dt}\vec{p}$$

$$\vec{F}_{net} \cdot d\vec{r} = \frac{d\vec{p}}{dt} \cdot d\vec{r} \quad \rightarrow \quad \vec{F}_{net} \cdot d\vec{r} = \frac{d\vec{p}}{dt} \cdot \frac{d\vec{r}}{dt} dt \quad \rightarrow \quad \vec{F}_{net} \cdot d\vec{r} = \frac{d\vec{p}}{dt} \cdot \vec{v} dt$$

$$\vec{F}_{net} \cdot d\vec{r} = \frac{d\vec{p}}{dt} \cdot \frac{\vec{p}}{m} dt = \left(\frac{d\vec{p}}{dt} \cdot \vec{p}\right)\frac{dt}{m}$$

We can simplify this expression since

$$\frac{d}{dt}\left(\vec{p} \cdot \vec{p}\right) = \frac{d\vec{p}}{dt} \cdot \vec{p} + \vec{p} \cdot \frac{d\vec{p}}{dt} = 2\frac{d\vec{p}}{dt} \cdot \vec{p} \quad \rightarrow \quad \frac{d\vec{p}}{dt} \cdot \vec{p} = \frac{1}{2}\frac{d}{dt}\left(\vec{p} \cdot \vec{p}\right)$$

Hence,

$$\vec{F}_{net} \cdot d\vec{r} = \frac{1}{2m}\frac{d}{dt}\left(\vec{p} \cdot \vec{p}\right)dt = \frac{1}{2m}d\left(\vec{p} \cdot \vec{p}\right) = d\left(\frac{\vec{p} \cdot \vec{p}}{2m}\right)$$

If we integrate both sides, we have

$$\int \vec{F}_{net} \cdot d\vec{r} = \int d\left(\frac{\vec{p} \cdot \vec{p}}{2m}\right) \quad \rightarrow \quad \int \vec{F}_{net} \cdot d\vec{r} = \Delta\left(\frac{\vec{p} \cdot \vec{p}}{2m}\right) \quad \rightarrow \quad \int \vec{F}_{net} \cdot d\vec{r} = \Delta K \qquad \textbf{(E-1)}$$

In Equation E-1, translational kinetic energy is expressed in terms of linear momentum.

$$K = \frac{\vec{p} \cdot \vec{p}}{2m} \qquad \textbf{(E-2)}$$

E-2 Newton's 2nd Law for Rotational Motion

We begin with the definition of linear momentum.

$$\vec{p} = m\vec{v}$$

Since the momentum vector is parallel to the velocity vector, the cross product of these two vectors must be zero.

$$\vec{v} \times \vec{p} = 0$$

Hence,

$$\vec{v} = \frac{d\vec{r}}{dt} \quad \rightarrow \quad \frac{d\vec{r}}{dt} \times \vec{p} = 0$$

Now, let's take the cross product of the position vector with both sides of the equation for Newton's 2nd law.

$$\vec{F}_{net} = \frac{d\vec{p}}{dt} \quad \rightarrow \quad \vec{r} \times \vec{F}_{net} = \vec{r} \times \frac{d\vec{p}}{dt}$$

Since $\dfrac{d\vec{r}}{dt} \times \vec{p} = 0$, we can also write this result as

$$\vec{r} \times \vec{F}_{net} = \vec{r} \times \frac{d\vec{p}}{dt} + \frac{d\vec{r}}{dt} \times \vec{p} \quad \rightarrow \quad \vec{r} \times \vec{F}_{net} = \frac{d}{dt}\left(\vec{r} \times \vec{p}\right)$$

Hence,

$$\vec{\tau}_{net} = \frac{d}{dt}\vec{L} \tag{E-3}$$

Now, let's assume that our system consists of a single object, or a system of objects, that moves as one rigid system. For such a system,

$$\vec{L} = I\vec{\omega}$$

Taking the dot product of both sides of Equation E-3 with a differential change in the angular position vector gives us

$$\vec{\tau}_{net} \cdot d\vec{\theta} = \frac{d\vec{L}}{dt} \cdot d\vec{\theta} \quad \rightarrow \quad \vec{\tau}_{net} \cdot d\vec{\theta} = \frac{d\vec{L}}{dt} \cdot \frac{d\vec{\theta}}{dt} dt \quad \rightarrow \quad \vec{\tau}_{net} \cdot d\vec{\theta} = \frac{d\vec{L}}{dt} \cdot \vec{\omega} dt$$

For our system, we have

$$\vec{L} = I\vec{\omega} \quad \rightarrow \quad \vec{\tau}_{net} \cdot d\vec{\theta} = \frac{d\vec{L}}{dt} \cdot \frac{\vec{L}}{I} dt \quad \rightarrow \quad \vec{\tau}_{net} \cdot d\vec{\theta} = \left(\frac{d\vec{L}}{dt} \cdot \vec{L}\right)\frac{dt}{I}$$

We can simplify this expression since

$$\frac{d}{dt}\left(\vec{L}\cdot\vec{L}\right)=\frac{d\vec{L}}{dt}\cdot\vec{L}+\vec{L}\cdot\frac{d\vec{L}}{dt}=2\frac{d\vec{L}}{dt}\cdot\vec{L}\;\;\rightarrow\;\;\frac{d\vec{L}}{dt}\cdot\vec{L}=\frac{1}{2}\frac{d}{dt}\left(\vec{L}\cdot\vec{L}\right)$$

Hence,

$$\vec{\tau}_{net}\cdot d\vec{\theta}=\frac{1}{2I}\frac{d}{dt}\left(\vec{L}\cdot\vec{L}\right)dt=\frac{1}{2I}d\left(\vec{L}\cdot\vec{L}\right)=d\left(\frac{\vec{L}\cdot\vec{L}}{2I}\right)$$

If we integrate both sides, we have

$$\int\vec{\tau}_{net}\cdot d\vec{\theta}=\int d\left(\frac{\vec{L}\cdot\vec{L}}{2I}\right)\;\;\rightarrow\;\;\int\vec{\tau}_{net}\cdot d\vec{\theta}=\Delta\left(\frac{\vec{L}\cdot\vec{L}}{2I}\right)\;\;\rightarrow\;\;\int\vec{\tau}_{net}\cdot d\vec{\theta}=\Delta K_{rot} \qquad \textbf{(E-4)}$$

In Equation E-4, rotational kinetic energy is expressed in terms of angular momentum.

$$K_{rot}=\frac{\vec{L}\cdot\vec{L}}{2I} \qquad \textbf{(E-5)}$$

APPENDIX F

An exact differential is an infinitesimal change that can be expressed as the differential of another function (*i.e.*, an exact differential is the antiderivative of another function). For example, the infinitesimal change in gravitational potential energy (dU_g) is an exact differential since it is found from the differentiation of the function for the gravitational potential energy (U_g).

$$dU_g = \left(\frac{\partial U_g}{\partial y} \right) dy$$

Indeed, any infinitesimal change in potential energy is an exact differential since it can be determined from the differentiation of a function, namely, the potential energy function. It follows that a change associated with the integration of an exact differential is independent of the path over which the change occurred. For example,

$$\Delta U_g = \int dU_g \quad \rightarrow \quad \Delta U_g = \left(U_g \right)_f - \left(U_g \right)_i$$

The change in the gravitational potential energy depends upon only the initial and final positions of the object. Infinitesimal changes in the total energy and the entropy of a system are also exact differentials.

In contrast, the infinitesimal change associated with an inexact differential cannot be found from the differentiation of another function. An example of this is the infinitesimal work done by a non-conservative force, such as the force of kinetic friction acting over an infinitesimal displacement of an object. There is no equivalent "*potential energy*" function for the work done by the force of kinetic friction since the work done by the force of kinetic friction depends upon the path taken by the object. In other words, we cannot determine the work done by the force of kinetic friction if we know only the initial and final positions of the object. To distinguish this infinitesimal change as an inexact differential, we use the symbol $đ$ rather than d. Hence,

$$W = \int đW$$

Similarly, an infinitesimal exchange of heat is also an inexact differential.

$$Q = \int đQ$$

It is interesting to note that the 1st law of thermodynamics relates an exact differential to two inexact differentials.

$$dE = đQ - đW$$

Although the infinitesimal changes in energy associated with heat and work are both path dependent, an infinitesimal change in the energy of the system is path independent. This makes sense since the energy of the system is a function of the positions and velocities of the objects in the system. These quantities specify the energy of the system regardless of how the objects came to possess them.

F-2 Principle of Minimum Potential Energy

The entropy of a system can be written as a function of the energy and the volume of the system.

$$S = (E, V)$$

The exact differential associated with an infinitesimal change in entropy is

$$dS = \left(\frac{\partial S}{\partial E}\right)_V dE + \left(\frac{\partial S}{\partial V}\right)_E dV$$

Thus, from the 1st law of thermodynamics, we have

$$dS = \frac{1}{T}dE + \frac{P}{T}dV \quad \rightarrow \quad \left(\frac{\partial S}{\partial E}\right)_V = \frac{1}{T} \quad \left(\frac{\partial S}{\partial V}\right)_E = \frac{P}{T}$$

Now, since dS is an exact differential, the mixed partial derivatives of entropy must be equal.

$$\left(\frac{\partial^2 S}{\partial E \, \partial V}\right) = \left(\frac{\partial^2 S}{\partial V \, \partial E}\right)$$

Similarly, the energy of a system can be written as a function of the entropy and the volume of the system.

$$E = (S, V)$$

The exact differential associated with an infinitesimal change in energy is

$$dE = \left(\frac{\partial E}{\partial S}\right)_V dS + \left(\frac{\partial E}{\partial V}\right)_S dV$$

From the 1st law of thermodynamics, we have

$$dE = TdS - PdV \quad \rightarrow \quad \left(\frac{\partial E}{\partial S}\right)_V = T \quad \left(\frac{\partial E}{\partial V}\right)_S = P$$

Finally, since dE is also an exact differential, the mixed partial derivatives of energy must be equal.

$$\left(\frac{\partial^2 E}{\partial S \partial V}\right) = \left(\frac{\partial^2 E}{\partial V \partial S}\right)$$

Putting everything together gives us

$$\left(\frac{\partial E}{\partial V}\right)_S = -\frac{\left(\frac{\partial S}{\partial V}\right)_E}{\left(\frac{\partial S}{\partial E}\right)_V} \quad \rightarrow \quad \left(\frac{\partial E}{\partial V}\right)_S = -T\left(\frac{\partial S}{\partial V}\right)_E = 0$$

$$\left(\frac{\partial^2 E}{\partial V^2}\right)_S = \frac{\partial}{\partial V}\left(-\frac{\left(\frac{\partial S}{\partial V}\right)_E}{\left(\frac{\partial S}{\partial E}\right)_V}\right)$$

$$\left(\frac{\partial^2 E}{\partial V^2}\right)_S = -\left(\frac{\left(\frac{\partial^2 S}{\partial V^2}\right)_E}{\left(\frac{\partial S}{\partial E}\right)_V} - \left(\frac{\partial S}{\partial V}\right)_E \frac{\frac{\partial^2 S}{\partial V \partial E}}{\left(\left(\frac{\partial S}{\partial E}\right)_V\right)^2}\right)$$

From the 2nd law of thermodynamics, we know that the entropy of the system is a maximum at equilibrium.

$$\left(\frac{\partial S}{\partial V}\right)_E = 0 \quad \left(\frac{d^2 S}{dV^2}\right)_E < 0$$

Hence,

$$\left(\frac{\partial S}{\partial V}\right)_E = 0 \;\rightarrow\; \left(\frac{\partial E}{\partial V}\right)_S = 0$$

$$\left(\frac{\partial S}{\partial V}\right)_E = 0 \;\rightarrow\; \left(\frac{\partial^2 E}{\partial V^2}\right)_S = -\left(\frac{\left(\dfrac{\partial^2 S}{\partial V^2}\right)_E}{\left(\dfrac{\partial S}{\partial E}\right)_V}\right) \;\rightarrow\; \left(\frac{\partial^2 E}{\partial V^2}\right)_S = -T\left(\frac{\partial^2 S}{\partial V^2}\right)_E$$

Thus,

$$\left(\frac{d^2 S}{dV^2}\right)_E < 0 \;\rightarrow\; \left(\frac{\partial^2 E}{\partial V^2}\right)_S > 0$$

The energy of the system is a minimum at equilibrium.

CPSIA information can be obtained
at www.ICGtesting.com
Printed in the USA
FSOW03n0459270815
10409FS

9 781626 614352